MATHEMATICS: The Man-made Universe

A Series of Undergraduate Books in Mathematics

R. A. Rosenbaum, EDITOR

Golden Gate Editions

MATHEMATICS

The Man-made Universe

An Introduction to the Spirit of Mathematics

By SHERMAN K. STEIN

University of California, Davis

W. H. FREEMAN AND COMPANY

SAN FRANCISCO AND LONDON

TO HADASSAH

PREFACE

We all find ourselves in a world we never made. Though we get used to the kitchen sink, we do not understand the atoms which compose it. The kitchen sink, like all the objects surrounding us, is a convenient abstraction.

Mathematics, on the other hand, is completely the work of man. Each theorem, each proof, is the product of the human mind. In mathematics all the cards can be put on the table. In this sense, mathematics is concrete, whereas the world is abstract.

This book exploits that concreteness to introduce the general reader to mathematics. The "general reader" might be either the college student or the high school student, whatever his special interest might be, or the curious adult. This book grew out of a college course designed primarily to give students in many fields an appreciation of the beauty, extent, and vitality of mathematics. I had searched several years for a suitable text, but those I found were either too advanced or too specialized.

The subjects, chosen from number theory, topology, set theory, geometry, algebra, and analysis, can be presented to the reader having little mathematical background (some chapters use only grammar school arithmetic). Each topic illustrates some significant idea and lends itself easily to experiments and problems.

The reader is advised to take advantage of the concrete nature of mathematics as he reads each theorem and proof; to take nothing on faith; to be suspicious and vigilant; to examine each step of the reasoning; and to take seriously such suggestions as "the reader may provide an example of his own" or "the reader should check this theorem for some special cases before going on to the proof." It would be wise to read this book with pencil and paper always at hand.

The exercises at the end of each chapter vary in difficulty; some are just routine checks, whereas others raise questions that no one has answered. They give the reader a chance to test and apply his understanding of the material. Many of the exercises offer either alternate proofs of theorems proved in the text or further results. Some point out relations to other chapters.

Using the Map and Guide (page ix), the reader or teacher may choose his own route through this book. The recommended route takes the chapters in order.

I would like to thank my students at the University of California at Davis for their comments on mimeographed versions of most of the chapters; my colleagues, Henry Alder and Curtis Fulton, for their encouragement and advice; and the artist, William Brown, who read several chapters and agreed that a proof can be beautiful.

It is a special pleasure to acknowledge the invaluable assistance of Robert Blair of Purdue University and George Raney of Wesleyan University, both of whom read the complete manuscript and made countless suggestions.

August 1962   SHERMAN K. STEIN

MAP AND GUIDE

In this map of the book "$a \longrightarrow b$" means that Chapter b depends in part on some material in Chapter a. The chapters are linked as follows.

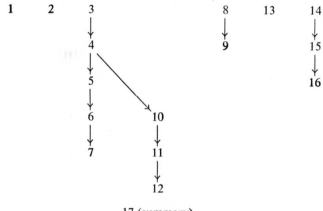

17 (summary)

Although, as the map indicates, the chapters need not be read in order, the recommended route does take the seventeen chapters in order. Many chapters refer for comparisons, contrasts, or exercises to earlier chapters. The map does not record these relations.

Chapters 1 and 2 introduce the mathematical style of thinking. Though referred to later, they are not used in the logical development of later chapters. Chapter 5 uses the main result of Chapter 4 (The Fundamental Theorem of Arithmetic). Chapter 11 uses results from Chapter 10 in the proof of Theorem 2. The proofs of Theorems 3 and 5 in Chapter 12 depend on Chapter 11. Chapter 15 uses the ordinary decimal representation of real numbers discussed in Chapter 14. Chapter 16 requires only Theorem 6 from Chapter 15. Chapter 17 is a general view and review.

Appendix A treats the four operations of arithmetic and algebra: addition, subtraction, multiplication, and division. The reader may use it simply as a reference, if and when needed, or he may choose to read it as a unit. It shows that the various manipulations met in arithmetic and algebra can all be based on eleven simple rules.

Appendix B treats the harmonic and geometric series, with an application of the latter to probability. This is a reference for Chapters 3, 14, and 15.

Appendix C defines spaces of any dimension. It is a reference for Chapter 15.

Throughout the text, E stands for exercise and R for reference. A starred reference presupposes more mathematical training than the general reader is expected to have; it is intended primarily as an aid to a teacher seeking background information. The contents of some references overlap.

Chapters 4, 7, 10, 11, 12, 13, 14, 15, and 16 use some high school algebra.

CONTENTS

Chapter **1**

THE WEAVER

In this chapter and the next we introduce the reader to the mathematical way of thinking and, in particular, to the concepts of proof and theorem. All that we will need in these two chapters is the distinction between the *odd numbers*, beginning with one $(1, 3, 5, \cdots)$ and the *even numbers*, beginning with zero $(0, 2, 4, \cdots)$. From such a simple notion we will deduce important and surprising consequences. Indeed, the ancient duality of odd and even, which separates the *natural numbers* $0, 1, 2, 3, 4, 5, \cdots$ into two types, will be of use several times in the course of this book; for example, in paths over highway systems, algebras, coloring of maps, and roots of polynomials—topics appearing in Chapters 8, 11, 13, and 15, respectively.

It is a puzzled weaver of hatbands who first introduces us to the mysteries of odd and even. To make his hatbands, this weaver braids several threads together, interchanging two at a time. Moreover, no two of his threads are of the same color. For instance, when he has only two threads, his pattern looks like

"After one switch," the weaver tells us, "neither thread is directly below its starting position. After the second switch, each is directly below its starting position. After three switches, each is again out of place; after four, they are back in place. Since I want these bands to go around a hat and not show the seam, my designs must have an even number of switches—at least if I have only two threads.

"Now, it seems to me that with more than two threads I should be able to make a seamless band with an odd number of switches. But, hard as I have tried, I have found no such design. Can you help me?"

1

Let us try to help the weaver find his design. Here is an experiment with three threads:

This diagram records the effect of four switches. Each switch interchanges two threads, as the weaver demands. The remaining thread is brought straight down (this is recorded by the vertical lines). Each of the three threads has been returned to its starting place, and so no seam will show. Regrettably, however, the number of switches is even; we did not find the weaver a design having an odd number of switches.

Let us try again. Here is a seamless design made with four threads:

The vertical lines record threads that are not switched; since there are four threads, two will not be switched at each stage.

The reader will notice that each of the four threads is back in place after six switches, again an even number. The reader is invited, at this point, to do some experimenting of his own with three, four, five, or more threads and to try designing a seamless hatband having an odd number of switches.

After several attempts we find ourselves in a disturbing position. We have found no design with an odd number of switches; we feel none can be found, but we are not sure of this. Perhaps there does exist a seamless design with very many threads and an odd number of switches.

What are we going to tell the weaver? He showed us why no two-thread seamless design having an odd number of switches could be found. It seems likely that if no designs exist at all—designs having any number of threads and an odd number of switches—then we ought to be able to explain why there are none. Experiments in mathematics prove nothing; they only point to a possible truth. Since no one can ever write down the endless list of all possible designs, we must somehow see into all designs at once and find a general principle that will tell us why the number of switches can never be odd.

We might find a clue to the more general question in the weaver's analysis of designs using only two threads. In order to simplify our diagrams, let us number his threads "1" and "2." The starting position is 1, 2. After one switch he has the backward position 2, 1; 2 is now to the left of 1. After another switch he has the original order 1, 2. The weaver's design of four switches we record simply as

$$
\begin{array}{cc}
1 & 2 \\
2 & 1 \\
1 & 2 \\
2 & 1 \\
1 & 2
\end{array}
$$

We could translate the weaver's analysis into: after an odd number of switches, 1 and 2 are backward; after an even number of switches they are forward, in their usual order, 2 to the right of 1.

With this as a clue, let us look at our four-switch experiment with three threads, which we now record as

$$
\begin{array}{ccc}
1 & 2 & 3 \\
2 & 1 & 3 \\
3 & 1 & 2 \\
1 & 3 & 2 \\
1 & 2 & 3
\end{array}
$$

Looking only at threads 1 and 2, we notice that, unfortunately, they do not alternate "forward" and "backward" with each of the four switches. In fact, after each of the last three they are forward. Clearly, if there were more threads, then threads 1 and 2 might not be displaced at all. If we are to extend the weaver's analysis, we will have to pay attention to threads other than just 1 and 2.

In order to treat all the threads without favoritism, perhaps we should examine each pair of threads and see whether it is forward or backward. This might help; but then again it might not.

At the beginning position (position 1 2 3), each pair [(1, 2), (1, 3), (2, 3)] is forward; none is backward. At the next position, 2 1 3, the pair (2, 1) is backward, and (2, 3) and (1, 3) are forward. At 3 1 2 the pairs (3, 1) and (3, 2) are backward, and (1, 2) is forward. At 1 3 2 we have the one backward pair (3, 2), whereas (1, 3) and (1, 2) are forward. Finally, all are forward again.

The number of backward pairs for each arrangement runs successively through 0, 1, 2, 1 and returns to 0. With just two threads these numbers alternate 0, 1, 0, 1, and so on, as the weaver has told us. Clearly we do not have quite so simple a situation in our experiment with three threads.

Now let us look at our design with four threads and six switches, which we record as

$$
\begin{array}{cccc}
1 & 2 & 3 & 4 \\
3 & 2 & 1 & 4 \\
3 & 4 & 1 & 2 \\
2 & 4 & 1 & 3 \\
4 & 2 & 1 & 3 \\
1 & 2 & 4 & 3 \\
1 & 2 & 3 & 4
\end{array}
$$

For simplicity, let us call the number of backward pairs of an arrangement B; for example, B of 1, 2, 3, 4 is 0. As the reader may check, B for each of the seven arrangements is successively 0, 3, 4, 3, 4, 1, 0. For example, the third arrangement, 3, 4, 1, 2, has the backward pairs (3, 1), (3, 2), (4, 1), (4, 2). Thus B is 4, or we might write $B(3, 4, 1, 2) = 4$. Similarly, $B(1, 2, 3, 4) = 0$.

Now look at the two sequences we found; namely, 0, 1, 2, 1, 0 and 0, 3, 4, 3, 4, 1, 0. Naturally each begins and ends with 0. But, chaotic as they are, they do have something else in common: *each alternates even, odd, even, odd, and so on.* For two-thread designs the alternation is restricted simply to 0, 1, 0, 1, $\cdots$, which is again even, odd, even, odd, $\cdots$. So we have a very promising clue for solving the weaver's problem. *All would be answered* if we could prove this statement:

If one switch is made in an arrangement of natural numbers, then the number of backward pairs always changes by an odd number.

We have reduced the question from one concerning weavers' designs that may involve billions of switches to one concerning the effect of a single typical switch. The thorough study of what happens when just one switch is made can be carried out with enough generality (if we make the bookkeeping sufficiently flexible) to cover completely the effect of any switch whatsoever.

We must scrutinize what happens to B when one switch is made in an arrangement. To be sure that our thinking will be valid for any switch in any arrangement, we will put hoods over all the natural numbers in question. This we can do quite easily by calling the left one of the two switched natural numbers "c" and the other "d." All we know is that c and d are two natural numbers; c may be less than d, or d may be less than c. The arrangement will look like

where the lines indicate that there may be more natural numbers in the arrangement left of c, between c and d, or right of d. After switching c and d, we obtain the new arrangement

$$\underline{\hspace{2cm}}d\underline{\hspace{2cm}}c\underline{\hspace{2cm}}\ .$$

Let us look at those pairs which might have influenced the *change* in B as we went from the first arrangement to the second. First of all, if neither number of a pair is c or d, then such a pair contributes nothing to the change in B; it is unaffected by switching c and d. Second, what about pairs that include either c or d but not both, such as (b, c) or (b, d)? If b lies to the left of both c and d,

$$\underline{\hspace{1.5cm}}b\underline{\hspace{1.5cm}}c\underline{\hspace{1.5cm}}d\underline{\hspace{1.5cm}}\ ,$$

then in the new arrangement,

$$\underline{\hspace{1.5cm}}b\underline{\hspace{1.5cm}}d\underline{\hspace{1.5cm}}c\underline{\hspace{1.5cm}}\ ,$$

b remains left of c and d. Thus if (b, c), for example, is forward in the first arrangement, it remains so in the second. Such pairs do not, of course, influence the *change* in B. Similar reasoning holds if b is right of both c and d.

But let us look closely at the pairs (c, b) and (b, d), where b is between c and d. The first arrangement is

$$\underline{\hspace{1.5cm}}c\underline{\hspace{1.5cm}}b\underline{\hspace{1.5cm}}d\underline{\hspace{1.5cm}}\ ,$$

and the second is

$$\underline{\hspace{1.5cm}}d\underline{\hspace{1.5cm}}b\underline{\hspace{1.5cm}}c\underline{\hspace{1.5cm}}\ .$$

If we assume that c is smaller than d, there are then three possibilities:

1. b is smaller than c (hence smaller than d);
2. b is larger than c but smaller than d;
3. b is larger than d (hence larger than c).

In case (1) our bookkeeping runs like this. At first (c, b) is backward, and (b, d) is forward. In the new arrangement (d, b) is backward, and (b, c) is forward. The total effect on the *change* in B is *zero*.

Let us look at the bookkeeping for case (2). At the start, (c, b) and (b, d) are forward. In the new arrangement (d, b) and (b, c) are backward. The total effect on the *change* in B is *two*.

The bookkeeping in case (3), similar to that for case (1), is left to the reader.

Now we treat the pair (c, d). If c is less than d, then (c, d) is forward at the beginning and backward after the switch. The effect of this pair on the *change* in B is *one*.

Combining all the possibilities, we see that the *change* in B is an even number plus one, hence *odd*. The reader may dispose of the case in which *c* is larger than *d* in a similar manner.

We have kept our bookkeeping flexible enough to cover any switch in an arrangement. Having proved that the change is odd in all possibilities, we can summarize our conclusion formally in this

THEOREM. *When one switch is made in an arrangement, the number of backward pairs changes by an odd number.*

For simplicity we will call an arrangement with an even number of backward pairs "*even*," and one with an odd number of backward pairs "*odd*." From our theorem follow several corollaries.

COROLLARY 1. *One switch turns an even arrangement into an odd arrangement, and an odd arrangement into an even arrangement.*

From Corollary 1 it follows that, if we start with an even arrangement and apply an odd number of switches, we end up with an odd arrangement. In particular, we have this reply to the weaver's question, in the form of

COROLLARY 2. *A seamless hatband woven of any number of threads must have an even number of switches.*

The reader may have noticed something peculiar about our reasoning. Though the weaver's question involves only the notion of odd and even, our solution involves, in addition, the notion that one natural number is smaller or larger than another natural number. He might complain, "Though the weaver is now happy, I am not. It seems to me that we should be able to find a proof that stays within the given notions—a proof that doesn't make use of those backward pairs." Actually there is such a proof, but reading it requires more mathematical background than the typical reader is assumed to have (see R 3).

After having worked so hard to make a tool (Corollary 1), let us use it to solve another problem, "The Fifteen puzzle." This little game, sold in almost every dime store, drugstore, and toy store, consists of a square frame holding 15 small movable squares, numbered 1 through 15, and one empty square. We are allowed to switch the blank square with a square next to it as often as we wish. The challenge is to move by a sequence of switches from a given position, such as

1	2	3	4
5	6	7	8
9	10	11	12
13	14	15	

to another specified position, such as

15	14	13	12
11	10	9	8
7	6	5	4
3	2	1	

The reader who would like to test his luck, but who has no Fifteen puzzle handy, can use paper, pencil, and eraser.

It so happens that it is impossible to go from the first position to the second. To see why, we will make use of the concept of backward pairs.

Place the puzzle on top of a red and white checkerboard having squares the size of the movable squares of the puzzle, with a red square in the lower right corner. The blank square begins on red. On the first move, it changes to white. Clearly, with every switch it changes color. In the final position, the blank square, having been returned to the lower right corner, is again red. So the *number of moves* in any solution of this particular problem must be *even*.

Next, we shall relate the positions of a Fifteen puzzle and the moves to arrangements of sixteen numbers in a row and certain switches of these numbers. Calling the blank square 16, we can read off the opening position as we read a printed page, from left to right and top to bottom

$$1, 2, 3, 4, 5, 6, 7, 8, 9, 10, 11, 12, 13, 14, 15, 16.$$

We wish to reach the arrangement that we would read

$$15, 14, 13, 12, 11, 10, 9, 8, 7, 6, 5, 4, 3, 2, 1, 16.$$

Every time we move the blank square we obtain a new arrangement of the sixteen numbers, differing from a preceding arrangement by one switch (of 16 with one of the numbers $1, 2, \cdots, 15$). Since B for the opening position is zero, it is even. The final arrangement has 105 backward pairs (as the reader may check) and hence is odd. If this particular Fifteen puzzle had a solution, then the number of moves would have to be *odd*, since we are traveling from an even arrangement to an odd arrangement.

Since no number is both *odd* and *even*, we can conclude that there is no way of going from the first to the second position through a sequence of switches of the blank square with its neighbors.

An article appearing in the *American Journal of Mathematics* of 1879, which gave the above reasoning, had this footnote from the editors:

> The "15" puzzle for the last few weeks has been prominently before the American public, and may safely be said to have engaged the attention of nine out of ten persons of both sexes and of all ages and conditions of the community. But

this would not have weighed with the editors to induce them to insert articles upon such a subject in the *American Journal of Mathematics*, but for the fact that the principle of the game has its root in what all mathematicians of the present day are aware constitutes the most subtle and characteristic conception of modern algebra, viz: the law of dichotomy applicable to the separation of the terms of every complete system of permutations into two natural and indefeasible groups, a law of the inner world of thought, which may be said to prefigure the polar relation of left- and right-handed screws or of objects in space and their reflexions in a mirror.

Alas, we cannot now go thoroughly into the prefigured relations of left and right on the line, clockwise and counterclockwise in the plane, left-handed and right-handed screws (or gloves) in space. They all rest on the part of algebra called "the theory of determinants," which in turn rests on the distinction between even and odd arrangements. An adequate treatment of determinants would require a small book all to itself.

We can, however, give an inkling of the relation of clockwise and counter-clockwise to our notion of even and odd arrangements. Draw a triangle on a piece of paper and label its corners 1, 2, and 3, such that a bug traveling over the three corners of the triangle in the order 1, 2, 3 will move clockwise, as in this figure:

There are six routes a bug might choose: 1 2 3 (just mentioned), 1 3 2, 2 1 3, 2 3 1, 3 1 2, and 3 2 1. Some will be clockwise, some counterclockwise; some will be even arrangements, some odd. The reader who checks the six cases will see that the even arrangements are also the clockwise, whereas the odd arrangements are the counterclockwise. A similar relation exists for a pyramid (see E 20, E 21, and E 22).

The weaver's problem has taken us far indeed: from threads and seamless hatbands, through the relative size of natural numbers into backward pairs, to the Fifteen puzzle, and finally to clocks and counterclocks. In the next chapter we will set out from the same base, the weaver's two threads, and soon find ourselves on quite a different path.

Exercises

1. Compute $B(2, 5, 1, 4, 3)$, $B(1, 2, 3, 4, 5, 6)$, $B(2, 1)$.

2. What can we say about the number of switches whenever we go from the arrangement 2, 7, 5, 1, 4, 3, 6 to the arrangement 6, 4, 1, 5, 3, 7, 2?

3. Scattered in a room are ten people sitting on ten fixed chairs. Every so often two people switch places while the remaining eight stay fixed. After many switches everyone is in his original chair. What can be said about the number of switches made?

4. (a) Show how we can go from 5, 4, 3, 2, 1, 10, 9, 8, 7, 6 to 10, 9, 8, 7, 6, 5, 4, 3, 2, 1 in five switches.
   (b) Is it possible to go from the first arrangement in (a) to the second arrangement in 142 switches?

5. Prove that we can always go from one arrangement of the natural numbers from 1 through 20 to any other arrangement of them in 19 or fewer steps.

6. The reader probably noticed that we proved our theorem only with the assumption that c is less than d. Take care of the case in which c is larger than d.

7. Can we go from

1	2	3	4
5	6	7	8
9	10	11	12
13	14	15	▨

to

▨	1	2	3
4	5	6	7
8	9	10	11
12	13	14	15

?

8. Can we go from

1	2	3	4
5	6	7	8
9	10	11	12
13	14	15	▨

to

13	14	15	▨
1	2	3	4
5	6	7	8
9	10	11	12

?

9. Can we go from

1	2	3	4
5	6	7	8
9	10	11	12
13	14	15	▨

to

1	2	3	4
13	14	15	▨
9	10	11	12
5	6	7	8

?

Be careful! (See R 2.)

10. (a) How many arrangements of 1, 2, 3, 4 have their B equal to 0?
    (b) How many arrangements of 1, 2, 3, 4 have their B equal to 1? To 2?
    (c) The same for B equal to 3, 4, 5, or 6.

11. (a) List all possible arrangements of 1, 2, 3, 4 (there are 24).
    (b) How many have their B even?
    (c) How many have their B odd?

12. The same as E 11 for the six arrangements of 1, 2, 3 (instead of the arrangements of 1, 2, 3, 4).

13. (a) Inspecting your list of E 11, show that, when you switch the 1 with the 2 in any arrangement with even B, you obtain an arrangement with odd B (what result in the chapter promises this?).
    (b) Why does (a) tell us that there are at least as many arrangements of 1, 2, 3, 4 with odd B as with even B?
    (c) Similarly, show why there must be at least as many arrangements with even B as with odd B.
    (d) From (b) and (c) conclude that there must be the same number of arrangements with even B as with odd B.

14. Prove that the number of arrangements of 1, 2, 3, 4, 5, 6, 7, 8, 9, 10 with even B is the same as with odd B. (*Hint:* Use the ideas of E 13.)

15. (a) Without computing any B, show that the number of switches in going from

1	2	3	4			2	1	4	3
5	6	7	8			6	5	8	7
9	10	11	12	to		10	9	12	11
13	14	15	≋			14	13	≋	15

    must be even. (Show that, if we are allowed to lift numbers out of the box and switch any pair, we could get from the first to the second in 8 switches.)
    (b) Prove that the puzzle in (a) is not solvable.

16. Without computing any B, determine whether one can go from

1	2	3		1	4	7
4	5	6	to	2	5	8
7	8	≋		3	6	≋

    in what might be called "The Eight puzzle." (See E 15.)

17. (a) Draw the position of the Fifteen puzzle recorded by the arrangement

    1, 2, 3, 4, 5, 6, 7, 8, 9, 10, 11, 12, 13, 14, 15, 16.

    (b) Draw the position of the Fifteen puzzle recorded by the arrangement

    1, 2, 3, 4, 13, 14, 15, 16, 9, 10, 11, 12, 5, 6, 7, 8.

    (c) Can one go from (a) to (b) by moves of the Fifteen puzzle?

18. On the three corners of a cardboard equilateral triangle lying on the floor are written the numbers 1, 2, and 3. The triangle is slid about the floor until it occupies once again its original place, though the three numbers might now be in different positions.

    Below the arrangement 1 2 3 write the arrangement that replaces it when you carry out the above experiment (that is, below 1 write the number that occupies the place on the floor originally occupied by 1, and likewise, below 2 and 3, their replacements). Show that you can get all three even arrangements of 1, 2, and 3 in this manner.

19. Show that if we allow ourselves to lift the triangle of E 18 off the floor and flip it over, then all six arrangements of 1, 2, and 3 can be obtained.

20. By definition, a right-handed screw, when turned clockwise, goes into the wood. Number the four corners of a triangular pyramid 1, 2, 3, and 4 in order that when the triangle 1, 2, 3 is taken as the top of a right-handed screw and 4 as the point, and is turned in the direction given by 1 to 2 to 3, 4 goes into the wood. In all that follows keep this labeling fixed on the pyramid.

    Consider the arrangement 4 1 2 3. Regard 4 1 2 as determining the top of the screw and 3 as the point. Show that when you turn the (pyramidal) screw in the direction 4 to 1 to 2, then 3 goes out of the wood.

21. Keep the labeling of E 20. In any of the 24 arrangements of 1 2 3 4 regard the right-hand number as the point, and the first three as the top of a right-handed screw, their order indicating the direction in which we turn it.
    (a) Verify that 1 2 3 4 has even *B* and sends the point into the wood.
    (b) Verify that 4 1 2 3 has odd *B* and sends the point out of the wood.
    (c) Verify that 2 4 3 1 has an even *B* and sends the point into the wood.

22. This continues E 21. Still keeping the labeling of the four corners of the pyramid of E 20, list the 24 arrangements of 1 2 3 4, and record for each whether *B* is even or odd and also whether the point moves into or out of the wood. What do you notice? Your list should reveal a relation similar to the one we found for the wandering bug on the triangle.

References

1. B. L. van der Waerden, *Science Awakening*, Noordhoff Ltd., Groningen, Holland, 1954. (Pages 108–110 discuss the history of even and odd.)

2. W. E. Story, Note on the '15' puzzle, *American Journal of Mathematics*, vol. 2, 1879, pp. 399–404. (This article shows that the puzzles that might be solvable indeed are solvable. That is, if the red-white and *B* reasoning leads to no contradiction, then the puzzle is solvable.)

3. *J. L. Brenner, A new proof that no permutation is both even and odd, *American Mathematical Monthly*, vol. 64, 1957, pp. 499–500. (This presents a proof, which does not use the notion of "greater and less," that a hatband must have an even number of switches.)

Chapter 2

THE COMPLETE
TRIANGLE

One morning I left my cat, Mackie, inside the house. When I returned in the evening I again found her inside. I wondered whether she had gone out during the day, and if so, how many times she had gone through the door.

It was not a hard riddle to solve. Maybe she had stayed in the house all day. But if she had gone out, then, after using the door once, she would have been outside; after using it twice, she would have been inside again. In general, after an odd number of trips through the door, Mackie would have been outside; after an even number, inside. Thus, while I was away, she would have had to go through the door an even number of times.

This reasoning is actually a variation of the weaver's analysis of designs with two threads. In fact, Mackie's riddle is simply a disguised version of the weaver's problem with just two threads.

But Mackie will now lead us in a different direction. Let us draw the diary of her day as a line segment stretching from morning to evening. It might look like this:

$$\underline{A \qquad B \quad B \quad A \qquad B \qquad A}\,,$$

morning   ·   evening

which is short for: started inside (A); went outside (B); stayed out awhile (B); went inside (A); went out again (B); then came back inside (A). The letters cut the original line segment into little segments; in this example there are five little segments. Each little segment with an A at one end and a B at its other end records a passage through the door. The total number of little segments having an A at one end and a B at the other is therefore even. And if Mackie was inside in the morning and outside in the evening, we could conclude that she had used the door an odd number of times. *Calling a little segment having one end labeled A and the other labeled B a* **complete segment,** we can state this miniature theorem, obtained with Mackie's help:

THEOREM 1. *If we divide a given line segment into little segments by means of dots, and then label these dots (including the two ends of the given line seg-*

12

ment) either A or B, then there is this relation between the number of complete segments and the two end dots of the given line segment:

1. *If the two end dots are labeled A and B, then there are an odd number of complete segments.*

2. *If the two end dots are both labeled A (or are both labeled B), then there are an even number of complete segments.*

The reader may be wondering, "Must we use a cat to prove Theorem 1? Surely there is a proof that can be expressed within the structure of the original line segment that we are dividing, since Theorem 1 concerns just that line." It is easy to satisfy such a scrupulous reader. We may imagine dividing the line into little segments by drawing and labeling dots one after the other. Though these divisions can be made in many ways, we can separate them into three types and see what *change* results in the number of *complete* segments each time we draw a dot.

Each time we draw a dot we introduce it into a segment whose ends are *A* and *A*, *B* and *B*, or *A* and *B*.

In the first case we have

new dot

A   *A*

If we label the new dot *A*, we create no complete segments; if we label it *B*, we create two new complete segments. In both cases the change is even. The same holds if we draw a dot in a segment having ends *B* and *B*, as the reader may check.

In the last case we have

new dot

A   *B*

If we label the new dot *A*, then we have replaced a complete segment with one complete segment and one with a segment having ends *A* and *A*. Thus we have no change in the total number of complete segments. A similar conclusion holds if we label the new dot *B*.

Consequently every time we draw and label a dot, the number of complete segments changes by an even number. If we start out with the line labeled *AB* (one complete segment), we continue to have an odd number of complete segments. If we start with the line labeled *AA*, or the one labeled *BB* (zero complete segments), we still have an even number of complete segments. This reasoning, pulling no cat out of the hat, should please that demanding reader.

Before we go on, let us rephrase Theorem 1 in order to emphasize the role of even and odd:

THEOREM 1 (rephrased). *If we divide a given line segment into little segments by means of dots, and then label these dots either A or B (including the two at the ends of the line), then there is this relation between the number of complete segments and the two end dots of the line:*

1. *If an odd number of the two end dots are labeled A, then there are an odd number of complete segments.*

2. *If an even number of the two end dots are labeled A, then there are an even number of complete segments.*

(*Of course we could have used the letter B instead of A in statements 1 and 2.*)

A mathematician who proves something about the line is not at peace until he learns whether his result is related to (usually more interesting) truths in the higher dimensions of the plane and space. If he finds no analogue in higher dimensions, he is disappointed. If he does find analogues, then he feels that he has penetrated a mystery that the line half concealed, half revealed. Perhaps he will find to his dismay that the proof that worked so easily on the line gives him no clue for dealing with the plane or with space. If so, he will seek a proof for the line that does help him treat the higher dimensions.

Now where do we go from Theorem 1, which is so close to that instance of the weaver's problem that involves only two threads? The weaver himself suggested the deeper problem that lay beyond: designs with three or more threads. But Mackie gives us no clue as to what might be the theorem corresponding to the three letters *A*, *B*, and *C*, instead of just *A* and *B*. If there is anything to be discovered, we shall have to discover it for ourselves.

Let us try. The basic idea was the *complete segment*. With three letters at our disposal we might think of a **complete triangle,** *a triangle furnished with all three of the letters A, B, and C at its corners.* Instead of cutting up a line segment into little segments, perhaps we should experiment with cutting up a triangle into little triangles by means of dots. Then we will label these dots either *A*, *B*, or *C*, and see what, if anything, we can find out.

This time we begin with a big triangle and draw dots inside it and on its border. We keep joining these dots with straight lines until we have cut up the big triangle into little triangles that, together, cover the big triangle. The dots become corners of the little triangles. Next we label each dot *A*, *B*, or *C* until each little triangle has a letter at each of its three corners.

Is there any relation between the number of complete little triangles and some property of the border of the big triangle? If there is, then we will have an analogue in the plane of Theorem 1. Let us make some experiments and, keeping odd and even in mind, try to unearth a relation between complete triangles and the border—if there is any such relation.

Not knowing what might be the relation between the number of complete triangles and the border, we record various data in the hope of finding a clue. Here is one experiment:

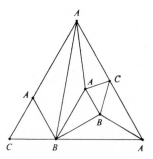

The data from this experiment appear in the first line of the table below. Four other experiments (not drawn here) lead to additional facts, which we record in the appropriate columns.

Complete				On the Border						
Triangles	Dots A	Dots B	Dots C	Edges: AA	BB	CC	AB	AC	BC
3	3	1	2	1	0	0	1	3	1
2	2	3	3	0	1	1	2	2	2
5	2	6	1	0	4	0	3	1	1
3	3	3	4	0	0	3	5	1	1
3	4	4	1	3	3	0	1	1	1

The reader is invited to make his own experiments.

Now let us see what we can find out. Our first instinct is to see whether the number of dots *A* on the border influences the number of complete triangles, as it did in Theorem 1 (rephrased). The answer is no; with two dots *A* we have both two and five complete triangles, as our list of experiments shows. Similarly, we can dispose of dots *B* and *C* and edges *AA*, *BB*, and *CC*.

But there seems to be a simple relation between complete triangles and edges *AB*, *AC*, or *BC*. Directing our attention to edges *AB*, for example, we are tempted to conjecture this analogue of rephrased Theorem 1:

THEOREM 2. *If we divide a triangle into little triangles by means of dots, and then label these dots either A, B, or C (including the three at the corners of the big triangle), then there is this relation between the number of complete little triangles and the edges on the border:*

1. *If an odd number of the edges on the border have their two ends labeled A and B, then there is an odd number of complete triangles.*

2. *If an even number of the edges on the border have their two ends labeled A and B, then there is an even number of complete triangles.*

Of course we could replace *AB* by *BC* or *AC* and still obtain a reasonable conjecture.

It certainly is not obvious that our conjectured Theorem 2 is always true. After all, if it were true, it would say in particular that if we have an odd number of edges of the type *AB* on the border, then there must be at least one complete triangle. It is hard to imagine that the border can influence the inside of the triangle so much. Therefore the reader may be surprised at the results of his own experiments if he starts at the border with an odd number of *AB* edges and tries to avoid forming a complete triangle as he labels the dots inside the big triangle.

After a few more experiments the reader may feel certain that Theorem 2 is indeed true. But how shall we go about proving it? If we look back at our catless proof of Theorem 1, we might think of watching what happens if a dot is drawn in a little triangle: does the number of complete triangles *change* by an even number?

For example, what happens when we draw a dot in a complete triangle? No matter how we label it, we end up with one complete triangle, as the reader may see by glancing at this picture:

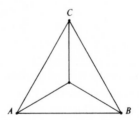

In this case there is no change in the number of complete triangles.

As another example, if we draw a dot inside

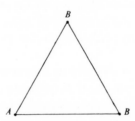

we end up with either zero or two complete triangles, again an even *change*.

The reader may easily check the other cases and see that, each time, the change in the number of complete triangles is even. Unfortunately this gets us nowhere. Though such reasoning worked on the line, it is inadequate for triangles.

Some divisions of the triangle can, of course, be obtained by the process described above; for example this division can be obtained by using the process twice:

But a division such as

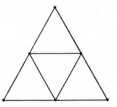

cannot be obtained by such a method.

If we are to prove Theorem 2, we will have to use new ideas. Perhaps the best thing to do now is to go back and try to find a new proof of Theorem 1, a proof which neither uses a cat nor draws a dot at a time. Perhaps the idea behind such a new proof might help us with Theorem 2. So let us backtrack for a moment and study the line once again.

Let us look at the various kinds of little segments that can appear in a division of a line segment. There are three types:

A ─── A B ─── B and the complete $\dfrac{A \quad\quad B}{B \quad\quad A}$

A complete little segment contributes one A, whereas the other types contribute either zero A's or two A's. More briefly, a complete segment contributes one A, whereas all the other little segments contribute an even number of A's. From this fresh observation we might be able to get a new proof of Theorem 1. Let us try.

Imagine that we have a division of a line segment into little segments. Let us say that T of these little segments are complete. Of course, T might be zero, but in any case, we want to find a relation between T and the number of A's at the ends of the original line. We want to use our fresh observation.

Consider a typical little segment. Place a pebble above any of its ends labeled A. Do this for each little segment. For example, if we have this division, then we end up with the pebbles piled as follows:

Any dot labeled *A* inside the original line segment has two pebbles, because it is the end of two little segments. Any dot labeled *A* at an end of the original line segment collects one pebble. These observations hold not only in this example but in any division of a line segment into little segments.

Let us now do some bookkeeping for the general case. Each complete little segment has one *A*, and hence contributes one pebble; all the other little segments contribute an even number of pebbles (either zero or two). Thus the total number of pebbles is *T plus an even natural number*, where *T* is the number of complete little segments.

Now let us look at the total number of pebbles in a different way. Any dot at the end of the original segment and labeled *A* has one pebble. Any inside dot labeled *A* has two pebbles. No other dot has pebbles. Thus the total number of pebbles is equal to *the number of A's at the ends of the original segment plus some even natural number*.

Combining these two views of the pebbles (and the fact that even + odd = odd, and even + even = even), the reader may easily obtain a new proof of Theorem 1.

Does this third proof of Theorem 1 give us a method for attacking Theorem 2? The key is that a complete little segment contributes one *A*, whereas all other little segments contribute an even number of *A*'s. We will now examine closely the way in which little triangles contribute edges of the type *AB*, for Theorem 2 concerns such edges. There are ten types of little triangles:

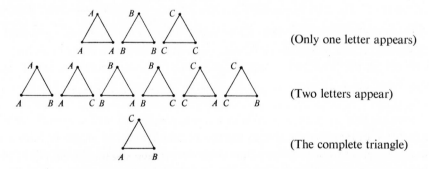

Of the ten triangles, seven have no *AB* edges; two have two *AB* edges; and the complete triangle has one *AB* edge. In short: a complete triangle contributes one *AB*, whereas all the other little triangles contribute an even number of *AB*'s. Can we base a proof of Theorem 2 on this fact?

Imagine that we have a division of the big triangle into little triangles. Let us say that T of these little triangles are complete. Of course, T might be zero, but in any case, we want to find a relation between T and the number of AB's on the border of the big triangle.

Again, a little bookkeeping. Consider a typical little triangle. Place a pebble on any of its edges labeled AB. Do this for each little triangle. Let us now look at the total number of pebbles in two ways.

First, each complete little triangle contributes one pebble; all the other little triangles contribute an even number of pebbles (either zero or two). Thus the total number of pebbles is *T plus an even natural number*.

Second, any edge AB on the border of the original triangle has one pebble. Any edge AB inside the big triangle has two pebbles. No other edges have pebbles. Thus the total number of pebbles is also equal to the *number of AB's on the border plus some even natural number*.

Combining these views we obtain the equation

$$T + \frac{\text{an even}}{\text{natural number}} = \frac{\text{number of } AB\text{'s}}{\text{on the border}} + \frac{\text{some even}}{\text{natural number.}}$$

Thus, if the number of AB's on the border is even, then so is the number of complete triangles. And if the number of AB's on the border is odd, so is the number of complete triangles. We have succeeded in proving Theorem 2; and only our third proof of Theorem 1 was of use. For this reason we can claim that the third proof of Theorem 1 is preferable, since it extended to the plane, whereas the other two did not.

The third proof has another distinction. It treats as a whole the division of the line into segments, whereas the others involve the manner in which the dots are inserted. The first two proofs are adequate for the line, since the divisions into little segments are relatively simple, but they fail to cope with the more complex divisions of the triangle.

From Theorem 2 we can deduce immediately

THEOREM 3. *If there is an odd number of AB's on the border of the big triangle, then there must be at least one complete little triangle.*

Since Theorem 3 is just a consequence of Theorem 2, we might think that it would be easier to prove. But I know of no elementary proof of Theorem 3 that bypasses the more general result—Theorem 2. It frequently happens in mathematics that it is simpler to prove more than to prove less; the general case exposes more and might even suggest the ideas on which to base a proof, whereas the special case might simply mislead. Suppose, for example, that the weaver of Chapter 1 had asked us: "Can I make a seamless hatband with 315 switches and 315 threads?" We would not have known where to turn. But he asked the seemingly tougher question, "Can I design a seamless hatband with an odd number of switches?" This helped us to concentrate on the number of switches, not the number of threads.

Historically, one special form of Theorem 2 is of importance here. It is the basis of several results in topology, a branch of mathematics that we shall discuss in later chapters. In honor of the Polish mathematician who discovered it in 1928, it is named

SPERNER'S LEMMA. *Label the three corners of the big triangle A, B, and C. Label dots inside the big triangle either A, B, or C. Label dots on the edge AB of the big triangle either A or B. Label dots on the edge BC of the big triangle either B or C. Label dots on the edge AC of the big triangle either A or C. Then the number of complete little triangles is odd.*

The reader can easily prove Sperner's lemma with the aid of Theorems 1 and 2.

Among the consequences of Sperner's lemma is the following. Let us say that in the morning you pass by a circular puddle of water completely covered with oil. A gentle breeze blows all day, moving the oil about the surface of the puddle, but not breaking the oil film. Then (it can be proved) when you pass by the puddle in the evening, at least one molecule of oil will be exactly where you saw it in the morning. Stating this a little more formally, we have

BROUWER'S FIXED POINT THEOREM. *Every smooth distortion of a circular disk into itself leaves at least one point fixed.*

The proof of Brouwer's theorem from Sperner's lemma is rather involved; it can be found in R 1. Brouwer's theorem, in turn, has many applications inside and outside of mathematics. Recently it has even assumed importance in economic theory. In the 1959 *SIAM Review*, A. T. C. Koopmans and A. F. Bausch report that

> The extent to which equilibria exist in actual markets is a matter for observation. The concern here is whether the [mathematical] model—extensively used to draw various conclusions about equilibrium—is capable of insuring the possibility of an equilibrium under the conditions it specifies.· · · There is little point in knowing that a competitive equilibrium, if possible, achieves efficient allocations of resources, if in fact it is a logical impossibility. The problem of the existence of a competitive equilibrium . . . is a topological one, and all recent proofs have made use of some topological result equivalent to Brouwer's fixed point theorem, or a generalization thereof.

Sperner's lemma also plays a key role in defining the dimension of a space. (This is touched on in Appendix C.)

We have come quite far from the problem that opened the chapter. Though the riddle of the cat and that of the weaver of two threads are really the same, they have led us to theorems whose only similarity is that they both involve the fundamental distinction between the even and the odd natural numbers. One led us into algebra, the other into topology.

Exercises

1. Prove that Theorem 1 (rephrased) remains true if we consider dots labeled *B* instead of *A*.

2. Does Theorem 2 remain true if we look at border edges labeled *BC* instead of *AB*? Justify your answer.

3. Prove that if the number of edges *AA* on the border of the big triangle is odd, then there is at least one little triangle with the letter *A* appearing on at least two of its three corners.

4. Prove that if the number of edges *AA* on the border of the big triangle is odd, then there are an odd number of little triangles with the letter *A* appearing on at least two of its three corners. (*Hint:* Do bookkeeping with contributions of *AA* edges.)

5. Contrast E 3 and E 4 with Theorems 3 and 2.

6. If only the letter *C* appears on the border of the big triangle, what can we say about the number of complete little triangles?

7. Prove Sperner's lemma.

8. The surface of a sphere is cut into triangles (with curved sides) by means of dots, which are then labeled *A*, *B*, or *C*. How many complete triangles are there?
   (a) Experiment three times (perhaps on a ping-pong ball); record the number of complete triangles each time.
   (b) Make a conjecture.
   (c) Prove your conjecture.

9. On the border of a circle, dots are drawn and labeled either *A*, *B* or *C*. Find a relation between the number of arcs *AB*, the number of arcs *BC*, and the number of arcs *AC*.
   (a) Experiment three times.
   (b) Make a conjecture.

10. (a) Prove E 9 (b) using Theorem 2 and E 2.
    (b) Prove E 9 (b) by studying what happens each time a dot is drawn and labeled.

11. (a) Theorem 1 is to the line segment as Theorem 2 is to the triangle as (?) is to the triangular pyramid.
    (b) Prove (?).

12. Does Theorem 1 remain true if the line is drawn wiggly, or have we used straightness in our proof?

13. Does Theorem 2 remain true if all the lines are drawn wiggly, or have we used straightness in our proof?

14. On the border of a circle, dots are drawn and labeled either A, B, C, or D. Is there any relation between the number of little segments AB and the number of little segments AC?

15. What do you think must be true about the dots of a division of the big triangle into little triangles if all the dots can be labeled in such a way that each little triangle is complete? Consider (a) dots inside the big triangle and (b) dots on the border of the big triangle.

16. If Mackie was at the foot of the stairs in the morning and at the top in the evening, we could deduce something stronger than Theorem 1. We could be sure that she went up the stairs once more than she went down them. In terms of the line segment picturing Mackie's diary, we could say that *the number of complete little segments with B right of A is one more than the number of complete little segments with B left of A*. Prove, without using Mackie, this refined version of Theorem 1. (Observe that the left end of the big line segment is A and that the right end is B; then examine what happens each time a dot is introduced and labeled.)

17. Left and right are to the line segment as clockwise and counterclockwise are to the triangle. Let us call a complete triangle clockwise if a bug making a journey A to B to C along its vertices moves clockwise; and similarly for counterclockwise. Assume that the dots by which the big triangle is cut up are labeled as in Sperner's lemma.
    (a) Make five experiments in which you count the number of clockwise, and also the number of counterclockwise, complete little triangles.
    (b) What do you notice?

18. Let us strengthen Sperner's lemma as we strengthened Theorem 1 in E 16. Assume that the dots are labeled in accordance with the restriction in Sperner's lemma and that the three corners of the big triangle are labeled A, B, and C in clockwise order.

    (a) Show that this
        THEOREM. *There is one more clockwise, complete little triangle than the number of counterclockwise complete little triangles.*
    agrees with your experiments.
    (b) Show that this theorem implies Sperner's lemma.

19. We now outline the steps for proving the theorem of E 18. Consider a bug who always travels around triangles in a clockwise direction. Whenever he moves along an edge that has both an A at one end and a B at the other, he does so in one of two possible ways: either he meets the A first and then the B (which we record then as $\overrightarrow{AB}$) or he meets the B first and then the A (which we record then as $\overrightarrow{BA}$). Do bookkeeping with contributions of $\overrightarrow{AB}$ and $\overrightarrow{BA}$. Using suitable drawings, show that

(a) In a clockwise complete triangle the bug sweeps out one $\overrightarrow{AB}$.

(b) In a counterclockwise complete triangle the bug sweeps out one $\overrightarrow{BA}$.

(c) In a triangle whose corners are labeled A, A, and B, the bug sweeps out one $\overrightarrow{AB}$ and one $\overrightarrow{BA}$.

(d) In a triangle whose corners are labeled B, B, and A, the bug sweeps out one $\overrightarrow{AB}$ and one $\overrightarrow{BA}$.

(e) In all other triangles the bug sweeps out no $\overrightarrow{AB}$'s and no $\overrightarrow{BA}$'s.

(f) Now prove the theorem of E 18 by counting contributions of $\overrightarrow{AB}$ and $\overrightarrow{BA}$ (recall E 16).

20. Prove that if dots are drawn on the border of a triangle and labeled either A or B, then there is an even number of edges having both an A and a B by
    (a) making use of Theorem 3;
    (b) employing an argument that uses only the border.

21. The surface of a sphere is divided into little triangles (with curved sides) by dots, which are then labeled A, B, C, or D. Prove that if the number of ABC triangles is odd, then so is the number of DBC triangles. (*Hint:* Count contributions of BC edges carefully.)

22. The surface of a sphere is divided into little triangles (with curved sides) by dots, which are labeled A, B, C, or D. Prove that the number of little triangles with more than one A at its corners is even.

23. Prove that if a triangle is cut into an odd number of little triangles by dots, then there must be an odd number of edges on the border of the big triangle.

24. Is it possible to cut the surface of a sphere into little triangles by dots in such a way that there are an odd number of little triangles?
    (a) Experiment (on a ball, if one is available).
    (b) Make a conjecture.
    (c) Prove it.
    (*Hint:* Do bookkeeping with edges and note that each triangle contributes three edges.)

25. (a) Cut a triangle into little triangles by means of dots.
    (b) Count the number of little triangles in (a).
    (c) With the *same* dots, cut the big triangle into little triangles in another way. (If you wish, you might make a copy of the big triangle with its dots.)
    (d) Count the number of little triangles in (c).
    (e) Using the same dots, carry out the experiment again, and count the number of little triangles.
    (f) Make a conjecture. (A proof can be based on material in Chapter 13, in particular E 45 of Chapter 13.)

References

1. *P. S. Aleksandrov, *Combinatorial Topology*, vol. 1, Graylock Press, Rochester, 1956. (Chapter 5 is devoted to Sperner's lemma and its applications.)

THE PRIMES

The even numbers are those natural numbers that can be written as the sum of 2's; natural numbers that are not even are odd. The duality of even and odd rests, then, on the number 2. But 2 is important also as being the first of the primes. To these natural numbers, the object of study for well over two thousand years, we now turn.

In order to define the primes, we shall need the notion of the divisors of a natural number. *A natural number A* **divides** *a natural number B if there is a natural number Q such that*

$$B = Q \times A.*$$

If A divides B, we call A a **divisor** *of B and B a* **multiple** *of A*. For example, 6 has four divisors, 1, 2, 3, and 6; the multiples of 2 are precisely the even numbers. Any natural number A is a divisor of 0, since $0 = 0 \times A$. The only natural number with precisely one divisor is the number 1. Any other natural number has at least two divisors, namely itself and 1. *The natural numbers with only two divisors are called the* **primes.** The reader may check that the first twenty primes are

2, 3, 5, 7, 11, 13, 17, 19, 23, 29, 31, 37, 41, 43, 47, 53, 59, 61, 67, 71,

and may easily extend this brief list. A prime can also be described as a natural number (larger than 1) that is not the product of two smaller natural numbers.

As we compute more and more primes, various questions come to mind. How many primes are there? How far apart can adjacent primes be (in the above list the largest gap is 6)? How many pairs of primes differ by 1 (for example, 2 and 3)? How many pairs of primes differ by 2 (for example, 3 and 5, 5 and 7, 11 and 13)? How many pairs of primes differ by 3 (for example, 2 and 5)? How many pairs of primes differ by 4 (for example, 3 and 7, 7 and 11)? Some of these questions can be answered easily, but others are so hard that nobody knows their answer. Let us take them up one by one.

Our first question—"How many primes are there"?—was answered by the

---

* The product of two numbers a and b will be denoted either $a \times b$ or ab.

Greeks some 2300 years ago. Their solution, which appears as Proposition 20 in Book 9 of Euclid, is based on their *Prime-manufacturing Machine*. When anyone feeds primes into this machine, it spews out brand new primes—primes that are different from those fed into it. Let us first watch it in operation; we will explain afterward why it always works.

Let us feed the machine the primes 3, 5, and 11, which we have chosen at random. The machine multiplies them all together, getting 165. Then it adds 1 to this result, getting 166. Then it produces all the primes that divide 166; namely, 2 and 83. We see that 2 and 83 are indeed brand new, being different from the three primes we fed the machine. The reader may check that when he feeds the machine the primes 2, 3, and 5 it produces just the one new prime, 31. That the primes manufactured by the machine are indeed different from those fed into it is the content of

THEOREM 1. *Any prime dividing the natural number that is 1 larger than the product of several primes is different from any of those primes.*

PROOF. Let us, like Adam naming the creatures, give names to the several primes in question so that we can speak of them. If we called them A, B, C, $\cdots$, then we would limit ourselves to feeding the machine at most twenty-six primes. We can avoid this artificial limit by naming the first prime we feed the machine F_1 (the letter F standing for Feed), the second prime we feed the machine F_2, and so on. When we feed the machine twenty-seven primes we name them

$$F_1, F_2, \cdots, F_{27}.$$

Now let us feed the machine N primes,

$$F_1, F_2, \cdots, F_N.$$

The machine forms their product $F_1 \times F_2 \times \cdots \times F_N$ and then adds 1 to this product to obtain the natural number

$$1 + (F_1 \times F_2 \times \cdots \times F_N),$$

which we will call M. Thus

$$M = 1 + (F_1 \times F_2 \times \cdots \times F_N).$$

We must prove that none of the primes $F_1, F_2, \cdots, F_N$ divides M. To do this, we first observe that no natural number bigger than 1 can divide two natural numbers that differ by 1, for when a natural number divides two natural numbers it also divides their difference. But each of the $F_1, F_2, \cdots, F_N$ clearly divides the product $F_1 \times F_2 \times \cdots \times F_N$. Hence none of the F's can divide the natural number M, which is one larger than $F_1 \times F_2 \times \cdots \times F_N$. Thus the machine produces only new primes. Our proof is done.

The wary reader might say, "Almost done. After all, how can we be sure that *M* always has a prime divisor?" The answer to this question is not hard, and is sketched in E 7.

With the help of the machine, we can now provide an answer to "How many primes are there?" in the form of

THEOREM 2. *There is no end to the primes.*

PROOF. Let us assume that there is an end to the primes. Feed a list of all the primes into the machine. The machine, operating on them as it does with any list of primes, spews out primes different from all we fed into it. But our list was supposed to be a complete inventory of all the primes. Our assumption must be mistaken, for we have reached a contradiction—a list that is both complete and incomplete. Therefore, there is no end to the primes. This proves Theorem 2.

The proof itself deserves some comment. It is an illustration of a frequently used technique in mathematics, called "proof by contradiction." Rather than proving an assertion directly we show that the denial of the assertion leads to nonsense. We used this same technique in proving that certain Fifteen puzzle problems have no solution. We assumed that they did have a solution and deduced from this assumption that a certain number must be both odd and even, which is surely nonsense.

It is also interesting to note that, though our definition of prime involves only the notion of multiplication, our proof that there is no end to the primes also involves addition (we added 1). The reason for this is that, although "divisor" was defined only in terms of multiplication, it happens to behave nicely with respect to addition: a divisor of two natural numbers is also a divisor of their sum and of their difference.

We have already met another proof like that of Theorem 2, similar in that it goes outside of the structure in which the definitions are made and the theorems stated. In the weaver's problem we went outside of odd and even and used the idea of one number being larger or smaller than another. We will meet more proofs like these in Chapters 4 and 5.

The machine helped us answer our first question. Now let us turn to our second. "How far apart can adjacent primes be?" We answer this with

THEOREM 3. *There are gaps as big as we please between adjacent primes.*

PROOF. We illustrate the idea by proving that there are 999 consecutive natural numbers, none of which is prime. To do this, we first multiply to-gether all the natural numbers from 1 through 1000. Call their product 1000 factorial (abbreviated 1000!). Then we will show that none of the following 999 consecutive natural numbers is prime:

$$1000! + 2, \qquad 1000! + 3, \qquad 1000! + 4, \qquad \cdots, \qquad 1000! + 1000.$$

The first is divisible by 2, since 2 divides both 2 and 1000!. The second is divisible by 3, the third by 4, and so on. Thus we have produced 999 consecutive integers, none of which is prime. The same idea can, of course, be used to produce larger gaps between primes, and our proof is done.

It would seem more natural to have started with 1000! instead of 1000! + 2, but 1000! + 1 might be prime. After all, 3! + 1 is prime. This raises another question: How many natural numbers of the form $N! + 1$ are prime? No one knows. Nor is it known whether 1000! + 1 is prime.

But let us return to the next question we asked at the beginning of the chapter, "How many pairs of primes differ by 1?" This is an easy one. Clearly, 2 is the only even prime. Any two other primes, being odd, differ by at least 2. Thus, 2 and 3 are the only primes differing by 1. Similarly, 2 and 5 are the only primes differing by 3. And going on, we see that 2 and 7 are the only primes differing by 5 and that there are no primes differing by 7.

But what about pairs of primes differing by 2? Such pairs, called "twin primes," have been the object of some of the deepest research in number theory for half a century. Yet nobody knows whether they end. A long list of primes suggests that they go on and on, but become rarer and rarer as we go farther in the list. Primes differing by 4 have also concealed their secrets well, though they have yielded some clues. For instance, they seem to be about as frequent as twin primes.

The study of the gaps between primes is intimately connected with the way in which the primes increase in size as we go farther and farther in the list of primes. If the gaps tend to grow larger and larger, then the primes grow more quickly; and we have seen that there are gaps as large as we please between primes. But if the small gaps, like 2 or 4, occurred very frequently, then the primes would not grow very quickly. Inspection of our own table of primes shows that the gaps fluctuate quite chaotically.

Yet even within chaos, mathematicians can discover order. We might even say that when things become totally chaotic order reappears. When a penny is flipped with absolute randomness, we find in the midst of that chaos this law: in the long run heads will appear half the time. In the midst of the chaos of primes there is order. In the long run, the gaps between the primes also exhibit a certain orderliness.

To discuss how the primes behave as we go farther and farther in the list, let us introduce a notation for them. Let us call the first prime P_1; the second prime, P_2; and so on. Thus, for example, P_{10}, the *tenth* prime, is 29. Since the gap between primes is always at least 1, we can say that the Nth prime, P_N, is at least as large as N. But we could be more precise. Since the gaps are at least 2 (except between 2 and 3) once we go beyond the fourth prime, 7, we can say that P_N is at least as large as $N \times 2$. As a matter of fact, P_{10} is 29, which is 10×2.9. Now, P_{10} can be thought of as the sum of ten gaps: from 0 to P_1, from P_1 to P_2, from P_2 to P_3, $\cdots$, from P_9 to P_{10}. Hence we can say that the average of the first ten gaps is 2.9, since $P_{10} = 10 \times 2.9$; moreover, we see the intimate relation between the average gap up to the Nth prime and the size of the Nth prime. If we know one, we know the other, for P_N is simply N times the average of the first N gaps. By the time we reach the 20th prime, 71, the average gap has grown to 3.55, since we have $P_{20} = 71 = 20 \times 3.55$. Thus, any estimate we have of the average of the first N gaps gives us a way of estimating P_N without our having to list all the primes from P_1 to P_N.

In 1791, Gauss noticed by inspection of tables of primes that, though the gaps behaved wildly, the average gap grows slowly and is closely approximated by this formula: the average of the first N gaps is approximately $\frac{1}{1} + \frac{1}{2} + \frac{1}{3} + \frac{1}{4} + \cdots + \frac{1}{N}$. He conjectured but did not prove

THE PRIME NUMBER THEOREM. *P_N is approximately*

$$N \times \left(\frac{1}{1} + \frac{1}{2} + \frac{1}{3} + \cdots + \frac{1}{N} \right).$$

That is, the difference between P_N and $N \times \left(\frac{1}{1} + \frac{1}{2} + \frac{1}{3} + \cdots + \frac{1}{N} \right)$ is small in comparison with P_N when N is large.

The accuracy of Gauss's estimate of P_N is shown by this table:

N	$\left(\frac{1}{1} + \frac{1}{2} + \frac{1}{3} + \cdots + \frac{1}{N} \right)$	$N \times \left(\frac{1}{1} + \frac{1}{2} + \frac{1}{3} + \cdots + \frac{1}{N} \right)$	P_N
1	1	1	2
2	1.5	3	3
3	$1.833\cdots$	5.5	5
4	$2.083\cdots$	8.3	7
5	$2.283\cdots$	$11.4\cdots$	11
10	$2.928\cdots$	$29.2\cdots$	29
20	$3.597\cdots$	$71.9\cdots$	71
100	$5.187\cdots$	$518.7\cdots$	541
1000	$7.485\cdots$	7485	7919

But it was not until 1896 that a proof was discovered for Gauss's conjecture. In that year Hadamard and de la Vallée Poussin, working independently of each other, proved the Prime Number Theorem. Their proofs made use of the complex numbers and the calculus. Finally, in 1948, Selberg and Erdös independently discovered a proof that requires neither the complex numbers nor the calculus. This came as a surprise to the mathematical world, which for over a century and a half had searched in vain for such a proof.

It can be shown that the Prime Number Theorem is equivalent to the assertion that *the number of primes less than the natural number X is roughly*
$X/\left(\frac{1}{1} + \frac{1}{2} + \frac{1}{3} + \cdots + \frac{1}{X}\right)$. As X increases, the numerator grows quickly,
whereas the denominator grows very slowly. (See Appendix B for a discussion of the growth of the denominator.) Thus the quotient becomes very large, which tells us again that there is no end to the primes. From the very deep Prime Number Theorem we obtain a result for which we already had a simple proof.

The situation with twin primes is quite different. Although no one knows whether the twin primes end, there is much experimental evidence in favor of

THE TWIN PRIME CONJECTURE.* *The number of pairs of twin primes less than the natural number X is roughly*

$$1.32X/\left(\frac{1}{1} + \frac{1}{2} + \frac{1}{3} + \cdots + \frac{1}{X}\right)^{2}.$$

This conjecture, made in 1923 by Hardy and Littlewood, would in particular imply that there is no end to the twin primes (for once again, the denominator is the tortoise, and the numerator is the hare). When he conjectured the Prime Number Theorem, Gauss had at least been assured by the Greeks that there is no end to the primes. It might turn out to be easier to prove the Twin Prime Conjecture than to prove that there is no end to the twin primes. We have met such a peculiar situation before, in Chapter 2, where it was easier to prove that there is an odd number of complete triangles than it was to prove that there is at least one. But the Twin Prime Conjecture, so tantalizing in its simplicity and so strongly supported by experimental evidence, remains unproved. (For more in this direction see R 4.)

The twin primes illustrate a very dependable recipe for inventing difficult questions about the primes: ask something about the relation between primes and addition. Since the primes are defined using only multiplication, it would seem fortuitous if they behaved decently with respect to addition. After all, as we saw with the Prime-manufacturing Machine, if we add 1 to a natural number we completely change its prime divisors. And the twin primes involve the addition of 2.

---

* If A is any number, then A^2 denotes $A \times A$,

We must be especially grateful for any result that manages to relate the primes to addition. Let us cite, without proof, a theorem that was proved by Fermat in 1641: *every prime differing from 1 by a multiple of 4 can be written as the sum of two squares in precisely one way.* (A "square" is a number of the form N^2 for some natural number N.) For example, 5 is prime, differs from 1 by 4, and can be written $1^2 + 2^2$. (We regard $2^2 + 1^2$ as the same representation.) Similarly, 13 is prime, differs from 1 by 12, a multiple of 4, and can be written $2^2 + 3^2$.

Fermat's theorem concerns writing primes in terms of other natural numbers. In the opposite direction, there are many questions concerning writing natural numbers in terms of primes. Before we can phrase some of these questions we shall need the notion of a power of a natural number. *The* **powers** *of a natural number N are those natural numbers N, $N \times N$, $N \times N \times N$, $\cdots$ that are the product of N times itself several times.* The first few powers of 2, for example, are 2, 4, 8, 16, $\cdots$; the first few powers of 3 are 3, 9, 27, 81, $\cdots$. The number $N \times N$ is called the *square* of N; $N \times N \times N$ is called the *cube* of N. Rather than write the cumbersome $3 \times 3 \times 3 \times 3$, we write simply 3^4; similarly, we write $2 \times 2 \times 2 \times 2 \times 2$ simply as 2^5.

Now we can raise the questions mentioned in the preceding paragraph. Can every odd natural number larger than 3 be written as the sum of a prime and a power of 2? Can every odd natural number larger than 1 be written as the sum of a prime and twice a square? Can every even natural number larger than 2 be written as the sum of two primes?

A few computations suggest that the answer to all three is "yes." Examining the first question, for example, we have $5 = 3 + 2$, $7 = 5 + 2$, $9 = 7 + 2$, $11 = 7 + 4$, $77 = 13 + 64$, and so forth. If the reader extends the list he will observe that sometimes there may be more than one way of expressing a natural number as such a sum, for example, $7 = 5 + 2$, and $7 = 3 + 4$. Illustrating the second question we have $3 = 3 + 2(0)^2$, $5 = 3 + 2(1)^2$, $7 = 5 + 2(1)^2$, $9 = 7 + 2(1)^2$, $11 = 3 + 2(2)^2$, $57 = 7 + 2(5)^2$. For the third question we have $4 = 2 + 2$, $6 = 3 + 3$, $8 = 3 + 5$, $10 = 3 + 7$ or $5 + 5$, $100 = 89 + 11$, and so on.

These three questions, so similar in spirit, have not had the same fate. The first breaks down at 149—the reader is invited to check this; the second breaks down at 5777; but the third, in spite of the profound research it has inspired, still remains unanswered. Every even natural number that has been tested can be written as the sum of two primes, but no one has proved that every even natural number can be written that way. The first and third questions were raised by Goldbach, the first in 1752, the third in 1742. Clearly, it is not always possible to judge the depth of a question at first glance, though the brevity of the third has an immediate appeal that the first two lack.

Returning to the natural habitat of the primes, multiplication, we raise another question in the spirit of the last three: Can every natural number larger than 1 and not itself a prime be written as the product of primes? A list of experiments begins as follows:

Natural Number	Remark	Natural Number	Remark
2	prime	12	$2 \times 2 \times 3$
3	prime	13	prime
4	2×2	14	2×7
5	prime	15	3×5
6	2×3	16	$2 \times 2 \times 2 \times 2$
7	prime	17	prime
8	$2 \times 2 \times 2$	18	$2 \times 3 \times 3$
9	3×3	19	prime
10	2×5	20	$2 \times 2 \times 5$
11	prime		

Calling the natural numbers larger than 1 and not prime **composite,** we see that all composite natural numbers up to 20 are indeed the product of primes. Jumping ahead, let us see if 100 is the product of primes. Writing first $100 = 10 \times 10$ and then using the fact that $10 = 2 \times 5$, we have $100 = 2 \times 5 \times 2 \times 5$. This computation suggests a way of proving

THEOREM 4. *Every composite natural number is the product of primes.*

PROOF. If N is composite, it can be written as the product of two smaller natural numbers. If those two natural numbers are prime, we are through. If either of the two is composite, it is in turn the product of smaller natural numbers. Continuing this process until we meet only primes, we eventually have N written as the product of primes.

Theorem 4 indicates how the primes earned their name. They can be thought of as the primitive bricks out of which all natural numbers can be built by multiplication, yet they themselves cannot be further reduced by multiplication. The primes are the atoms of multiplication, just as 1 is the only atom of addition, each natural number being a sum of 1's.

The reader, in checking the computations up through 20, will observe that each composite natural number up to 20 can be written in only one way as the product of primes. Of course, $6 = 2 \times 3 = 3 \times 2$, and so, strictly speaking, 6 can be written as a product of primes in more than one way. To avoid this trivial and awkward detail, let us agree that from now on, when we write a natural number as the product of primes, we will record the primes with their size increasing from left to right. For example, we will write $6 = 2 \times 3$ or $100 = 2 \times 2 \times 5 \times 5$.

Let us see what happens with a large natural number, well beyond our list. Say that we want to write 2000 as the product of primes. We might notice first that $2000 = 20 \times 100$; then $20 = 4 \times 5$, and $100 = 10 \times 10$. But $4 = 2 \times 2$, and $10 = 2 \times 5$. Thus $2000 = 2 \times 2 \times 2 \times 2 \times 5 \times 5 \times 5$. Or we might have noticed first that $2000 = 40 \times 50$, and then written $40 = 5 \times 8$ and $50 = 5 \times 10$. But $8 = 2 \times 2 \times 2$ and $10 = 2 \times 5$. Assembling these computations, we have $2000 = 2 \times 2 \times 2 \times 2 \times 5 \times 5 \times 5$. Both times we end up with four 2's and three 5's in the expression of 2000 as the product of primes. The reader is encouraged to carry out his own experiments on the number of ways he can write a composite natural number as the product of primes.

Recall that an even natural number can sometimes be written as the sum of two primes in different ways; for example, $10 = 3 + 7 = 5 + 5$. It certainly is not obvious that the situation should be any different when it concerns natural numbers written as the product of several primes.

Indeed, if the mathematicians of the great academy of Lagado were with us today, they would be shocked if we were to think, even for a moment, that all natural numbers could be written as the product of primes in only one way. In case you have forgotten, this was the academy where, according to Lemuel Gulliver, the teaching of mathematics was attempted in the following manner: "The proposition and demonstration were fairly written on a thin wafer, with ink composed of cephalic tincture. This the student was to swallow upon a fasting stomach, and for three days following eat nothing but bread and water. As the wafer digested, the tincture mounted to the brain, bearing the proposition with it."

Gulliver, for lack of space, failed to report that the King of Laputa, under whom the academy flourished, had noticed that 1 is good, for there is one sun, 4 is good, for there are four seasons, 7 is good, for there are seven days in the week, and 10 is good, for he had ten fingers. His mathematicians replied, "Yes, your majesty, we understand. All natural numbers obtained from 1 by adding a multiple of 3 are good." "A profound insight," commented the King, "hence all other natural numbers must be bad, and I hereby exile them from my kingdom." "But," pleaded the horrified mathematicians, "can't we at least use the bad natural numbers to write down the good? Otherwise, we can't even speak of 13, which is good, though 3 is bad." "Henceforth," decreed the King, "the bad natural numbers can be used only in the notation for the good ones." Thus, in Lagado, they too spoke of prime and composite natural numbers. A good natural number is a Lagado prime if it has exactly two good divisors. In the Lagado system, 4 is prime (recall that 2 was exiled), and 10 is prime (for 2 and 5 were exiled). But 16, a good natural number, is composite, even in the Lagado system, for $16 = 4 \times 4$. In fact, 16 can be written as the product of

Lagado primes in precisely one way. The professors of Lagado made this table of all the ways in which the Lagado natural numbers up to 100 could be written as the product of Lagado primes.

Lagado Natural Numbers	Remarks	Lagado Natural Numbers	Remarks
1	Neither prime nor composite	52	4×13
4	Lagado prime	55	Lagado prime
7	Lagado prime	58	Lagado prime
10	Lagado prime	61	Lagado prime
13	Lagado prime	64	$4 \times 4 \times 4$
16	4×4	67	Lagado prime
19	Lagado prime	70	7×10
22	Lagado prime	73	Lagado prime
25	Lagado prime	76	4×19
28	4×7	79	Lagado prime
31	Lagado prime	82	Lagado prime
34	Lagado prime	85	Lagado prime
37	Lagado prime	88	4×22
40	4×10	91	7×13
43	Lagado prime	94	Lagado prime
46	Lagado prime	97	Lagado prime
49	7×7	100	4×25 or 10×10

All goes well until we reach 100. In the Lagado system, 100 can be written in two different ways as the product of Lagado primes.

Perhaps if we return to our own arithmetic and continue our own list (from which no numbers have been exiled) we too might eventually run into the same phenomenon as did the mathematicians of Lagado when they reached 100. And if we do not, then our good fortune will undoubtedly have something to do with the fact that we have banned no natural number.

Our next chapter will be devoted to proving that there is only one way to write each composite natural number as the product of primes. Not only are the primes the building blocks for all natural numbers, but they can be assembled in only one way to form each natural number. From this will flow a variety of implications, which we will examine in Chapters 5 and 6.

Exercises

1. Some primes can be written in the form $1 + N^2$ for some natural number N. For example, $5 = 1 + 2^2$, and $17 = 1 + 4^2$.
   (a) Find three more primes of the form $1 + N^2$.
   (b) Do you think that there is an end to such primes? (No one knows.)

2. Some primes are 1 less than a square; that is, they can be written in the form $N^2 - 1$ for some natural number N. For example, $3 = 2^2 - 1$.
   (a) Can you find other primes of the form $N^2 - 1$?
   (b) Make a conjecture.
   (c) Prove it.

3. Some primes are 1 more than a power of 2; for example, $5 = 1 + 2^2$, and $17 = 1 + 2^4$.
   (a) Find another such prime.
   (b) Do you think that there is an end to such primes? (No one knows.)

4. Some primes are 1 less than a power of 2; for example, $3 = 2^2 - 1$, and $7 = 2^3 - 1$.
   (a) Find two more such primes.
   (b) Do you think that there is an end to such primes? (No one knows.)

5. Prove that the Greeks could have designed their Prime-manufacturing Machine by forming the number $(F_1 \times F_2 \times \cdots \times F_N) - 1$ instead of the number M that they used.

6. The primes 17, 29, 41, 53 form an arithmetic progression (that is, each differs from the one before by the same amount—in this case, 12). (That there are other primes between them, such as 19, does not matter.)
   (a) Find an arithmetic progression formed of five primes.
   (b) Do you think that there is an arithmetic progression of 12 primes? (The longest known list has only 11 primes in it.)

7. Prove that the smallest natural number that is larger than 1 and divides a natural number larger than 1 must be prime.

8. (a) Write 1500 as the product of primes.
   (b) In how many ways do you think 1500 can be written as the product of primes?

9. In how many ways can you write 1728 as the product of primes?

10. Write 57 and 117 as the product of primes.

11. If you feed the Prime-manufacturing Machine 11 and 13, what primes does it produce?

12. If you feed the Prime-manufacturing Machine 2, 11, and 13, what primes does it produce?

13. If N is a natural number bigger than 1, is there always a prime between N and $2 \times N$?
    (a) Experiment for all N less than 50.
    (b) Make a conjecture.

14. If N is a natural number, is there a prime between N^2 and $(N + 1)^2$?
    (a) Experiment for all N less than 20.
    (b) Make a conjecture. (Though it is known that the answer to E 13 is "yes," the answer to E 14 is not known.)

15. Show that 6 is equal to the sum of its divisors other than itself. Find another natural number (less than 30) that is equal to the sum of its divisors other than itself. Such natural numbers are called *perfect*. It is not known whether there are

any odd perfect numbers; nor is it known whether there is an end to the even perfect numbers. (See R 1 and R 5 of this chapter and E 11 of Chapter 17.)

16. Compare the number of primes less than N to the quotient $N/(\frac{1}{1} + \frac{1}{2} + \cdots + \frac{1}{N})$ for (a) $N = 6$, (b) $N = 10$, (c) $N = 20$.

17. Which odd natural numbers can be written as the sum of three primes (allowing a prime to be duplicated)? Experiment, and make a conjecture. (See R 1.)

18. Prove that even in the Lagado system every composite natural number is the product of primes.

19. Is it true that whenever 10 divides the product of two natural numbers it must divide at least one of them?

20. Is it true that whenever 5 divides the product of two natural numbers it must divide at least one of them? Make some experiments and a conjecture.

21. (a) Show that the last digit of any even number is 0, 2, 4, 6, or 8.
    (b) Using (a) prove that if 2 divides the product of two natural numbers, then it must divide at least one of them.

22. (a) Show that the last digit of a multiple of 5 is either 0 or 5.
    (b) Using (a) prove that if 5 divides the product of two natural numbers, then it must divide at least one of them.

23. Do you think that whenever 3 divides the product of two numbers it must divide at least one of them? Experiment, and make a conjecture.

24. Let $N!$ denote the product of all the natural numbers from 1 through N. For example, $6! = 1 \times 2 \times 3 \times 4 \times 5 \times 6 = 720$.
    (a) Prove that when N is composite and larger than 4, then N is a divisor of $(N - 1)!$.
    (b) Prove that when N is composite, N is not a divisor of $(N - 1)! + 1$.
    (c) If N is prime, do you think that N divides $(N - 1)! + 1$? (Experiment with at least four primes.) We return to this question in E 32, 33, 34 of Chapter 10.

25. (a) Show that 220 is a good natural number in the Lagado system and can be written in more than one way as the product of Lagado primes.
    (b) Show that 484 is a good natural number in the Lagado system and can be written as the product of Lagado primes in more than one way.

26. If a prime divides $A + B$, then must it divide at least one of A and B?

27. (a) Prove that if every even natural number is the sum of two primes, then every odd natural number is the sum of three primes.
    (b) Give an example of an odd natural number that is the sum of three primes but not the sum of two primes. [In 1937 Vinogradov proved that every odd natural number beyond some point (which he did not determine) is the sum of three primes. It is also known that each odd natural number less than 100,000 is the sum of three primes.] (See R 1.)

28. Let us feed into the Prime-manufacturing Machine the primes $F_1, F_2, \cdots, F_N$. The machine produces $G_1, G_2, \cdots, G_P$. Let us feed the machine $G_1, G_2, \cdots, G_P$. It pro-

duces H_1, H_2, $\cdots$, H_Q. Now feed the H's into the machine. What happens if we keep repeating this process when we start with
(a) $F_1 = 2$ and $F_2 = 3$,   (b) $F_1 = 3$, $F_2 = 5$, $F_3 = 7$?

29. Let us feed the Prime-manufacturing Machine a number of primes, which we call the input. It spews out another number of primes, which we call the output. Now let us feed the machine the original input together with the output. It produces new primes. Now feed into the machine all the primes it has produced up to this point together with our original input. It produces still more primes. Do you suppose the machine would eventually produce every prime if this process were not stopped? Experiment with the original input consisting of just the one prime 2. (The answer is not known.)

The number 1.32 in the Twin Prime Conjecture is just a two-decimal estimate of a number whose precise definition is quite fascinating. Exercises 30–34 are devoted to a description of this number.

30. For each natural number N that is greater than 1, we can form the product

$$A_N = \left(1 - \frac{1}{2^2}\right) \times \left(1 - \frac{1}{3^2}\right) \times \left(1 - \frac{1}{4^2}\right) \times \cdots \times \left(1 - \frac{1}{N^2}\right).$$

For example,

$$A_2 = \left(1 - \frac{1}{2^2}\right),$$

which is simply $\frac{3}{4}$, or decimally, 0.75. As another example,

$$A_3 = \left(1 - \frac{1}{2^2}\right) \times \left(1 - \frac{1}{3^2}\right),$$

which is just $\frac{3}{4} \times \frac{8}{9}$. Note that this is equal to $\frac{2}{3}$, or decimally, 0.666$\cdots$. Compute, to three decimals, (a) A_4, (b) A_5, and (c) A_6.

31. See E 30. Observe that

$$1 - \frac{1}{2^2} = \frac{2^2 - 1}{2^2} = \frac{(2 - 1) \times (2 + 1)}{2 \times 2} = \frac{1 \times 3}{2 \times 2}.$$

In a similar manner show that

(a) $1 - \frac{1}{3^2} = \frac{2 \times 4}{3 \times 3}$;   (b) $1 - \frac{1}{4^2} = \frac{3 \times 5}{4 \times 4}$;   (c) $1 - \frac{1}{5^2} = \frac{4 \times 6}{5 \times 5}$.

32. Continuing E 31. (a) What equations, analogous to those in E 31 (a), (b), and (c) hold for

$$1 - \frac{1}{6^2}; \qquad 1 - \frac{1}{7^2}?$$

(b) Show that A_4 can be rewritten

$$\frac{1 \times 3}{2 \times 2} \times \frac{2 \times 4}{3 \times 3} \times \frac{3 \times 5}{4 \times 4}.$$

Therefore, after the cancellations

$$\frac{1}{2} \times \frac{3}{2} \times \frac{2}{3} \times \frac{4}{3} \times \frac{3}{4} \times \frac{5}{4},$$

A_4 is seen to be equal to $\frac{1}{2} \times \frac{5}{4}$.

(c) **In a similar manner show that** A_5 **is equal to** $\frac{1}{2} \times \frac{6}{5}$.

(d) Show that as N grows larger and larger, A_N shrinks and gets closer and closer to $\frac{1}{2}$.

33. For each natural number N that is larger than 1, we can form the product

$$B_N = \left(1 - \frac{1}{(P_2 - 1)^2}\right) \times \left(1 - \frac{1}{(P_3 - 1)^2}\right) \times \cdots \times \left(1 - \frac{1}{(P_N - 1)^2}\right),$$

where, as in the text, P_N is the Nth prime; $P_2 = 3$, $P_3 = 5$, and so on. Thus

$$B_2 = 1 - \frac{1}{(3 - 1)^2},$$

which, as the reader may check, is 0.75. Also,

$$B_3 = \left(1 - \frac{1}{(3 - 1)^2}\right) \times \left(1 - \frac{1}{(5 - 1)^2}\right),$$

which reduces to $\frac{3}{4} \times 1\frac{5}{16}$, or, to three decimals, 0.703.

(a) Compute B_N to 3 decimals for $N = 4$, 5, and 6. (As a check, $B_4 = 0.683\cdots$.)

(b) Why does B_N shrink as N increases?

(c) Why is B_N always larger than the A_N of E 30?

(d) Prove that for any N, B_N is larger than $\frac{1}{2}$. [*Hint:* E 32 (d) and E 33 (c).]

34. In E 33, B_N shrinks as N increases, but stays above $\frac{1}{2}$. With the aid of an electronic computer, it can be shown that the B_N is approaching a number C that is approximately 0.660. Instead of 1.32 in the Twin Prime Conjecture, we should have written $2 \times C$. (See R 4 for more details.)

35. (a) Prove that if a number is a square, then it has an odd number of divisors.

(b) Prove that if a number is not a square, then it has an even number of divisors.

36. We defined a^n, for any natural numbers a and n larger than 0, as $a \times a \times \cdots \times a$ (where a appears n times).

(a) Verify that $2^3 \times 2^5 = 2^8$.

(b) Verify that $5^1 \times 5^2 = 5^3$.

(c) Prove that $a^m \times a^n = a^{m+n}$ for any natural numbers m and n larger than 0.

37. See E 36. We did not give the symbol a^0 any meaning. Show that if we want the rule $a^m \times a^n = a^{m+n}$ to hold even when m or n is 0, then we must assign to a^0 the value 1. For this reason, we (the masters) *define* a^0 to be 1.

38. This triangular array of natural numbers

$$
\begin{array}{ccccccc}
2 & 3 & 5 & 7 & 11 & 13 & 17 \\
 & 1 & 2 & 2 & 4 & 2 & 4 \\
 & & 1 & 0 & 2 & 2 & 2 \\
 & & & 1 & 2 & 0 & 0 \\
 & & & & 1 & 2 & 0 \\
 & & & & & 1 & 2 \\
 & & & & & & 1 \\
\end{array}
$$

is formed as follows.

    (i) All primes from 2 through 17 form the first line.

    (ii) Their gaps form the second line.

    (iii) Differences of adjacent numbers in the second line form the third line.

    (iv) Differences of adjacent numbers in the third line form the fourth line.

    (v) The process continues until the triangle is formed.

  (a) Do the same for all primes from 2 through 37 (instead of from 2 through 17).

  (b) Do the same for all primes from 2 through 59.

  (c) What do you notice about the entries forming the left side of the triangle in each case? (What you notice has been checked for all primes less than 792, 722. Whether it always holds is not known. See R 7.)

References

1. O. Ore, *Number Theory and its History*, McGraw-Hill, New York, 1948. (Pages 81, 84, and 85 discuss the representation of natural numbers as the sum of primes; pp. 91–94 discuss perfect numbers.)

2. R. D. James, Recent progress in the Goldbach problem, *Bulletin of the American Mathematical Society*, vol. 55, 1949, pp. 246–260.

3. W. Sierpinski, On some unsolved problems of arithmetics, *Scripta Mathematica*, vol. 25, 1960, pp. 125–136. (This expository article presents many unsolved problems concerning primes and rational numbers.)

4. G. Polya, Heuristic reasoning in the theory of numbers, *American Mathematical Monthly*, vol. 66, 1959, pp. 375–384. [An exploration, based on electronic computers and shrewd guessing, of the differences between (not necessarily consecutive) primes.]

5. P. J. McCarthy, Odd perfect numbers, *Scripta Mathematica*, vol. 23, 1957, pp. 43–47.

6. E. T. Bell, *Men of Mathematics*, Simon and Schuster, New York, 1937. (Contains chapters devoted to Gauss and Fermat.)

7. *R. B. Killgrove and K. E. Ralston, On a conjecture concerning primes, *Mathematical Tables and Other Aids to Computing*, National Research Council, Washington, D.C., vol. 13, 1959, pp. 121–122.

8. T. Dantzig, *Number, the Language of Science*, Macmillan, New York, 1954. (Chapter 3 discusses the primes.)

9. R. G. Archibald, Goldbach's theorem, *Scripta Mathematica*, vol. 3, 1935, pp. 44–50 and pp. 153–161. (This examines the number of ways an even natural number can be written as the sum of two primes. The footnote on p. 153 notes misprints on pp. 46–48.)

Chapter 4

THE FUNDAMENTAL
THEOREM
OF ARITHMETIC

As we proved easily in the last chapter, every composite natural number is the product of primes. We approach now the question: In how many ways can a composite natural number be written as the product of primes? The few experiments we made in Chapter 3 suggested that the answer is: Precisely one way. The proof that this answer is correct is far more interesting than the proof that every composite natural number can be written as the product of primes, and will occupy this whole chapter.

Here is what we want to prove. If we have managed by some means or other to express a natural number as the product of primes, say, the product of n primes $A_1 \times A_2 \times \cdots \times A_n$, and if someone else manages to express the same number as the product of primes, say, as the product of m primes, $B_1 \times B_2 \times \cdots \times B_m$, then m must be the same as n, and the B's just a rearrangement of the A's. In other words, what we want to prove is this theorem, usually called

THE FUNDAMENTAL THEOREM OF ARITHMETIC. *If* $A_1, A_2, \cdots, A_n$ *and* $B_1,$ $B_2, \cdots, B_m$ *are primes, written in order of increasing size, and if*

(1) $A_1 \times A_2 \times \cdots \times A_n = B_1 \times B_2 \times \cdots \times B_m,$

then $A_1 = B_1, A_2 = B_2, \cdots,$ *and hence* $m = n.$

It would be reasonable to prove first that $A_1 = B_1$. Let us try. From (1) we see that A_1 is a divisor of the product of all the A's and hence of all the B's. If we knew that this forced A_1 to be a divisor of at least one of the B's, we would be well on the way to a proof. For if A_1 divides, say, B_1, then, since B_1 is a prime, A_1 would have to equal B_1. This would be a fine start. Unfortunately, we are not sure at this point whether a prime that divides the product of several natural numbers must divide at least one of them. After all, our definition of a prime depends on the way natural numbers divide it, not on the way it divides other natural numbers.

To check whether a natural number is prime, we only have to look at the numbers less than that number and check whether they divide it. To check the way a given natural number divides products of numbers would seem a superhuman task. Yet we must undertake it.

Let us call a natural number larger than 1 **special** *if, whenever it divides the product of two natural numbers, it divides at least one of them.* For example, let us prove that 2 is special. We must show that whenever 2 divides $A \times B$, then 2 must divide at least one of A and B. In the language of even and odd, we wish to prove that if $A \times B$ is even, then at least one of A and B is even. To prove this, we will prove that the product of two odd numbers must be odd.

If A is odd, it can be written in the form $2a + 1$ for some natural number a. If B is odd, it can be written in the form $2b + 1$ for some natural number b. Let us examine the product $A \times B$ and show that it is also odd. We have*

$$A \times B = (2a + 1) \times (2b + 1) = 4ab + 2a + 2b + 1,$$

which is 1 more than the number $4ab + 2a + 2b$, which is clearly even. Thus 2 is special. (A simpler proof is found in E 21 of Chapter 3.)

Clearly it is more difficult to prove that 2 is special than to prove that 2 is prime. The reader might like to prove that 3 is special (see E 33) and that 5 is special (see E 22 of Chapter 3). It is easier to show that a natural number is not special than to show that it is. For example, since 6 divides 3×4, yet divides neither 3 nor 4, we see that 6 is not special. In fact, we could have been more economical in showing that it is not special. After all, 6 divides 2×3, yet divides neither 2 nor 3. This second argument suggests that no composite natural number can be special. We will prove

THEOREM 1. *Every special number must be prime.*

PROOF. Let N be special. Assume, for the moment, that N is also composite. Then N can be written as the product $Q \times A$, where Q and A are both smaller than N. Since N divides N, we see that N divides $Q \times A$. But, because Q and A are smaller than N, N can divide neither Q nor A. Thus N is not special, hence our assumption that N is composite must be wrong. Therefore every special number is also prime.

Let us not be too hasty in jumping to the conclusion that every prime is special. Recall that it took some effort just to prove that 2 is special, and nowhere in that proof did we make use of the fact that 2 is prime. Also, recall

---

* This is justified in Example 6 of Appendix A.

that, in the Lagado system, 10 is a prime, but is not special, since it divides 4×25 and yet divides neither 4 nor 25. As it turns out, the proof that every prime is special in our usual arithmetic will fill most of this chapter.

Before we turn to the problem of whether every prime is special, we ought to go back briefly to what led us to define the special numbers. We were interested in the question: If a prime divides the product of several natural numbers, must it divide at least one of them? As a small step toward answering this question we have

THEOREM 2. *If a special number divides the product of several natural numbers, then it divides at least one of them.*

PROOF. We illustrate the argument for the case in which the special number happens to divide the product of three natural numbers. Let S be a special number that divides $A \times B \times C$. We wish to prove that S divides at least one of A, B, and C.

It is clear that S divides the product of the two natural numbers A and $B \times C$. Since S is special, it must divide at least one of A and $B \times C$. If S divides A, we are done. If S divides $B \times C$, then, since S is special, S must divide at least one of B and C. Thus we see that whenever a special number divides the product of three natural numbers, then it must divide at least one of them.

The same argument can be applied to the product of more than three natural numbers. The reader can take care of the case in which a special number divides the product of four natural numbers, and also see how the proof of Theorem 2 can be carried out in general.

We have been able to go this far without getting involved with addition. Neither the notions of prime and special nor Theorems 1 and 2 and their proofs have made any mention of addition. But the proof that every prime is special leans heavily on addition. Thus the Fundamental Theorem of Arithmetic is really a theorem about multiplication and addition.

The proof that we will present is basically the one that appears in Book 7 of Euclid, published about 300 B.C., and is probably the work of a whole school of mathematicians. The reader should note carefully just where addition makes its appearance on stage and where it exits; it appears nowhere in the statement of the Fundamental Theorem of Arithmetic, but only in the proof leading up to it.

We shall break up Euclid's proof that every prime is special into several small pieces. The diagram on p. 42 tells how these pieces fit together. As the reader goes through the proof, he can find where he is in the whole argument by looking back at the diagram. When he has grasped the details of the various proofs, he can then go back to the diagram to see how the separate lemmas really form one large result. The first time through, though, he may not be able to see the forest for the trees.

We shall first need the notion of a common divisor of two natural numbers. *A natural number that is a divisor of both A and B is called a* **common divisor** *of A and B.* For example, 3 is a common divisor of 9 and 12. So is 1 a common divisor of 9 and 12. Of particular interest will be the *greatest common divisor* of *A* and *B*, which we will denote by (A, B). For example, $(9, 12) = 3$. The reader may verify that $(7, 12) = 1$, $(5, 15) = 5$, and $(0, 3) = 3$. We should point out that $(0, 0)$ does not exist, since there is no largest divisor of 0.

Now we can draw the promised diagram of Euclid's proof:

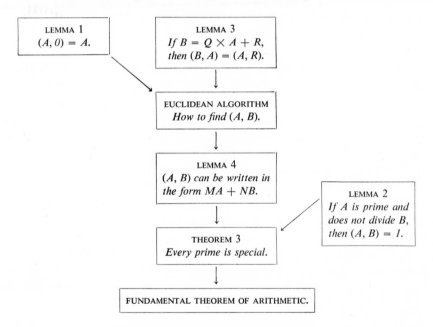

The main flow of thought is down the column; notice the presence of addition in Lemmas 3 and 4. Now let us begin the proof.

LEMMA 1. *For any natural number A, other than 0, $(A, 0) = A$.*

PROOF. Any natural number *D* is a divisor of 0, since $0 = 0 \times D$. Thus the largest common divisor of *A* and 0 is simply the largest divisor of *A*, namely *A*.

LEMMA 2. *If A is prime and does not divide B, then $(A, B) = 1$.*

PROOF. The only divisors of *A* are 1 and *A*. Since *A* does not divide *B*, it follows that the only common divisor of both A and B is 1. Thus 1 is the greatest common divisor of A and B.

Addition appears on the scene in

LEMMA 3. *If A, B, Q, and R are natural numbers in the relation $B = (Q \times A) + R$ (where A and B are not both equal to zero), then $(B, A) = (A, R)$.*

Before entering the proof, let us consider this illustration. Since $57 = (4 \times 12) + 9$, Lemma 3 asserts that $(57, 12) = (12, 9)$, a fact that the reader may check.

PROOF. Though we are interested only in the greatest common divisor, we shall actually prove more; namely, that the common divisors of A and B are the same as the common divisors of A and R. From this, Lemma 3 follows easily.

Let D be a natural number dividing both A and R. Then D divides $Q \times A$, and hence also the sum $(Q \times A) + R$, which is B. Thus D divides A and B. Hence any common divisor of A and R is a common divisor of B and A.

Let us consider the opposite direction. Let d be any natural number dividing both B and A. Then d divides $Q \times A$. Thus d divides the difference $B - (Q \times A)$, which is R. Therefore d is a common divisor of A and R. Thus any common divisor of B and A is a common divisor of A and R. This ends the proof.

A laborious way of computing (A, B) consists in listing all divisors of A and then all divisors of B, and picking out the largest divisor that appears in both of the lists. Lemma 3 is the basis for a far more efficient method of finding (A, B), known as the *Euclidean Algorithm*. Let us illustrate this technique, which works for any (A, B), by applying it to the case $(72, 20)$.

Step 1. Divide 20 into 72, and find the remainder. We have $72 = 3 \times 20 + 12$ (the remainder is 12). By Lemma 3, $(72, 20) = (20, 12)$.

Step 2. Divide 12 into 20, and find the remainder. We have $20 = 1 \times 12 + 8$ (the remainder is 8). By Lemma 3, $(20, 12) = (12, 8)$.

Step 3. Divide 8 into 12, and find the remainder. We have $12 = 1 \times 8 + 4$ (the remainder is 4). By Lemma 3, $(12, 8) = (8, 4)$.

Step 4. Divide 4 into 8, and find the remainder. We have $8 = 2 \times 4 + 0$ (the remainder is 0). By Lemma 3, $(8, 4) = (4, 0)$.

But Lemma 1 asserts that $(4, 0) = 4$. Combining all the steps, we conclude that $(72, 20) = 4$.

The Euclidean Algorithm *involves repeatedly dividing and finding remainders until we reach the remainder 0.* Each step produces a remainder smaller than the remainder from the previous step. Eventually we must obtain the remainder 0. The remainder before 0 is the greatest common divisor. This is the technique. The reader is invited to apply the Euclidean Algorithm to (117, 51). He might also compare the ease of the Euclidean Algorithm to the labor of making lists in the computation of (433, 144). (Of course, the number of steps need not be four; one keeps going till the remainder 0 is met.)

For the first time in this book we shall need the numbers $-1, -2, -3,$ $-4, \cdots$. Without them, Lemma 4 would be false. After all, $(2, 3) = 1$, yet there are certainly no natural numbers M and N such that $1 = M \times 2 + N \times 3$. But $(2, 3)$ does equal $(-1) \times 2 + 1 \times 3$.

The numbers
$$\cdots, -3, -2, -1, 0, 1, 2, 3, \cdots$$
we shall call **integers.** Thus, every natural number is also an integer. We can extend our definition of divisor to include the integers by saying that the integer A divides the integer B if there is an integer Q such that $B = Q \times A$. For example, since $-6 = (-3) \times 2$, 2 divides -6. We will make great use of this notion in Chapter 10.

The next lemma will be the chief tool for proving that every prime is special. Just as $(2, 3) = (-1) \times 2 + 1 \times 3$ and just as $(72, 20)$, which we know to be 4, can be expressed as $2 \times 72 + (-7) \times 20$, Lemma 4 asserts that (A, B) for any natural numbers A and B, where both are not zero, can be expressed similarly in terms of A and B.

LEMMA 4. *For any natural numbers A and B (not both 0) there are integers M and N (positive or negative) such that*
$$(A, B) = M \times A + N \times B.$$

If A and B are small, we might find M and N quickly with just a little figuring. For example, if A is 5 and B is 8 [and (A, B) is therefore 1], we can easily find these three examples:
$$1 = 5 \times 5 + (-3) \times 8,$$
$$\text{or} \quad 1 = (-3) \times 5 + 2 \times 8,$$
$$\text{or} \quad 1 = (-11) \times 5 + 7 \times 8;$$
and the reader might add further illustrations.

But when A and B are large, it might not be at all obvious that M and N can be found. We would know only that if the integers M and N did exist, then one of them must be positive, the other negative. Now we shall turn to the proof of Lemma 4, which not only will prove that M and N can be found, but will provide a technique for finding them (though it may not produce the smallest possible M and N).

In order to find M and N we shall unwind the Euclidean Algorithm. Let us illustrate the technique by two examples.

The computation of $(7, 29)$ by the Euclidean Algorithm involves these steps:

$$29 = 4 \times 7 + 1,$$
$$7 = 7 \times 1 + 0;$$

hence $1 = (29, 7)$. Using just the first step, we have $1 = 29 - 4 \times 7$, which can be written

$$1 = 1 \times 29 + (-4) \times 7.$$

We have found an M and an N such that $1 = M \times 29 + N \times 7$. We may check that our M and N work by noticing that $1 \times 29 = 29$ and that $4 \times 7 = 28$.

Now for a slightly longer example. The computations for $(230, 32)$ by the Euclidean Algorithm run as follows (the underline identifies the A and B in the relation $B = Q \times A + R$):

$$\underline{230} = 7 \times \underline{32} + 6,$$
$$\underline{32} = 5 \times \underline{6} + 2,$$
$$\underline{6} = 3 \times \underline{2} = 0;$$

thus $2 = (230, 32)$. We will unwind these steps to find M and N such that $2 = M \times 230 + N \times 32$. We can begin by expressing 2 in terms of $\underline{32}$ and $\underline{6}$, using the next to the last step:

$$2 = \underline{32} - 5 \times \underline{6}.$$

A natural impulse would be to multiply $5 \times \underline{6}$ and subtract the result from $\underline{32}$ (we would just get 2), but instead let us keep $\underline{32}$ and $\underline{6}$ intact.

Using the first step of the Euclidean Algorithm we can write

$$\underline{6} = \underline{230} - 7 \times \underline{32}.$$

Now substitute this expression for $\underline{6}$ into our expression for 2; we have

$$2 = \underline{32} - 5 \times \underline{6} = \underline{32} - 5 \times (\underline{230} - 7 \times \underline{32}).$$

Keeping the $\underline{32}$ and $\underline{230}$ intact, and recalling* that $(-5) \times (-7) = 35$, we have

$$2 = \underline{32} - 5 \times \underline{230} + 35 \times \underline{32}.$$

Collecting the $\underline{32}$'s, we end up with

$$2 = (-5) \times \underline{230} + 36 \times \underline{32}.$$

---

* Proved in Theorem 11 in Appendix A.

So we have found values of M and N that satisfy

$$2 = M \times 230 + N \times 32.$$

We can easily check our answer with a little arithmetic: $-5 \times 230 = -1150$, $36 \times 32 = 1152$, and $-1150 + 1152$ does equal 2.

Using the same technique, the reader might like to find M and N such that $(72, 20) = M \times 72 + N \times 20$. Clearly the technique applies to any (A, B), and we see why Lemma 4 is true.

With Lemma 4 in our possession, we are ready to prove

THEOREM 3. *Every prime is special.*

PROOF. Let P be a prime that divides $A \times B$. We wish to prove that P must divide at least one of A and B. To do this we will prove that if P does not divide A, then P must divide B.

Since P does not divide A, we have, by Lemma 2,

$$(P, A) = 1.$$

Lemma 4 then promises us that there are M and N such that

$$1 = M \times P + N \times A.$$

If we multiply both sides of this equation by B, we obtain the new equation

$$B = M \times P \times B + N \times A \times B.$$

Now, P divides $M \times P \times B$; and since P divides $A \times B$, we see that P divides $N \times A \times B$. Hence P divides the sum

$$M \times P \times B + N \times A \times B.$$

But that sum is just B. Therefore P divides B. Theorem 3 is proved.

This ends Euclid's proof that every prime is special. Note precisely where addition walked onto the stage; contrast this proof with the much simpler one for the converse "every special number is prime."

Now that we know that every prime is special, we can give the long-awaited

PROOF OF THE FUNDAMENTAL THEOREM OF ARITHMETIC. We have the n primes $A_1, A_2, \cdots, A_n$ and the m primes $B_1, B_2, \cdots, B_m$ in the relation

$$A_1 \times A_2 \times \cdots \times A_n = B_1 \times B_2 \times \cdots \times B_m.$$

We wish to prove that $A_1 = B_1$, $A_2 = B_2$, and so on.

Let us first prove that $A_1 = B_1$. Since A_1 divides $B_1 \times B_2 \times \cdots \times B_m$, it must divide at least one of the B's (by Theorem 3 and Theorem 2). Since the B's are all prime, A_1 must coincide with the B that it divides. Thus A_1 is one of the B's. Therefore A_1 is at least as large as B_1, the smallest of all the B's.

Similar reasoning, beginning with the fact that B_1 divides

$$A_1 \times A_2 \times \cdots \times A_n,$$

proves that B_1 is at least as large as A_1.

Combining the facts:

A_1 is at least as large as B_1

and

B_1 is at least as large as A_1,

we see that $A_1 = B_1$.

To prove that $A_2 = B_2$, we first note that

$$A_1 \times A_2 \times \cdots \times A_n = A_1 \times B_2 \times \cdots \times B_m$$

and then divide both sides by A_1. This gives us the equation

$$A_2 \times \cdots \times A_n = B_2 \times \cdots \times B_m.$$

With the same kind of reasoning that proved $A_1 = B_1$, we can show that $A_2 = B_2$.

Step by step, we peel away the primes from each side until we have proved $A_1 = B_1$, $A_2 = B_2$, $A_3 = B_3$, and so on. Since we pair off the A's with the B's, we also see that $m = n$. This ends the proof.

Thus we see that the Fundamental Theorem of Arithmetic is an immediate consequence of the fact that every prime is special. Not content with this discovery, a mathematician instinctively asks, "Is the fact that every prime is special an immediate consequence of the Fundamental Theorem of Arithmetic?" He is really wondering, "Are the two assertions of equal depth? Must I expect that any proof of the Fundamental Theorem of Arithmetic will involve some ingenious step? If I could somehow prove the Fundamental Theorem of Arithmetic without using the fact that each prime is special, could I then go on to prove from this that each prime is special?" It is not enough to know what is true; how the truths interlock to form a mathematical structure is equally important. It happens to be a simple matter to satisfy the mathematician's curiosity with

THEOREM 4. *If the Fundamental Theorem of Arithmetic is true, then every prime is special.*

PROOF. (We disregard all the work of this chapter. It is of no concern to us at this moment whether the Fundamental Theorem of Arithmetic is true or whether each prime is special. We are studying only the influence of one speculation upon another.)

Let P be a prime that divides the natural number $A \times B$. We wish to prove, with the aid of the Fundamental Theorem of Arithmetic, that P must divide at least one of A and B.

Since P divides $A \times B$, there is a natural number Q such that

$$A \times B = Q \times P.$$

Let us write A as the product of primes,

$$A = A_1 \times A_2 \times \cdots \times A_n;$$

B as the product of primes,

$$B = B_1 \times B_2 \times \cdots \times B_m;$$

and Q as the product of primes,

$$Q = Q_1 \times Q_2 \times \cdots \times Q_p.$$

Since $A \times B = Q \times P$, we have

$$A_1 \times A_2 \times \cdots \times A_n \times B_1 \times B_2 \times \cdots \times B_m = Q_1 \times Q_2 \times \cdots \times Q_p \times P.$$

The Fundamental Theorem of Arithmetic, which we are assuming, assures us that P, one of the primes on the right, must appear somewhere on the left; that is, P must be one of $A_1, A_2, \cdots, A_n$ or of $B_1, B_2, \cdots, B_m$. If P is one of $A_1, A_2, \cdots, A_n$, then P divides A; if P is one of $B_1, B_2, \cdots, B_m$, then P divides B. We have thus shown that P is special, hence Theorem 4 is proved.

In the Lagado system, the Fundamental Theorem of Arithmetic does not hold, nor are all the primes special. But there is a theorem, true both for us and for the mathematicians of the academy of Lagado, which sheds much light on our writing of natural numbers as the product of primes. Let us call this

THE CONCEALED THEOREM. *If* $A_1, A_2, \cdots, A_n$ *and* $B_1, B_2, \cdots, B_m$ *are all special* (*with the A's and B's increasing from left to right*), *and their products are equal,*

$$A_1 \times A_2 \times \cdots \times A_n = B_1 \times B_2 \times \cdots \times B_m,$$

then $A_1 = B_1$, $A_2 = B_2$, *and so on.*

The Concealed Theorem, so similar to the Fundamental Theorem of Arithmetic, is quite simple to prove—so simple, in fact, that we do not need to use addition to prove it. In outline the proof goes like this. Recall that every special is prime (Theorem 3, whose proof involves no addition). Then, with the aid of Theorem 2 (whose proof involves no addition), we can carry through the identical (peeling away) argument that we provided for the Fundamental Theorem of Arithmetic.

Without using addition, we can (as could the mathematicians of Lagado) prove these theorems:

    I. *Every special number is prime.*

   II. *Every composite natural number can be written as the product of primes in at least one way.*

  III. *Every natural number can be written as the product of special numbers in at most one way (maybe not at all).*

With the aid of addition, we can then prove

  IV. *Every prime is special.*

In ordinary arithmetic the primes are the same as the special numbers. With this information we can merge Theorems II and III into the one elegant result: *every composite natural number is the product of primes in exactly one way.*

Not only does this result have many applications, but it also suggests new problems. These we discuss in the next chapter.

Exercises

1. (a) List all the divisors of 100.   (c) List all the common divisors of 75 and 100.
   (b) List all the divisors of 75.   (d) What is (75, 100)?

2. Do the same as in E 1 for the numbers 90 and 76.

3. By making the complete list of divisors, find (a) (24, 51) and (b) (57, 133).

4. Prove that the smallest divisor, other than 1, of a natural number, is prime.

5. Using the Euclidean Algorithm compute (24, 51) and (57, 133).

6. Using the Euclidean Algorithm compute
   (a) (164, 72),   (b) (91, 39),   (c) (73, 21).

7. Find four different pairs of integers M and N such that $(2, 3) = M \times 2 + N \times 3$.

8. Find three different pairs of integers M and N such that $(3, 5) = M \times 3 + N \times 5$.

9. Using the technique given in this chapter, find a pair of integers M and N such that
   (a) $(24, 51) = M \times 24 + N \times 51$,
   (b) $(57,133) = M \times 57 + N \times 133$.

10. Verify that your answers in E 9 are correct by computing both sides of the equations.

11. Find an M and an N for each of these pairs of A and B:
    (a) 72, 164,   (b) 39, 91,   (c) 21, 73.

12. Check your answers in E 11 by computing $M \times A + N \times B$ in each case and comparing it to (A, B).

13. Let A and B be natural numbers. If there are integers M and N such that $1 = M \times A + N \times B$, what can be said about (A, B)?

14. Let A and B be natural numbers. If there are integers M and N such that $4 = M \times A + N \times B$, what can be said about (A, B)?

15. Prove that if A and B are distinct primes, then there are natural numbers M and N such that $M \times A$ and $N \times B$ differ by 1.

16. Prove that every common divisor of A and B is a divisor of (A, B). (*Hint:* Use Lemma 4.)

17. Prove the Concealed Theorem.

18. Prove that if a special number divides the product of four natural numbers, then it must divide at least one of them.

19. Using the Fundamental Theorem of Arithmetic, prove that every divisor of 2^{100} must itself be a power of 2. (Since we define 2^0 to be equal to 1, then 1 is thus a power of 2; see Chapter 3, E 37.)

20. See E 19. How many divisors does 2^{100} have?

21. Prove that every divisor of $2^5 \times 3^{11}$ must be a power of 2 times a power of 3. (*Hint:* Prove that 2 and 3 are the only primes that can occur when a divisor of $2^5 \times 3^{11}$ is expressed as the product of primes.)

22. Using the Fundamental Theorem of Arithmetic, prove that
    (a) $(2^5 \times 3^7, 2^7 \times 3^2) = 2^5 \times 3^2$,
    (b) $(3^4 \times 7^6, 3^4 \times 11) = 3^4$.

23. Prove that no power of 3 is equal to a power of 7. (Except, of course, $3^0 = 1 = 7^0$; see Chapter 3, E 37.)

24. Prove that if $(A, B) = 1$, then $(A^2, B^2) = 1$.

25. Prove that $(A, B) = (A, A + B)$.

26. Show that, in the Lagado system, 100 is not the product of Lagado special numbers.

27. Prove that if $(A, B) = 1$ and $(A, C) = 1$, then $(A, B \times C) = 1$.

28. Give an example of natural numbers A, B, and C such that A divides C and B divides C, yet $A \times B$ does not divide C.

29. See E. 28. If $(A, B) = 1$ and both A and B are divisors of C, then prove that $A \times B$ is a divisor of C, using
    (a) Lemma 4,
    (b) the Fundamental Theorem of Arithmetic.

30. Prove that if 6 divides the square of an integer, then it divides the integer itself.

31. Show that, in the Lagado system, $(4, 10) = 1$, but that there are no integers M and N for which $1 = M \times 4 + N \times 10$.

32. If the King of Lagado had decided that 1 and the even numbers other than 0 are good and that the odd numbers other than 1 are bad, he would have created a rather interesting arithmetic.
    (a) Find the primes of this new arithmetic.
    (b) Show that 180 can be written as the product of primes in this arithmetic in more than one way.

(c) Prove that if $A_1, \cdots, A_n$ and $B_1, \cdots, B_m$ are primes in this arithmetic, with $A_1 \times \cdots \times A_n = B_1 \times \cdots \times B_m$, then $m = n$ (even though the A's need not be the same as the B's).

33. Without using the material of this chapter, prove that 3 is special. (*Hint:* Observe that every natural number, when divided by 3, leaves a remainder of 0, 1, or 2. Thus every natural number is of the form $3x$, $3x + 1$, or $3x + 2$ for some natural number x. Show that the product of two natural numbers of the last two types is not of the form $3x$.)

34. Using the technique of E 33, prove that 7 is special.

35. A regular n-gon is a polygon of n equal sides and equal angles. For example, a regular 4-gon is a square. Given a regular 3-gon and regular 5-gon, inscribed in a circle, one can easily find the side of a regular 15-gon. (*Hint:* Prove that the arc PQ is one-fifteenth of the circle by using the relation $\frac{1}{15} = \frac{2}{3} - \frac{3}{5}$.)

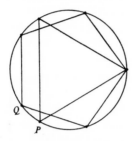

36. (a) Prove that if $(A, B) = 1$, then there are natural numbers C and D such that $1/(A \times B) = C/A - D/B$ or, perhaps, $C/B - D/A$.
   (b) Use (a) to show that if $(A, B) = 1$, then from a regular A-gon and a regular B-gon inscribed in a circle and sharing a vertex, it is easy to construct a regular $A \times B$-gon. (*Hint:* See E 35.)

37. With straightedge and compass construct the following regular polygons:
   (a) 3-gon,   (d) 8-gon,
   (b) 4-gon,   (e) 12-gon.
   (c) 6-gon,

38. (a) Show how to obtain by straightedge and compass a regular $2N$-gon from a regular N-gon.
   (b) Show how to obtain by straightedge and compass a regular N-gon from a regular $2N$-gon.
   (c) Why do (a) and (b) reduce the problem of constructing regular polygons to the construction of those with an odd number of sides?

39. See E 37 and E 38. In 1796 Gauss proved that a regular N-gon, with N odd, can be constructed with straightedge and compass only when N has the following property: when N is written as the product of primes no prime appears twice, and each prime is one more than a power of 2.
   (a) Using Gauss's theorem, show that a regular 9-gon, or regular 11-gon, or regular 25-gon cannot be constructed with straightedge and compass.

(b) Using Gauss's theorem, show that a regular 5-gon, or regular 3-gon, or regular 17-gon can be constructed with straightedge and compass.

(c) What role does the Fundamental Theorem of Arithmetic play in the statement of Gauss's theorem?

References

1. I. Niven and H. S. Zuckerman, *An Introduction to the Theory of Numbers*, Wiley, New York, 1960. (An alternate proof of the Fundamental Theorem of Arithmetic is given on p. 14.)

2. R. Courant and H. Robbins, *What is Mathematics?*, Oxford University Press, New York, 1960. (On p. 23 is the same proof as is given in R 1. The proof given in R 1 and R 2 is quite short. The proof given in the present chapter was chosen for two reasons. First, it generalizes to structures called "Euclidean Rings," which include polynomials, integers, and complex integers as special cases. Second, in Chapters 10, 11, and 12 we will need Lemma 4.)

3. *B. L. van der Waerden, *Modern Algebra*, vol. 1, Ungar, New York, 1949. (The theory of Euclidean rings is presented on pp. 32–62; unique factorization is discussed on pp. 55–61.)

4. *G. Birkhoff and S. MacLane, *Survey of Modern Algebra*, Macmillan, New York, 1953. (Unique factorization into primes is discussed for natural numbers on p. 18, for polynomials on pp. 75–77, and for complex integers on p. 415.)

5. H. Davenport, *The Higher Arithmetic*, Harper and Brothers, New York, 1960. (Another short proof of the Fundamental Theorem of Arithmetic is given on pp. 19–20.)

6. J. B. Roberts, *The Real Number System in an Algebraic Setting*, Freeman, San Francisco, 1962. (Another proof that each prime is special is given on pp. 34–36.)

Chapter **5**

RATIONALS AND
IRRATIONALS

As long as we use numbers just for counting, we can get along quite well with just the natural numbers 0, 1, 2, 3, 4, 5, $\cdots$. In Chapter 1 we counted switches and backward pairs; in Chapter 2, edges and triangles of special types. But in Chapter 4 we used the negative integers -1, -2, -3, $\cdots$ to simplify the statement and proof of Lemma 4, which asserts that for any positive integers A and B there are integers M and N such that $(A, B) = M \times A + N \times B$. For some purposes, however, such as measuring temperature or distance, we require numbers that are not positive or negative integers.

We can think of the integers as descriptions of certain regularly spaced points on a thermometer or ruler:

$$\cdots \; -2 \quad -1 \quad 0 \quad 1 \quad 2 \quad 3 \quad 4 \quad 5 \; \cdots$$

Once this scale is fixed, then to every point on the line there corresponds a number, and to every number there corresponds a point on the line. [A proof of this requires a close study of the geometric notion "line" and of the algebraic notion "number," and is quite technical (see R 6, R 7, R 8)]. In view of this fact, we might refer to "the point 3," meaning, of course, the point corresponding to the number 3.

For more accurate measurements, we usually introduce a finer division than the integers by cutting each segment into 4, 8, 16, or 32 identical pieces, if we are working with inches, or into 10, 100, or 1000 pieces, if we are working with the metric system. There is nothing sacred about these particular numbers. The mathematicians of Babylonia, some 4000 years ago, chose to divide each segment into 60 pieces. If we wish, we can divide each segment into 117 pieces, but no civilization has ever chosen to do so.

Let us look at the points of division when we cut each segment into, say, five pieces:

$$\cdots \; -2 \quad -1 \quad 0 \quad 1 \quad 2 \quad 3 \quad 4 \quad 5 \; \cdots$$

The finer unit of measure is now $\frac{1}{5}$. The points of division are labeled

$$\cdots \frac{-7}{5}, \frac{-6}{5}, \frac{-5}{5}, \frac{-4}{5}, \frac{-3}{5}, \frac{-2}{5}, \frac{-1}{5}, \frac{0}{5}, \frac{1}{5}, \frac{2}{5}, \frac{3}{5}, \frac{4}{5}, \frac{5}{5}, \frac{6}{5}, \frac{7}{5}, \cdots$$

Of course, $\frac{0}{5}$ is just the point 0, and $\frac{5}{5}$ is 1. Perhaps the reader has the impulse to change $\frac{7}{5}$ to $1\frac{2}{5}$, which is short for $1 + \frac{2}{5}$, but let him restrain himself. Whether such a change complicates or simplifies depends on the application we have in mind. For the purpose of this chapter, it will turn out that to insist on writing $\frac{7}{5}$ as $1 + \frac{2}{5}$ will only complicate matters.

If we divided each segment into, say, twenty-seven pieces instead of five, then we could label all points that can be written in the form $M/27$ for some integer M. More generally, when we divide each segment into N pieces, then the points of division will correspond to numbers of the form M/N.

Numbers of the form M/N, for some integers M and N (N, of course, not 0), we shall call rationals. That is, a rational is a number describing a point that appears as one of the marks of division in some refinement of our original fixed scale 0, 1, 2, 3, $\cdots$. Observe that every integer is a rational; for example, $6 = \frac{6}{1}$, $-7 = -\frac{7}{1}$, and so on; and, generally, $N = N/1$. We might think that every point on the line is described by some rational—that is, we might think that each point is the division mark of some perhaps extremely small refinement of the given scale. After all, as we draw in more and more division points of smaller and smaller refinements, we seem to be filling up the line gradually with an unbroken blur of ink. It is hard to imagine that a point could escape being a mark of at least one refining scale or, what amounts to the same thing, that there are numbers that are not rational.

Though it is hard to imagine, we must try; for, some 2400 years ago, the Pythagoreans, much to their astonishment, discovered numbers that are not rational. Let us see what kind of problems led them to their discovery of the world of numbers beyond the realm of rationals. (For the history of this discovery see R 4.)

Over 1000 years before Pythagoras, the mathematicians of Babylonia had a formula relating the two shorter sides of a right triangle to the side opposite the right angle. If the lengths of the three sides of the right triangle are given by the numbers a, b, and c, as in this diagram, then, say the perfectly preserved Babylonian clay tablets,

$$a^2 + b^2 = c^2.$$

Though they used this formula for over a thousand years, there is no evidence that they had a proof for it. But, using it, they knew that if $a = 3$ and $b = 4$, then $c = 5$ ($3^2 + 4^2 = 5^2$) and that if $a = 8$ and $b = 15$, then $c = 17$ (as the reader may check).

Hundreds of proofs now exist for the *Pythagorean Theorem, which asserts that in all right triangles* $a^2 + b^2 = c^2$. Some of these date back to the Greeks, perhaps even to Pythagoras himself. The proof that we shall present here depends on a pictorial interpretation of the three numbers a^2, b^2, and c^2.

The area of a square of side a is a^2. Similarly, b^2 and c^2 can be thought of as the areas of squares of sides b and c, respectively. With this point of view, we are therefore concerned with the three squares shown in this figure:

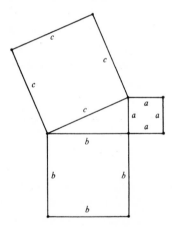

To prove the Pythagorean Theorem, we will prove that the two smaller squares together have an area equal to that of the big square. To do so, let us look closely at these two big squares (of side $a + b$):

Squares I and II have equal area. If we take away from each the same area, namely, the four triangles, then what we are left with in each case must be the same. In square I we are left with the two small squares; in square II we are left with the big square of side c. We have proved the Pythagorean Theorem.

The reader who objected to Mackie the cat in Chapter 2 is probably quite exasperated. "Look here, you with your areas and your squares. You are proving a theorem that concerns lengths and angles. What's the idea of dragging in area?" Once again this scrupulous reader has a point. Fortunately, there is a proof involving only angle and length, and he can find it in E 4, E 5, and E 6.

Now we are ready to observe how geometry presents numbers that are not rationals. When we apply the Pythagorean Theorem to the simplest right triangle anyone might think of,

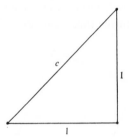

we get into trouble in trying to describe c numerically. Since

$$1^2 + 1^2 = c^2,$$

we know that $c^2 = 2$. But what is c? Clearly c is somewhere between 1 and 2. In fact, the Babylonians estimated that c is about $1 + 24/60 + 51/(60)^2 + 10/(60)^3$ (see R 1), which is decimally about 1.414, or, if you prefer to write our decimals, similarly, as sums of certain rationals, $1 + 4/(10) + 1/(10)^2 + 4/(10)^3$. In any case, c is trapped between the rationals $1414/1000$ and $1415/1000$. Perhaps c is of the form M/N, where N is not a power of 10. For example, we might try to find M such that $(M/13)^2 = 2$. Now, as the reader may check, $(18/13)^2$ is less than 2, whereas $(19/13)^2$ is more than 2. Thus no rational with denominator equal to 13 can have its square equal to 2. Similarly, the reader can check that no rational M/N with N less than 13 has its square equal to 2. And, if he has time, he might easily eliminate $N = 14$, 15, 16, or 17, and so on (depending on the time available) as possibilities.

But the Greeks disposed of all M/N in one sweeping analysis that rests on the theory of odd and even. We shall present a different proof, one that employs the Fundamental Theorem of Arithmetic and that will help us study far more than the single case $c^2 = 2$. (The Greeks' proof is sketched in E 11.)

We shall prove that there is no rational whose square is 2; that is, we shall prove that the number c in question, which is a little bigger than 1.414, is not rational. To prove that c is not rational we shall reason by contradiction, as we did with the Fifteen puzzle, where we proved that a certain assumption leads us to a natural number that is both odd and even. To begin, we assume that there are natural numbers M and N with

$$(M/N) \times (M/N) = 2,$$

and, from this assumption, deduce that there is a natural number that is both odd and even. Such an assumption, leading us to nonsense, must itself be nonsense. Thus our proof will show that c is not rational.

Multiplying both sides of the above equation by $N \times N$, we have

$$M \times M = 2 \times N \times N,$$

an equation involving only the multiplication of natural numbers (it asserts that one square natural number is twice another square natural number). We wish to prove that there are no natural numbers M and N (other than 0) in the relation $M \times M = 2 \times N \times N$. To do this, we are going to examine how often 2 appears when both $M \times M$ and $2 \times N \times N$ are written as the product of primes. We must remember, of course, that $M \times M$ and $2 \times N \times N$ are just different versions of the same natural number.

Imagine that M is written as the product of primes. Among these the prime 2 appears a certain number of times, say, D times; if D is 0, this just means that 2 does not appear at all. When $M \times M$ is written as the product of primes, the prime 2 appears $D + D$ times, twice as often as in M. Thus 2 appears an *even* number of times among the primes whose product is $M \times M$.

Now consider N. In the expression of N as the product of primes, 2 appears, say, E times. Thus, in the expression of $N \times N$ as the product of primes, 2 appears $E + E$ times. When $2 \times N \times N$ is written as the product of primes, 2 appears an *odd* number of times.

But $M \times M$ and $2 \times N \times N$ are just the same natural number in different costumes. The Fundamental Theorem of Arithmetic promises us that the number of times 2 appears among the primes whose product is $M \times M$ is the same as the number of times 2 appears among the primes whose product is $2 \times N \times N$. Thus the number of appearances of 2 is both *odd* and *even*, which is nonsense. Our assumption that there is a rational whose square is 2 must be wrong. We have thus proved that the number whose square is 2 is not rational.

For convenience, let us call the positive number whose square is 2 "*the square root of 2.*" Similarly, we could speak of the square root of 25, which happens to be 5. The square root of the natural number A we will write simply $\sqrt{A}$. We know that $\sqrt{2}$ is a little larger than 1.414 and is not a rational.

A number that is not rational we will call irrational. The rationals and irrationals together describe all points on the line. Thus there are two types of numbers, rational and irrational. We have proved

THEOREM 1. *The number $\sqrt{2}$ is irrational.*

Now that we know that $\sqrt{2}$ is irrational, we can easily manufacture more irrationals. For example, $7 \times \sqrt{2}$ must also be irrational. For if $7 \times \sqrt{2} = M/N$, we would have $\sqrt{2} = M/(7 \times N)$, and $\sqrt{2}$ would itself be rational. More generally, we have

THEOREM 2. *If F is rational and not 0, then $F \times \sqrt{2}$ is irrational.*

The reader may provide a proof for Theorem 2 himself. Note that with the aid of Theorem 2 we can sprinkle irrationals quite generously about the line. For example, using only those F of the form $M/2000$, M being an integer, we can lay out an endless string of irrationals, with each adjacent pair separated by $\sqrt{2}/2000$, which is less than $1/1000$.

We have wandered away from what rightfully should have been the next item on the agenda. Having discovered that $\sqrt{2}$ is irrational, we wonder about the square root of other natural numbers. Clearly the natural numbers $1, 4, 9, 16, \cdots$, being squares, have rational square roots. For instance, $\sqrt{9} = 3$. But $\sqrt{8}$ is $2 \times \sqrt{2}$ [since $(2 \times \sqrt{2}) \times (2 \times \sqrt{2}) = 2 \times 2 \times \sqrt{2} \times \sqrt{2} = 2 \times 2 \times 2 = 8$] and hence is irrational. But what about $\sqrt{3}$ and $\sqrt{5}$, and so on?

Let us tackle $\sqrt{3}$. Assume that $\sqrt{3} = M/N$, where M and N are natural numbers. Will we be able to get a contradiction as with $\sqrt{2}$? We readily obtain

$$3 \times N \times N = M \times M$$

by the same process as before. Now what should we do? Before, we counted appearances of the prime 2; so this time let us watch the prime 3. The reader may easily verify that the number of appearances of 3 when $3 \times N \times N$ (alias $M \times M$) is written as the product of primes must be both odd and even. The same reasoning works for $\sqrt{A}$, for any prime A, and establishes

THEOREM 3. *The square root of any prime is irrational.*

The first unsettled case is $\sqrt{6}$. Is $\sqrt{6}$ rational, or is it irrational? Let us try to prove that $\sqrt{6}$ is irrational.

If $\sqrt{6} = M/N$, then, as before,

$$6 \times N \times N = M \times M.$$

Since 6 is not a prime, we must be careful at the next step, for it would be useless to ask: "How many times does 6 appear when a natural number is written as the product of primes?" The answer would, of course, be: "Not at all."

We must also consider the way 6 itself is written as the product of primes. The prime 2, for example, appears once when 6 is written as the product of primes. Thus 2 appears an odd number of times when $6 \times N \times N$ is written as the product of primes and an even number of times when $M \times M$ is written as the product of primes. Again, since $6 \times N \times N$ and $M \times M$ are the same number, we have, by the Fundamental Theorem of Arithmetic, the same contradiction as before. Thus we have proved

THEOREM 4. *The square root of 6 is irrational.*

The next square root to examine, $\sqrt{7}$, is irrational according to Theorem 3; and $\sqrt{8}$ is irrational, as we happened to notice earlier. Since 9 is a square, $\sqrt{9}$ is rational. The reader may easily prove that $\sqrt{10}$ is irrational. Theorem 3 shows that $\sqrt{11}$ is irrational.

The next challenge is $\sqrt{12}$. Assuming that it is a rational M/N, we obtain

$$12 \times N \times N = M \times M.$$

Let us count appearances of the prime 2 when $12 \times N \times N$ and $M \times M$ (two versions of the same natural number) are written as the product of primes. In $12 = 2 \times 2 \times 3$, 2 appears twice. In M, 2 appears, say, D times and in N, 2 appears, say, E times. By the Fundamental Theorem of Arithmetic, we must have

$$2 + (2 \times E) = 2 \times D.$$

Unfortunately for us, since both $2 + (2 \times E)$ and $2 \times D$ are clearly even, we have no contradiction at all. Imitation of our previous arguments this time brought us to a dead end. Before we look for another attack, or perhaps for a proof that $\sqrt{12}$ is rational, let us try to find out why we ran into a dead end.

We reached no contradiction because 2 appears an even number of times when 12 is written as the product of primes. Had 2 appeared an odd number of times, we would have arrived at a contradiction, which in our circumstances is preferable to a dead end. This explains the dead end.

Let us look again at $12 = 2 \times 2 \times 3$. Note that the prime 3 appears once, an odd number of times. If we tabulate appearances of 3 instead of 2, we will reach a contradiction instead of a dead end, as the reader may check. Thus $\sqrt{12}$ is irrational.

We could go on and on deciding for many natural numbers A, whether $\sqrt{A}$ is rational or irrational. So far, the only natural numbers whose square roots are rational are the squares. We begin to suspect that if A is a natural number, and $\sqrt{A}$ is rational, then A must be a square.

To see whether this is so, let us look back for a moment at our proof that $\sqrt{12}$ is irrational. It depends on the fact that 3 appears an odd number of times when 12 is written as the product of primes. The same kind of argument would have proved that if $A = 2 \times 2 \times 3 \times 3 \times 3 \times 3 \times 5 \times 5 \times 5$, then A is irrational; bookkeeping with the prime 5 would lead to a contradiction if we assumed that $\sqrt{A}$ is a rational (though bookkeeping with the primes 2 or 3 would lead to dead ends).

Thus, if A is a natural number that, when written as the product of primes, has at least one prime appearing an odd number of times, we see that $\sqrt{A}$ is irrational.

On the other hand, what can we say if, when we write A as the product of primes, each prime appears an even number of times? For example, what if A is $3 \times 3 \times 5 \times 5 \times 5 \times 5$? In this case, we can easily compute $\sqrt{A}$; it is simply $3 \times 5 \times 5$, the natural number formed by taking each prime half as often as it appears when A is written as the product of primes. That is, A is a square. The same kind of argument works for any A for which each prime occurs an even number of times. Summarizing the conclusions of the last two paragraphs in a nutshell, we have

THEOREM 5. *If the natural number A is not a square, then $\sqrt{A}$ is irrational. If A is a square, then $\sqrt{A}$ is rational (in fact, a natural number).*

The Fundamental Theorem of Arithmetic has shown its power. Not only did it help us prove that $\sqrt{2}$ is irrational, but it even helped us to determine all natural numbers that have irrational square roots. The Fundamental Theorem of Arithmetic, which depends on the addition and multiplication of natural numbers, has provided an insight into the irrationals.

Just as geometry raised a question about numbers and exposed the irrationals, so does the existence of irrationals in turn have an impact upon geometry. This we will examine in the next chapter, on covering rectangles with squares.

Exercises

1. Prove that the sum of the three angles of any triangle is 180° by drawing the dotted lines indicated in the figure below and using the facts that $A = D$, $B = E$.

2. In square II of the proof of the Pythagorean Theorem, we tacitly *assumed* that the figure whose four sides are all of length c is a square. Show that it is indeed a square by proving that each of its four corners is a right angle. (*Hint:* Use E 1.)

3. The reader may make the proof of the Pythagorean Theorem more vivid by cutting out of cardboard four right triangles of the same size, and three squares, each corresponding to one of the three sides of his cardboard triangle. With these he can then assemble the squares I and II of the proof.

4. Two triangles are similar if the three angles of one are equal to the three angles of the other. Prove that the triangles ADC, ACB, and CDB of this figure are similar:

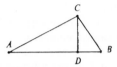

CD and AB are perpendicular; so are AC and CB.

5. It is proved in geometry that if a, b, and c are the lengths of the three sides of one triangle and a', b', c' the lengths of the three corresponding sides of a similar triangle, then*

$$\frac{a}{a'} = \frac{b}{b'} = \frac{c}{c'}.$$

Using this fact and E 4, prove that $b/p = c/b$ and $a/q = c/a$, where the letters are defined by this diagram:

This is the triangle of E 4

6. Continued from E 5. From the relations $p + q = c$, $b/p = c/b$ and $a/q = c/a$, prove that
   (a) $b^2 = pc$,   (c) $a^2 + b^2 = (p + q)c$,
   (b) $a^2 = qc$,   (d) $a^2 + b^2 = c^2$.

   (E 5 and E 6 provide a proof of the Pythagorean Theorem that uses length and angle but not area.)

7. (a) If the two shorter sides of a right triangle are 5 and 12, find the third side.
   (b) If the two longer sides of a right triangle are 29 and 21, find the smallest side.

8. Assume that the two short sides of a right triangle are both 30.
   (a) Show that the long side is $30 \times \sqrt{2}$,
   (b) Give a decimal estimate of $30 \times \sqrt{2}$,
   (c) Compare this estimate to your measurement of the long side of a right triangle with its two short sides each of length 30.

---

* See R 3.

9. Compare your estimate of E 8 (b) to the Babylonian estimate:

$$42 + \frac{25}{60} + \frac{35}{(60)^2}.$$

10. Prove that, if M and N are natural numbers, there are natural numbers A and B such that $(A, B) = 1$ and $A/B = M/N$.

11. The Pythagoreans based their proof of the irrationality of $\sqrt{2}$ on the distinction between odd and even, but did not require the Fundamental Theorem of Arithmetic. Carry out their proof, which we now sketch:

    (i) If $\sqrt{2}$ is a rational number, then we may assume that $\sqrt{2} = A/B$ with $(A, B) = 1$ (see E 10).

    (ii) From $2 \times B \times B = A \times A$, we see that A is even and thus can be written as $2 \times C$ for some natural number C.

    (iii) From $2 \times B \times B = 2 \times C \times 2 \times C$, we see that B is even.

    (iv) Thus (A, B) is at least 2, a contradiction with (i).

12. Without using Theorem 5, prove that $\sqrt{10}$ is irrational.

13. Without using Theorem 5, prove that $\sqrt{30}$ is irrational.

14. Without using Theorem 5, prove that $\sqrt{108}$ is irrational.

15. Prove that $1 + \sqrt{2}$ is irrational.

16. Prove that if N is an integer, then $N + \sqrt{2}$ is irrational.

17. Prove that if F is a rational number, then $F + \sqrt{2}$ is irrational.

18. (a) Prove that the sum of two rationals is again rational.
    (b) Show, by an example, that the sum of two irrationals might not be irrational.

19. Prove that $\sqrt{2} + \sqrt{3}$ is irrational.

20. Prove that $\sqrt{3} + \sqrt{5}$ is irrational.

21. Prove that there is no rational M/N such that $M/N \times M/N \times M/N = 2$.

22. If a and b are in the relation $a \times a \times a = b$, then we shall call a the *cube root* of b, and write a as $\sqrt[3]{b}$. For example, $2 = \sqrt[3]{8}$. In E 21, $\sqrt[3]{2}$ was seen to be irrational. Prove that the cube root of any prime is irrational.

23. See E 22. Prove that $\sqrt[3]{36}$ is irrational.

24. (a) What do you think would be the analogue of Theorem 5 for cube roots?
    (b) Prove it.

25. If $a \times a \times a \times a = b$, then we shall call a the *fourth root* of b, and write a as $\sqrt[4]{b}$. (Here a and b are positive numbers.) For example, $\sqrt[4]{81} = 3$, and $\sqrt[4]{10}$ is somewhere between 1 and 2.
    (a) Prove that the fourth root of a prime is irrational.
    (b) Prove that the fourth root of 32 is irrational.

26. (a) What do you think would be the analogue of Theorem 5 for fourth roots? (See E 25.)
    (b) Prove it.

27. Prove that if A divides both B and C, then A divides (B, C):
    (a) using Lemma 4 of Chapter 4,
    (b) using the Fundamental Theorem of Arithmetic.

28. If $(A, B) = 1$ and $(C, D) = 1$, must $(A \times C, B \times D) = 1$? If so, prove it.

29. If $(A, B) = 1$ and $(C, D) = 1$, must $(A + C, B + D) = 1$? If so, prove it.

30. A natural number is called *square-free* if 1 is the only square that divides it. How can you decide whether a natural number is square-free if you have it written as the product of primes?

31. See E 30.
    (a) How many square-free natural numbers are there from 1 to 100?
    (b) How many square-free natural numbers are there from 101 to 200?
    (c) How many square-free natural numbers are there from 201 to 300?

32. This continues E 31.
    (a) Compute $6/\pi^2$ to two decimals.
    (b) Compute to two decimals the fraction of natural numbers from 1 to 200 that are square-free.
    It is known that as we make longer and longer lists, the fraction of square-free natural numbers gets closer and closer to $6/\pi^2$.

33. (a) Prove that for natural numbers A and B, we have $\sqrt{A} \times \sqrt{B} = \sqrt{A \times B}$. (*Hint:* Square both sides.)
    (b) Show by an example that $\sqrt{A} + \sqrt{B}$ need not equal $\sqrt{A + B}$.

34. Prove that $\sqrt{\frac{5}{3}}$ is irrational.

35. (a) Using the distinction between odd and even, prove that $(\frac{3}{2})^{12}$ is not equal to 2^7.
    (b) Using the Fundamental Theorem of Arithmetic, prove that $(\frac{5}{3})^{10}$ is not equal to $(\frac{7}{5})^{16}$.

36. Compute $(\frac{3}{2})^{12}$ and 2^7 in decimals, and compare them.

37. The frequency of a note that is an octave above another is exactly twice the frequency of the lower note. The frequency of a note that is a fifth above another note is $\frac{3}{2}$ the frequency of the lower note. Starting at the lowest C on the piano, you will notice that going up 7 octaves will bring you to the highest C; going up 12 fifths will also bring you to the top C. Prove that if a piano could be tuned such that fifths as well as octaves were true, then $(\frac{3}{2})^{12}$ would equal 2^7 (but compare with E 35 (a) and E 36).

38. Prove Theorem 2.

39. Prove that between any two numbers there is an endless supply of both rationals and irrationals.

40. The three dimensions of a box are 1, 2, and 2. Find the length of the long diagonals (the diagonals not on the surface of the box).

41. (a) Is the product of two rationals always rational?
    (b) Is the product of two irrationals always irrational?

42. The three dimensions of a box are 2, 3, and 6. Find, as in E 40, the length of the long diagonals.

43. See E 36 and E 37 of Chapter 3. We have given the symbols 2^0, 2^1, 2^2, $\cdots$ meaning. Let us, since we are the masters, now give the symbol $2^{1/2}$ meaning.
    (a) If we want the rule $2^{m+n} = 2^m \times 2^n$ to hold even when m and n are not natural numbers, show that we would want $2 = 2^{1/2} \times 2^{1/2}$.
    (b) Show that (a) advises us to use $2^{1/2}$ as a new name for $\sqrt{2}$.

44. See E 43. We have not given the symbol 2^{-1} any meaning.
    (a) Show that if we want the rule $2^{m+n} = 2^m \times 2^n$ to hold even when m or n is negative, then we would want $2^0 = 2^1 \times 2^{-1}$.
    (b) Show that (a) tells that 2^{-1} should be a new name for $\frac{1}{2}$.

45. Using the ideas of E 43 and E 44, show that we should make (a) $25^{1/2} = 5$, (b) $3^{1/2} = \sqrt{3}$, (c) $3^{-2} = \frac{1}{9}$.

46. See E 45. Using the ideas of E 43 and E 44, show that we should make (a) $4^{3/2} = 8$, (b) $4^{-(3/2)} = \frac{1}{8}$.

47. (a) Show how two rulers or yardsticks can be used to make a slide rule for addition and subtraction.
    (b) To make a slide rule for multiplication and division, mark two strips of paper (or wooden slats) as follows. At the left end write the numeral 1. One inch from the left write the numeral 2. Two inches from the left write the numeral 4. Three inches from the left write the numeral 8. Continue in the same manner for several inches; that is, m inches from the left write the decimal form of 2^m. How can these two strips of paper be used to multiply powers of 2? Why is the relation $2^m \times 2^n = 2^{m+n}$ important here?

References

1. B. L. van der Waerden, *Science Awakening*, Noordhoff Ltd., Groningen, Holland, 1954. (A discussion of the Babylonian and Egyptian treatments of right triangles is to be found on pp. 6, 76–77. Plate 8, facing p. 65, has a photograph of the clay tablet showing a right triangle whose two short sides have length 30.)

2. O. Ore, *Number Theory and its History*, McGraw-Hill, New York, 1948. (The right triangle interested the ancients in the problem of finding all pairs of square natural numbers whose sum is again a square. The case of two cubes whose sum is a cube is discussed on pp. 204–207.)

3. I. Niven, *Numbers: Rational and Irrational*, Random House, New York, 1961. (The impact of the irrationals on the proof that corresponding sides of similar triangles are proportional is shown on pp. 46–49.)

4. K. von Fritz, The discovery of incommensurability by Hippasus of Metapontum, *Annals of Mathematics*, vol. 46, 1945, pp. 242–264.

5. O. Neugebauer, *The Exact Sciences in Antiquity*, Princeton University Press, 1952.

6. G. D. Birkhoff and R. Beatley, *Basic Geometry*, Chelsea, New York, 1959. (This is a specially fine text on high school geometry.)

For material on the geometry of points and the arithmetic of numbers and their relation, see R 8, R 9, and R 10 of Chapter 15.

Chapter 6

TILING

There is no barrier between one part of mathematics and another. In the last chapter a theorem in geometry led to a discovery in the algebra of numbers—the existence of the irrationals. To prove that, for example, $\sqrt{2}$ is irrational, we used the Fundamental Theorem of Arithmetic from the part of mathematics called number theory, which is concerned primarily with the study of the integers. The distinction between even and odd, also part of number theory, was of aid in our study of switches (part of algebra) and of labeling vertices (part of topology). We will find that the existence of irrationals has an impact on geometry; in particular, on the division of rectangles into squares.

It is a simple matter to tile a rectangle of dimensions 5 by 7 with nonoverlapping congruent squares. The rectangle shown in this diagram

has been cut into 35 squares. We could divide each of these squares into four smaller squares, all of equal size, and make a tiling of the rectangle with 140 squares.

Let us try to tile with congruent squares a more challenging rectangle, one whose dimensions are $4\frac{2}{3}$ by $8\frac{5}{7}$. We can rewrite $\frac{2}{3}$ as $\frac{14}{21}$ and $\frac{5}{7}$ as $\frac{15}{21}$; thus a square whose dimensions are $\frac{1}{21}$ by $\frac{1}{21}$ can tile this rectangle. We can even compute how many tiles are necessary. Since

$$4\frac{2}{3} = 4 + \frac{2}{3} = 4 + \frac{14}{21} = \frac{84}{21} + \frac{14}{21} = \frac{98}{21},$$

the little square whose sides are $\frac{1}{21}$ must be laid off 98 times along the width. Since

$$8\frac{5}{7} = 8 + \frac{5}{7} = 8 + \frac{15}{21} = \frac{168}{21} + \frac{15}{21} = \frac{183}{21},$$

the same little square must be laid off 183 times along the length. The total number of squares covering the rectangle is $98 \times 183 = 17,934$; but this number is of less interest than the 98 and 183 which already assure us that the tiling exists. The same reasoning proves

THEOREM 1. *A rectangle whose sides are rational can be tiled with congruent squares.*

What happens if the rectangle has irrational sides? For example, can we tile a rectangle whose dimensions are $10 \times \sqrt{2}$ by $5 \times \sqrt{2}$? Since this rectangle happens to be twice as long as it is wide, it can be tiled with two congruent squares, each with side $5 \times \sqrt{2}$. Thus even this rectangle, though it has irrational sides, can be tiled with congruent squares.

Next let us consider the rectangle

Is it possible to find a square, perhaps a very small one, that can be used to tile this rectangle of dimensions $\sqrt{2}$ by 1? That is, can we find a square that we can lay off along the width, and along the length, without having anything left over?

We can easily show that no such square can be found. Imagine, for the moment, that we have such a square and that its sides are of length A, perhaps some very small number. Since this square is supposed to tile the rectangle, there are natural numbers M and N such that

$$\sqrt{2} = M \times A$$

and

$$1 = N \times A.$$

From these two equations we deduce that

$$\frac{\sqrt{2}}{M} = A$$

and

$$A = \frac{1}{N},$$

and hence

$$\frac{\sqrt{2}}{M} = \frac{1}{N}.$$

Thus $\sqrt{2} = M/N$. But we have already proved that $\sqrt{2}$ is irrational. From this contradiction, we gather that our assumption must be wrong. We have proved

THEOREM 2. *The rectangle of dimensions $\sqrt{2}$ by 1 cannot be tiled with congruent squares.*

In a similar manner, the reader may prove that we cannot tile the $\sqrt{2}$ by $\sqrt{3}$ rectangle with congruent squares. What is the general rule for determining which rectangles can be tiled with congruent squares? It is not simply that both sides must be rational, since the $5 \times \sqrt{2}$ by $10 \times \sqrt{2}$ rectangle can be tiled. What is it, then, that made this case so simple? The answer is that the quotient $(10 \times \sqrt{2})/(5 \times \sqrt{2})$ is 2 (a rational), even though the dimensions are not rational.

We should probably look at the quotient of the two dimensions rather than the dimensions themselves. Perhaps the reader has already guessed

THEOREM 3. *A rectangle whose dimensions are L by W, with L/W a rational, can be tiled with congruent squares.*

PROOF. Since L/W is rational, we know that there are natural numbers M and N with

$$L/W = M/N.$$

Thus $L \times N = W \times M$. Dividing both sides by $M \times N$, we obtain

$$L/M = W/N.$$

This last equation tells us what size square can be used to tile the rectangle. A square of side L/M fits exactly M times along the length. Moreover, since L/M is equal to W/N, this square fits exactly N times along the width. Thus this little square, when laid down $M \times N$ times, tiles the rectangle. This proves Theorem 3.

Which rectangles cannot be tiled with congruent squares? It is reasonable to suspect those for which L/W is irrational. One can prove

THEOREM 4. *A rectangle whose dimensions are L by W, with L/W irrational, cannot be tiled with congruent squares.*

The proof, similar to that of Theorem 2, is left to the reader.

Having learned which rectangles can be tiled with congruent squares, let us go to the opposite extreme and ask: Which rectangles can be tiled with squares no two of which are the same size? We will keep our tacit restriction; namely, that a tiling has only a finite number of tiles.

This is a question on which mathematicians have worked only in the twentieth century. But the Egyptians, forty centuries ago, were involved with a similar question about rationals. In their daily computations they represented a rational as the sum of unit fractions, no two being the same size. (A unit fraction is a rational of the form $1/N$, with N a natural number.) For example, they expressed $\frac{2}{5}$ as $\frac{1}{3} + \frac{1}{15}$ and $\frac{2}{59}$ as $\frac{1}{36} + \frac{1}{236} + \frac{1}{531}$. On the other hand, it is a simple matter to represent $\frac{2}{5}$ as the sum of equal unit fractions, for example,

$$\frac{2}{5} = \frac{1}{5} + \frac{1}{5}.$$

Though their representation may strike us as peculiar, it is similar to our own decimal system. After all, when we write $\frac{5}{16} = 0.3125$ we are writing $\frac{5}{16}$ as the sum of rationals, no two the same size: $\frac{3}{10}, \frac{1}{100}, \frac{2}{1000}, \frac{5}{10000}$. When we write the numbers less than 1 decimally, we are actually expressing them as the sum of rationals of different sizes and of the form M/N, where M is at most 9 and N is a power of 10. (This is discussed in more detail in Chapter 14.)

But, after this detour, let us return to the problem of tiling a rectangle* with unequal squares, a problem remotely resembling the Egyptians' problem of writing rationals. There are two ways of approaching this question. We may either try to piece together squares and hope that after a while we succeed in forming a rectangle, or we may start with a rectangle and try to cut it into squares, no two of the same size. Let us first try to assemble a rectangle out of incongruent squares. Using just two squares we would have either

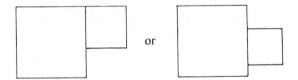

or

which surely are not rectangles. If we now add one square we get many possibilities, two of which are

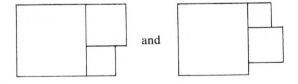

and

---

* If the rectangle happens to be a square, then it can of course be covered with one square. Such a trivial situation we will not call a tiling.

but neither of which forms a rectangle. Of course, if we allow two of the squares to be congruent, we could have this tiling of a rectangle:

The reader, in assembling four squares to form a rectangle, will see that there are essentially five ways

and that each has at least two congruent tiles. With five squares we can assemble a rectangle in many more ways, of which these are three samples:

Observe that in each rectangle there are congruent squares. The reader may add to the list and even go on to assemble six squares to form a rectangle. He will find, as we have seen so far, that each such tiling will have at least two congruent squares.

At this point we can either go on, trying to assemble seven incongruent squares into a rectangle, or we can seek a proof showing that it is impossible to tile a rectangle with incongruent squares. Or we could take the attitude of some research mathematicians who devote Monday to trying to prove a conjecture, Tuesday to trying to disprove it, Wednesday to trying to prove it, and so on, until either the conjecture is resolved or the mathematician is exhausted.

Already with five or six squares it is difficult to keep an accurate list of all possibilities and to be sure we have overlooked none. Going on to seven, therefore, is not promising. Thus, like the "alternating" mathematician, let us try to prove that it is impossible to tile a rectangle with incongruent squares.

In all our examples the smallest square is duplicated. This suggests that we should look closely at the smallest square and its neighboring squares. Imagine, for the moment, that the smallest square, S, lies on the border of the rectangle and that no two squares are congruent. We might have either

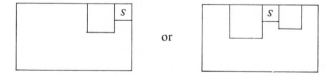

or

In either example, a square placed above *S* would have to be smaller than *S*. Thus we have

 THEOREM 5. *If a rectangle is tiled with incongruent squares, then the smallest square does not touch the border of the rectangle.*

Now all we must do is prove that the smallest square must touch the border, and we will have a proof that a rectangle cannot be tiled with incongruent squares. Let us try.

Let us assume that the smallest square does not touch the border. Looking closely at this square *S* and at its surrounding neighbors, we see that if *S* had two neighboring squares touching one of its edges, for example,

then adding another square, *T*, above *S*, would give us something like this (since *T* must be larger than *S*):

Thus another square, *U*, placed to the left of *S*, would give

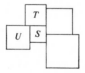

And similarly, any square placed below *S* would have to be smaller than *S*. Thus there can be only one square bordering *S* on its right (and only one on each of its other three sides), and the squares surrounding *S* will form a windmill.

We have proved

THEROEM 6. *If a rectangle is tiled with incongruent squares, then the smallest square is surrounded by four squares.*

Instead of obtaining a contradiction to Theorem 5, we just learned a little more about the smallest square. Perhaps, like our "alternating" mathematician, we should try again to tile a rectangle with incongruent squares.

Here is a way that might work. Draw a rectangle cut up into rectangles in such a way that there is a chance of distorting all the small rectangles into squares (and, incidentally, the big rectangle into one of different shape). In view of Theorem 6, we should be sure to include a rectangle surrounded by four rectangles. One candidate, with nine rectangles, looks like this:

Either D or H might become the smallest square.

To see what stretching and shrinking might accomplish, let us use a little algebra. Imagine that rectangle E becomes a square of side x and that rectangle H becomes a square of side y and that all the other rectangles become squares. Square F will then have side $x + y$. Thus I will have side $y + (x + y)$, or simply $x + 2y$. Then G will have side $y + (x + 2y)$, or simply $x + 3y$. If we call z the side that D must have, then we see that $z + x = (x + 3y) + y$. Thus $z = 4y$, and hence D will have side $4y$. Square C will have side $4y + (x + 3y)$, or simply $x + 7y$. Hence A will have side $(x + 7y) + 4y$, or simply $x + 11y$. Since the side of B is the sum of the side of E and the side of F, it is equal to $x + (x + y)$, or simply $2x + y$. If the top edge of A is to be a continuation of the top edge of B, we must have $(x + 11y) + 4y = (2x + y) + x$. This places a restriction on x and y. Collecting terms on each side of the equation, we get

$$x + 15y = 3x + y.$$

Subtracting x from both sides yields

$$15y = 2x + y.$$

Subtracting y from both sides yields

$$14y = 2x.$$

Dividing both sides by 2 yields

$$7y = x,$$

a relation between x and y. If we choose $y = 100$, then x must be 700. For convenience of arithmetic let us choose $y = 1$. Then $x = 7$, $x + y = 7 + 1 = 8$, and F becomes a square of side 8. Similarly, we can compute the sides of the other six squares. Luckily, none of their sides turns out to be zero or negative; moreover, no two are equal. We have finally obtained a partition of a rectangle into (nine) incongruent squares.

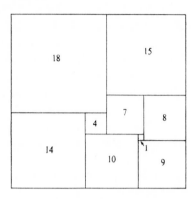

If we were to place a 33 by 33 square above this 32 by 33 rectangle, we would have ten incongruent squares tiling a 33 by 65 rectangle. Such a tiling, depending so much on a previous tiling, is not very appealing. Let us call a tiling of a rectangle by squares *simple* if no subcollection of the squares forms a rectangle. We see that a 32 by 33 rectangle has a simple tiling by incongruent squares, as does this square:

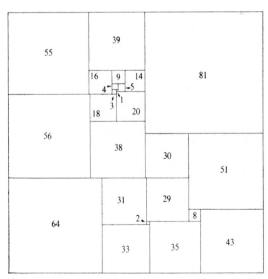

But no one knows which rectangles have simple tilings; for example, it is not known whether the 1 by 2 rectangle has a simple tiling.

Still keeping the restriction of incongruent tiles, we can go in various directions. We might ask: Can an equilateral triangle be tiled with incongruent equilateral triangles? Or we might move into space and ask: Can a box be filled with incongruent cubes?

Before he feels he understands the specific case of tiling rectangles, a mathematician will automatically examine such closely related questions. Perhaps he will find a general theorem to be true for tilings of many different objects. Such a theorem is more satisfying than knowledge of one special case, such as tiling by squares. And if he can find no all-inclusive theorem, no insight into a wide class of structures, then at least he knows the extent of his theory, and understands just what it is he is proving theorems about.

As it turns out, the case of an equilateral triangle, or of a box, is quite different from that for the rectangle. In R 1, Tutte proves

THEOREM 7. *It is impossible to tile an equilateral triangle with incongruent equilateral triangles.*

His proof is quite indirect and involved, and will be omitted; in E 28 we sketch what might be made the basis of a more direct and elementary proof.

The equilateral triangle thus behaves quite differently from the square. We should feel very fortunate that the square can be tiled with incongruent squares, yet we are disappointed that the theory is not so general as we hoped it would be. When we consider the problem of filling a box, we meet

THEOREM 8. *It is impossible to fill a rectangular box with incongruent cubes.*

PROOF. We will first assume that it is possible to fill a box with incongruent cubes, and then obtain a contradiction of this assumption. Specifically, we will construct in such a situation an *endless* tower of cubes, within the given limited supply of cubes.

Let us look at the smallest of the cubes resting on the bottom of the box. We know from Theorem 5 (which states that when a rectangle is tiled with incongruent squares, the smallest square does not touch the border) that this cube—call it C—does not touch the border of the bottom; hence it will have a position such as this:

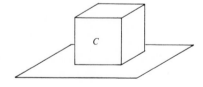

Thus the other cubes resting on the bottom of the box, and in touch with C, make a wall around the top of C. Hence the cubes resting on C are all smaller than C, and their bases tile the top of C with incongruent squares. Now if we look at the smallest of the cubes resting on C—give it the name D—we see that we have started a tower of cubes:

It can easily be seen that we can continue the tower endlessly (by looking at the smallest cube resting on D, and so on). Since we have a limited number of cubes at our disposal, we have reached a contradiction: there can be no endless tower. Thus it is impossible to fill a box with incongruent cubes.

The tiling of rectangles with incongruent squares is, in a sense, a piece of luck. It is a theory that exists for the plane, but not for space; for rectangles, but not for equilateral triangles.

However, within the theory of tiling rectangles is a result that is not only a vast generalization of Theorem 4, but will illustrate how the machinery developed in one branch of mathematics can be applied to another, seemingly unrelated, branch.

In Chapter 7 we will use the theory of electrical networks to prove that it is impossible to tile the 1 by $\sqrt{2}$ rectangle with squares, even if we remove all restrictions on their relative size.

Exercises

1. Tile a rectangle $21\frac{5}{7}$ by $17\frac{2}{5}$ with congruent square tiles.

2. What is the smallest number of congruent square tiles that will tile the rectangle of E 1?

3. Tile a rectangle $10\frac{3}{4}$ by $5\frac{1}{2}$ with congruent square tiles.

4. What is the smallest number of congruent square tiles that will tile the rectangle of E 3?

5. Can the following two rectangles be tiled with congruent square tiles?
   (a) $5 \times \sqrt{3}$ by $7 \times \sqrt{3}$,   (b) $7 \times \sqrt{2}$ by $11 \times \sqrt{3}$.

6. Can the following two rectangles be tiled with congruent square tiles?
   (a) $10 \times \sqrt{5}$ by $15 \times \sqrt{5}$,   (b) 10 by $12 \times \sqrt{2}$.

7. Cut out of paper or cardboard a quadrilateral having no two sides parallel, no two sides of equal length, and no indentations. Show that the plane can be tiled with copies of such a figure.

8. (a) Prove that the sum of the four inside angles of any four-sided figure such as the one of E 7 is 360°. See E 1 of Chapter 5.
   (b) Why is part (a) of importance in the tiling requested in E 7?

9. A box has dimensions L, W, and H. What must be true about the relation between those three numbers if the box can be filled with congruent cubes? Show why.

10. Prove that if a rectangle is tiled with incongruent squares, then the smallest tile touches exactly four other tiles. That is, check the proof of Theorem 5.

11. A triangle has angles 30°, 60°, and 90°. Prove that it can be tiled with incongruent triangles having the angles 30°, 60°, and 90°.

12. Prove that a right triangle whose two smaller angles, A and B, are not 45° can be tiled with incongruent triangles similar to the given triangle (that is, with triangles whose angles are A, B, and 90°).

13. Can a triangle with angles 90°, 45°, and 45° be tiled with incongruent triangles of the same angles? (No one knows.)

14. In finding a tiling of a rectangle by incongruent squares (see p. 72), we set the side of E equal to x and the side of H equal to y. But we need not have started with E and H. Find another tiling by setting the side of B equal to x and the side of E equal to y. Then proceed as we did on p. 72.

15. See E 14. Set the side of E equal to x and the side of F equal to y. Then proceed as we did on p. 72.

16. See E 14. Set the side of C equal to x and the side of D equal to y. Then proceed as we did on p. 72. It might be necessary to introduce more unknowns than x and y in the process.

17. Show that a rectangle 1 by $\sqrt{2}$ can be tiled with incongruent square tiles if we permit ourselves to use an endless supply of tiles.

18. Show that any rectangle can be tiled with square tiles if we permit ourselves an endless supply of tiles.

19. Cut 13 squares of cardboard to fit together to form the tiling

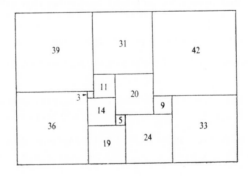

20. Reassemble the 13 squares of E 19 to form the tiling

21. Prove that for any natural number N, from 9 on, it is possible to put N incongruent squares together to form a rectangle.

22. Distort this tiling of a rectangle into a tiling of a rectangle with incongruent squares.

23. Two squares are "adjacent" if they touch at more than just a corner. Prove that if a rectangle is tiled with squares in such a way that no two adjacent squares are congruent, then none of the smallest squares touches the border of the rectangle.

24. Two cubes are "adjacent" if they touch at more than an edge. Prove that if a box is filled with cubes, then there exist two adjacent cubes that are congruent. In fact, they will share one of their six faces. (*Hint:* Use E 23.)

25. A rectangle is tiled with squares in such a way that no two adjacent squares are congruent. Prove that any smallest square of the tiling is surrounded by precisely four squares.

26. (a) Show all ways in which five squares (of various or equal sizes) can be fitted together to form a rectangle.
    (b) Which rectangles can be tiled with five squares? (There is no restriction on size of the squares; they may be all of the same size or of various sizes.)

27. (a) In how many ways can 36 congruent squares be put together to form a rectangle?
    (b) In how many ways can 37 congruent squares be put together to form a rectangle?

28. Consider a tiling of an equilateral triangle with small incongruent equilateral triangles.

(a) Prove that the smallest tile, S, touching the base of the big triangle meets the base at just one point:

(b) Prove that the smallest tile, T, touching the top side of S meets that side at just one point:

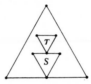

(c) Can this method be continued to produce an endless tower of little triangles, and thus a proof of Theorem 7?

29. Check the proof of Theorem 8.

Reference

1. W. T. Tutte, The dissection of equilateral triangles into equilateral triangles, *Proceedings of the Cambridge Philosophical Society*, vol. 44, 1948, pp. 463–482.

See also references of Chapter 7.

TILING AND
ELECTRICITY

In the last chapter we saw that rectangles whose dimensions are L by W, with L/W irrational, cannot be tiled with congruent squares. We will now prove much more: *such rectangles cannot be tiled with squares in any way whatsoever.* To carry out the proof, we will show that tiling a rectangle with rectangles is intimately related to the flow of electricity through wires. Then we will be able to use for our purposes the mathematics of electricity, which was developed a century ago. We will first present the electrical background.

Since it will be several pages before we return to the tiling of rectangles by rectangles, the reader is asked to be patient. After we have developed the electrical theory it will be a very simple matter to prove that a 1 by $\sqrt{2}$ rectangle cannot be tiled with squares in any way at all.

A collection of wires we will call a **network.** *A point where two or more wires meet we will call a* **vertex.** Here, for example, is a network with eight wires and six vertices.

We will assume that our networks are *connected;* that is, that a bug can get from any vertex to any other by traveling along the wires.

Each wire has the ability to conduct electricity. This ability is influenced by the material of which the wire is made (silver conducts electricity better than copper); the length of the wire (the shorter the wire, the lesser the distance the electricity must travel); and the radius of the wire (the bigger the cross section, the easier it is for electricity to pass through). With this in mind, let us cause electricity to flow in our network by hooking up a battery.

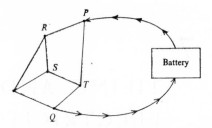

The electrons enter the network at P and leave it at Q. Some of the electrons will choose to flow through the wire PR; and others, through the wire PT. If PR conducts electricity better than PT, we might expect all the electrons to choose PR. But if they do, PR may get so crowded that some will choose PT. At R, S, and T, the electrons have more choices. For example, some electrons leaving T may choose to move toward S. Other electrons might move from S toward T. Nobody has developed a microscopic psychology of electrons. Yet it is important to be able to predict the current in each wire; too much current will blow a fuse, too little will result in dim lights.

After many experiments, physicists came to two simple conclusions about the flow of electrons through a network. With these two rules, they can predict the mass behavior of the electrons. They observed first that in the simplest network—a single wire—with both ends attached to a battery,

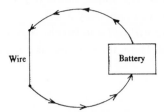

the current flowing in the wire is proportional to the strength of the battery. That is, if they doubled the strength of the battery (say, by hooking a second battery to the first) then the flow of electricity in the wire doubled; similarly, if they tripled the strength of the battery, the flow of electricity in the wire tripled. In short, if the strength of a battery was measured in volts, V, and the flow of electricity in amperes, A, it was observed that, for *each wire*, A/V was always a fixed number. *This number—called the* **conductance*** *of the wire—describes the ease with which the wire lets electricity pass through it*, and is denoted by the letter C. Thus $A/V = C$, or, avoiding division, we have

$$A = C \times V.$$

---

* Conductance can also be defined as the reciprocal of resistance.

Here V records the voltage and A the current. We may assume that the conductance of each wire is known.

Voltage can also be thought of as a pressure. With a voltmeter, physicists can measure the difference in pressure between any two vertices of a network. The difference in voltage causes the current, just as a difference in air pressure causes the wind. If we set the voltage at the bottom vertex of the network equal to zero (the "sea level" above which voltages are measured), then we can assign to each vertex a voltage equal to the reading of a voltmeter attached to that vertex and to the bottom vertex. Now, without a private interview with each electron, we are ready to state the first rule of electrical networks.

I. *If a wire in the network has conductance C and voltages V and V' at its two vertices, then the current A in the wire flows from the larger voltage (say, V) to the smaller (V'), and*

$$A = C(V - V').$$

We may read the preceding equation as: current is equal to conductance times the difference in pressure. (The difference in pressure, $V - V'$, is what we call the voltage drop in the wire.) In the psychology of the individual wire, we would say that the wire thinks it is hooked up to a battery with voltage $V - V'$ and knows nothing about the other wires of the network.

The second rule concerns only the currents.

II. *The total current flowing into each vertex equals the total current leaving that vertex.*

Rule II simply says that electrons do not accumulate at any vertex. Before discussing these two rules further, let us see how we can use them to predict the flow of electrons through a network. Take, for example, this network of two wires and two vertices.

The conductance of each wire is circled. The voltage at the bottom vertex is 0. The current flowing into the network is 14 amperes (we will no longer bother drawing the battery). We want to know the voltage at the top vertex and the current in each of the two wires. We would also like to know the current leaving the bottom vertex (we suspect that it will be 14 amperes).

The unknown voltage we will call V_1. The unknown currents will be A_1, A_2, A_3, as in this picture:

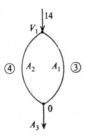

Rule I, applied to each of the two wires, gives

$$A_1 = 3(V_1 - 0),$$
$$A_2 = 4(V_1 - 0).$$

Rule II, applied to each of the two vertices, gives

$$14 = A_1 + A_2,$$
$$A_3 = A_1 + A_2.$$

The last two equations inform us that $A_3 = 14$, as we hoped. Thus we may dispense with the fourth equation. The first three are simply

$$A_1 = 3V_1, \qquad A_2 = 4V_1, \qquad 14 = A_1 + A_2.$$

These three equations yield

$$14 = 3V_1 + 4V_1.$$

Thus $14 = 7V_1$, and hence $V_1 = 2$. Having found V_1 we then find A_1 and A_2: $A_1 = 3 \times 2 = 6$, $A_2 = 4 \times 2 = 8$.

Are the answers $A_1 = 6$ and $A_2 = 8$ reasonable? Yes, for we would expect more current in the wire with the larger conductance. This example indicates that rules I and II seem to be adequate for predicting the currents and the voltages. That is, rules I and II seem to contain enough information to enable us to pinpoint all the unknowns.

Let us see if rules I and II are adequate for this fancier network.

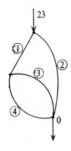

Here 23 amperes are flowing into a network with four wires and three vertices. We would like to know the current in each of the four wires and the voltage at each of the two vertices (the voltage at the bottom vertex is always taken as 0). As a check on our arithmetic, we might also compute the current leaving the bottom vertex (we suspect that it should be 23). We have seven unknowns, A_1, A_2, A_3, A_4, A_5, V_1, and V_2, as indicated in this figure.

Rule I, applied to each of the four wires, gives

$$A_4 = 1(V_1 - V_2),$$
$$A_1 = 2(V_1 - 0),$$
$$A_2 = 3(V_2 - 0),$$
$$A_3 = 4(V_2 - 0).$$

Rule II, applied to each of the three vertices, gives

$$23 = A_1 + A_4,$$
$$A_4 = A_2 + A_3,$$
$$A_5 = A_1 + A_2 + A_3.$$

We have seven equations in seven unknowns. Let us omit the last equation and use it only as a check after we have found A_1, A_2, and A_3 (A_5 should be 23). The six equations in six unknowns, slightly simplified, are:

$$A_4 = V_1 - V_2, \quad A_1 = 2V_1, \quad A_2 = 3V_2, \quad A_3 = 4V_2,$$
$$23 = A_1 + A_4, \quad A_4 = A_2 + A_3.$$

Now we use the information given by rule I to simplify the equations given by rule II. We combine $23 = A_1 + A_4$ with $A_4 = V_1 - V_2$ and $A_1 = 2V_1$ to deduce

$$23 = 2V_1 + (V_1 - V_2) = 3V_1 - V_2.$$

Similarly, from

$$A_4 = A_2 + A_3, \quad A_2 = 3V_2, \quad A_3 = 4V_2, \quad A_4 = V_1 - V_2,$$

we find that

$$V_1 - V_2 = 3V_2 + 4V_2.$$

Therefore we now have only two equations in two unknowns:

$$23 = 3V_1 - V_2,$$
$$V_1 - V_2 = 3V_2 + 4V_2.$$

The second of these equations can be shortened. Since $3V_2 + 4V_2 = 7V_2$, we have $V_1 - V_2 = 7V_2$. Adding V_2 to both sides yields $V_1 = 8V_2$. Thus we have the two equations

$$23 = 3V_1 - V_2,$$

and

$$V_1 = 8V_2.$$

We can now substitute $8V_2$ for V_1 into the first to obtain

$$23 = 3(8V_2) - V_2 = 24V_2 - V_2 = 23V_2.$$

Hence we have just one equation in one unknown,

$$23 = 23V_2.$$

Dividing both sides by 23 yields $V_2 = 1$. Now that we have found V_2 we can immediately find V_1, since $V_1 = 8V_2$. In fact, $V_1 = 8 \times 1 = 8$. Having found all the voltages, we can now compute all the currents:

$$A_4 = 1(V_1 - V_2) = 1(8 - 1) = 7,$$
$$A_1 = 2(V_1 - 0) = 2(8) = 16,$$
$$A_2 = 3(V_2 - 0) = 3(1) = 3,$$
$$A_3 = 4(V_2 - 0) = 4(1) = 4.$$

Finally, as a check, let us compute A_5. We obtain

$$A_5 = A_1 + A_2 + A_3 = 16 + 3 + 4 = 23,$$

as we suspected.

So, again, rules I and II were adequate for pinpointing all the unknown currents and voltages. So far, the answers have all been integers. This need not always be the case, of course, as the following example shows. This third example we will work out in detail also, to illustrate how rules I and II are sufficient to deal with an even more complicated network. After we finish this example, we will be ready to return to tilings of rectangles.

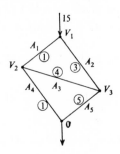

Here we have three voltages and five currents to find. Let us not bother with the current leaving the network; it will equal $A_4 + A_5$ and will serve as a check, since it should equal 15.

Rule I gives

$$A_1 = 1(V_1 - V_2), \qquad A_2 = 3(V_1 - V_3), \qquad A_3 = 4(V_2 - V_3),$$
$$A_4 = 1(V_2 - 0), \qquad A_5 = 5(V_3 - 0).$$

Rule II gives $15 = A_1 + A_2$, $A_1 = A_3 + A_4$, $A_2 + A_3 = A_5$.

As before, we use the equations given by rule I to eliminate the A's. We end up with three equations involving only the V's:

$$15 = 1(V_1 - V_2) + 3(V_1 - V_3),$$
$$1(V_1 - V_2) = 4(V_2 - V_3) + 1(V_2 - 0),$$
$$3(V_1 - V_3) + 4(V_2 - V_3) = 5(V_3 - 0).$$

Simplifying these three equations slightly, we have

$$15 = V_1 - V_2 + 3V_1 - 3V_3,$$
$$V_1 - V_2 = 4V_2 - 4V_3 + V_2,$$
$$3V_1 - 3V_3 + 4V_2 - 4V_3 = 5V_3.$$

Moving all unknowns to the right side,* we obtain

$$15 = 4V_1 - V_2 - 3V_3,$$
$$0 = -V_1 + 6V_2 - 4V_3,$$
$$0 = -3V_1 - 4V_2 + 12V_3.$$

This time we have three equations and three unknown voltages. What should we do with these three equations in order to find V_1, V_2, and V_3?

One possibility is this. Get rid of V_1 and hope we can find two equations in the two unknowns V_2 and V_3. That will be a step in the right direction.

From $15 = 4V_1 - V_2 - 3V_3$ and $0 = -V_1 + 6V_2 - 4V_3$ we can obtain an equation involving just V_2 and V_3. To do this, multiply the second equation by 4, which gives

$$0 = -4V_1 + 24V_2 - 16V_3,$$

and add the equation just obtained to

$$15 = 4V_1 - V_2 - 3V_3;$$

we thus have

$$15 = 23V_2 - 19V_3.$$

To find another relation between V_2 and V_3 we might get rid of V_1 between the two equations

$$0 = -V_1 + 6V_2 - 4V_3$$

and

---

* How this is done is shown in slow motion in Example 17 of Appendix A.

$$0 = -3V_1 - 4V_2 + 12V_3.$$

To do so, multiply $0 = -V_1 + 6V_2 - 4V_3$ by -3, and add the result to $0 = -3V_1 - 4V_2 + 12V_3$. Thus we will be adding

$$0 = 3V_1 - 18V_2 + 12V_3$$

to

$$0 = -3V_1 - 4V_2 + 12V_3.$$

The V_1's cancel when we add these two equations; their sum is

$$0 = -22V_2 + 24V_3.$$

As a result we have two equations that involve only V_2 and V_3:

$$15 = 23V_2 - 19V_3,$$
$$0 = -22V_2 + 24V_3.$$

We want just one equation in one unknown. We can devise such an equation by eliminating, say, V_2, from the last two equations. Using just the second of these, we have

$$22V_2 = 24V_3.$$

Dividing both sides by 22 we obtain

$$V_2 = \frac{24}{22} V_3,$$

or, if we prefer,

$$V_2 = \frac{12}{11} V_3.$$

Combining this relation with $15 = 23V_2 - 19V_3$ gives

$$15 = 23 \left(\frac{12}{11} V_3 \right) - 19V_3.$$

Thus

$$15 = \frac{276}{11} V_3 - 19V_3.$$

Multiplying both sides by 11 we obtain

$$165 = 276V_3 - 209V_3,$$

or simply

$$165 = 67V_3.$$

Dividing both sides by 67 we find

$$V_3 = \frac{165}{67}.$$

Having found V_3 it is a simple matter to reverse our steps and find V_2, then V_1, and finally the A's.

From $V_2 = \frac{12}{11}V_3$ we learn that $V_2 = \frac{12}{11} \times \frac{165}{67}$. Since $\frac{165}{11} = 15$, we see that

$$V_2 = (12 \times 15)/67.$$

Thus

$$V_2 = \frac{180}{67}.$$

Any of the equations involving V_1, V_2, and V_3 can now tell us what V_1 must be. Using, say,

$$0 = -V_1 + 6V_2 - 4V_3,$$

we find

$$0 = -V_1 + 6\left(\frac{180}{67}\right) - 4\left(\frac{165}{67}\right).$$

Thus

$$V_1 = 6\left(\frac{180}{67}\right) - 4\left(\frac{165}{67}\right),$$

or

$$V_1 = \frac{1080}{67} - \frac{660}{67}.$$

Hence

$$V_1 = \frac{420}{67}.$$

Once these voltages are known, the equations given by rule I tell us the currents. For example,

$$A_1 = 1(V_1 - V_2) = 1\left(\frac{420}{67} - \frac{180}{67}\right) = \frac{240}{67}.$$

The reader may easily compute A_2, A_3, A_4, and A_5.

In our third example, the input information (conductance and current) consisted entirely of natural numbers. The unknowns, as it turned out, were not natural numbers, but at least they were rationals. Even if the input information had consisted of rationals, the unknowns would still have been rationals, for all we did was multiply, divide, add, or subtract the numbers we had to work with. These operations, applied to rationals, yield only rationals, never an irrational such as $\sqrt{2}$.

In the three examples, rules I and II were sufficient to predict all the unknowns. It can be proved by the theory of determinants that rules I and II are sufficient to predict all the unknowns in any network. Rules I and II make it unnecessary to psychoanalyze myriads of individual electrons.

In particular, our technique of first writing down all the equations provided by rules I and II, finding equations involving only the V's, and then gradually getting rid of the V's until we have a single equation involving only one of the V's, will always work. All that we will require from the mathematics of electrical networks is this conclusion:

If the conductances in a network and the current entering the network are all rationals, then so are the voltages at all the vertices and the currents in all the wires.

We are finally prepared to show the intimate relation between electrical networks and the tiling of a rectangle. We will show that, from any tiling of a rectangle with rectangles (in particular, with squares) a network of wires, conductances, currents, and voltages can be derived that will satisfy rules I and II. Though we will illustrate the process with a particular example, we will describe it in terms general enough to be applied to any tiling of any rectangle by rectangles. Let us start with a rectangle tiled with rectangles as in this diagram:

The horizontal lines have been drawn heavier for emphasis. Observe that the sum of the horizontal dimensions of the rectangles hanging from a given horizontal line is equal to the sum of the horizontal dimensions of the rectangles resting on that horizontal line. This sounds a good deal like rule II and suggests that the horizontal dimension of each rectangle could be a current in a wire and that each darkened horizontal line could somehow be a vertex. This observation suggests the following steps—to be applied to any tiling of a rectangle with rectangular tiles—for the construction of an electrical network.

Step 1. Darken each horizontal line.

Step 2. The midpoint (or any other point on that line, if you prefer) *of each horizontal line shall be a vertex (for the network being constructed).*

Step 3. With each rectangle of the tiling associate a wire joining the midpoints of the two darkened lines that the rectangle touches on its top and bottom.

Step 4. The current in a wire shall be the horizontal dimension of the rectangle with which it is associated.

Step 5. The voltage at each vertex shall be the height of this vertex above the lowest horizontal line.

Thus the number of wires equals the number of rectangles; the number of vertices equals the number of horizontal lines.

We next define the conductance in each wire such that rule I is satisfied. Rule I reads

Current = Conductance × Difference in voltages.

Now, the difference in voltages between the ends of a wire is just the vertical dimension of the associated rectangle. The current is the horizontal dimension of that rectangle. So we must define the conductance C in each wire such that

$$\frac{Horizontal\ dimension\ of}{associated\ rectangle} = C \times \frac{Vertical\ dimension\ of}{associated\ rectangle.}$$

This brings us to

Step 6. Set the conductance of each wire equal to h/v, where h is the horizontal dimension and v the vertical dimension of the associated rectangle.

Step 7. The current flowing into the top vertex and out of the bottom vertex will equal the horizontal dimension of the tiled rectangle.

(Step 7 guarantees that rule I holds at the top and bottom vertices.) When applied to our example, these seven steps create this electrical network:

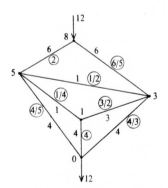

which satisfies rules I and II. The reader might check a few vertices and wires to assure himself that this electrical network, derived from a rectangle tiled with rectangles, satisfies rules I and II.

Now we are ready to prove a theorem that the reader should contrast with the weaker Theorem 2 of Chapter 6.

THEOREM 1. *The rectangle of dimensions $\sqrt{2}$ by 1 cannot be tiled with squares in any way whatsoever.*

PROOF. Orient the rectangle such that its horizontal dimension is 1 and its vertical dimension is $\sqrt{2}$.

If it could be tiled with squares, then we would have an electrical network with input current equal to 1 and all conductances equal to 1. By our previous reasoning, all the currents and voltages must be rational. In particular, the voltage at the highest vertex must be rational. But $\sqrt{2}$ is not a rational. Thus the 1 by $\sqrt{2}$ rectangle cannot be tiled with squares in any way whatsoever.

With a slight change in technique we can prove that a rectangle $\sqrt{2}$ by $\sqrt{3}$ cannot be tiled with squares. Were we simply to take $\sqrt{2}$ as the input current, we would not be able to conclude that all voltages are rational. But we notice that, by shrinking each dimension by the factor $\sqrt{2}$, we obtain a smaller rectangle of dimensions 1 by $\sqrt{3}/\sqrt{2}$,

which is of the same shape as the larger rectangle

To any tiling of the larger rectangle by squares there corresponds a tiling of the smaller rectangle by squares (obtained by shrinking all dimensions by the factor $\sqrt{2}$). Since $\sqrt{3}/\sqrt{2}$ is not rational, the smaller rectangle cannot be tiled with squares, and hence the larger cannot be.

Similar reasoning proves

THEOREM 2. *A rectangle with dimensions L by W, with L/W irrational, can not be tiled with squares.*

Combining Theorem 3 from Chapter 6 with Theorem 2, just obtained, we arrive at

THEOREM 3. *If a rectangle cannot be tiled with congruent squares, then it cannot be tiled with squares in any way whatsoever.*

The arguments leading to Theorems 1, 2, and 3 needed a device for recording how the squares fit together to form a rectangle. This was provided by the electrical network diagrams, which described in a somewhat skeletal fashion the relative positions of the tiles. What we knew about networks we then applied to tilings, which are just networks in disguise. To a mathematician, networks and tilings of a rectangle are just two examples of structures that satisfy rules I and II. Their main difference lies in our feeling about them; their underlying form is the same. And it is the form that a mathematician prefers to study. For this reason he strips away the specific setting as a camouflage, and, by abstracting, obtains a keener insight into the structure. The deeper his understanding of the pure structure, the freer will be his imagination to recognize, through the clutter of reality, an example, or model, of this structure.

Exercises

1. The conductance of a certain wire is 8. How many amperes flow in this wire if the difference in voltage between its two ends is (a) 7 volts, (b) 14 volts, (c) 10 volts?

2. The conductance of a certain wire is 5. How strong a battery is needed to push through this wire a current of (a) 10 amperes, (b) 20 amperes, (c) 12 amperes?

3. Find the unknown voltage and the three unknown currents for this network:

4. Check that the voltages and currents of E 3 satisfy rules I and II.

5. Find the unknown voltage and the three unknown currents for this network:

6. Check that the voltages and currents of E 5 satisfy rules I and II.

7. In our networks we have an unknown voltage at each vertex except the bottom one. We also have an unknown current in each wire and an unknown current leaving the bottom vertex. Prove that the number of equations provided by rules I and II is equal to the total number of unknowns.

8. Find all currents and voltages in this network:

9. Check your answers to E 8 by showing that they satisfy rules I and II.

10. Find all currents and voltages in this network:

11. Check your answers to E 10 by showing that they satisfy rules I and II.

12. Find the unknown voltages and currents in this network:

13. Check your answers to E 12 by determining whether the current leaving the network equals the current entering.

14. Find the unknown voltages and currents in this network:

15. Check your answers to E 14 by determining whether the current leaving the network equals the current entering.

16. Find the unknown voltages and currents in this network:

17. Draw the network, with its conductances, currents, and voltages, that is associated with the tiling at the top of p. 73.

18. Draw the network, with its conductances, currents, and voltages, that is associated with the tiling of E 19 of Chapter 6.

19. Draw the network, with its conductances, currents and voltages, that is associated with the tiling of E 20 of Chapter 6.

20. Draw the tiling of a rectangle into five rectangles that corresponds to this network:

21. Draw the tiling of a rectangle into six rectangles that corresponds to this network:

22. How can we derive an electrical network from a box filled with smaller boxes? (Think first of satisfying rule II.)

23. If we rotate through 90° a rectangle tiled with rectangles, the horizontal and vertical lines change roles. Thus the electrical network associated with the rotated rectangle is different from that associated with the original rectangle. Find the network associated with the rectangle of p. 88 rotated 90°.

24. The same as E 23, but for the rectangle of E 17.

25. The same as E 23, but for the rectangle of E 18.

26. Find x and y if $2x + 3y = 7$ and $4x - y = 11$. Check your answers by showing that they satisfy the two equations.

27. Find s and t if $4s - 9t = 5$ and $3s + 5t = 6$. Check your answers by showing that they satisfy the two equations.

28. Show that further examples of systems satisfying rule II are:
    (a) water flowing through narrow pipes,
    (b) traffic on a system of one-way roads, alleys, and boulevards.

29. Call a tiling of a rectangle "rational" if for each of the tiles the ratio of length to width is rational. Prove the following generalization of Theorem 2: *If a rectangle has dimensions L by W, with L/W irrational, then it has no rational tiling whatsoever.*

References

1. M. Gardner, Mathematical games, *Scientific American*, November, 1958, pp. 136–142. (Contains further examples of tiling by squares.)

2. ———, *The Second Scientific American Book of Mathematical Puzzles and Diversions*, Simon and Schuster, New York, 1961. (This includes R 1 and some new results obtained with the aid of electronic computers. See pp. 186–209.)

Chapter 8

THE HIGHWAY
INSPECTOR AND
THE SALESMAN

If we stare at a diagram of an electrical network long enough, it might, like an optical illusion, turn into a map of highways and towns. This diagram, for example, formed of ten wires and six vertices where the wires are soldered together,

might turn into a map of ten sections of highway joining six towns. Even if we lose all the numbers, the voltages, the currents, and the conductances, such a map still raises interesting questions, which concern not electrons, but a highway inspector and a salesman.

A thrifty highway inspector has this problem. He would like to find a route that takes him over each section of highway exactly once. After all, he does not want to waste the taxpayers' money on unnecessary inspections.

A traveling salesman has another problem. He would like a route that would take him through each town exactly once. He is not at all interested in covering each section of highway.

Let us try to find the inspector and the salesman their desired routes on this simple highway system of six towns and nine highway sections:

95

After a few tries, the reader might come up with this route for the inspector,

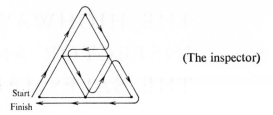

(The inspector)

and this for the salesman:

(The salesman)

Notice that the inspector has the added convenience of ending his inspection in the town where he started; he will not need two headquarters. The salesman happened to finish his journey in a town adjacent to the one where he started.

Let us try another highway system; for example, this one with five towns and five highway sections:

Working first on the inspector's problem, we notice that the terminal points of his route must be the towns d and D. As the reader can easily verify, each of the two routes from D to d fails to cover all the sections of highway. We must inform the inspector that for this highway there is no route that takes him exactly once over each section.

Working on the salesman's problem for the same highway system, we see that his route must also have its ends at *d* and *D*. Of the two routes from *d* to *D*, one of them, fortunately, takes the salesman through each town:

Here is a highway system of four towns and three sections, which, as the reader can check, makes both the inspector and the salesman unhappy, for neither has his desired route:

Finally, here is a system of nine towns and fourteen sections, which pleases the inspector but not the salesman.

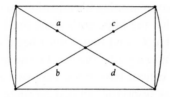

The inspector could follow this route:

But the salesman, in order to visit the towns labeled *a*, *b*, *c*, and *d*, would be forced to visit the town in the center more than once.

But the mere accumulation of examples is not mathematics any more than a dictionary is a novel. What we want is an insight into highway systems that will enable us to decide which highway systems have a route for the inspector or the salesman and which do not. Is there a way of knowing whether such routes can be found in a particular highway system without going through perhaps thousands of trials? We will consider the inspector's problem first.

Let us probe more deeply the inspector's problem by a close examination of this system:

We first concentrate our attention on town A. Assume, for the moment, that the inspector does not begin his tour at town A. When he drives through A he inspects two of the sections at A; one as he approaches A and the other as he leaves A. This leaves him one section at A that he still must inspect. When he does inspect this third section he will find himself at A, with no exit. If he is to inspect each section once, he must do so before he gets stuck in A—that is, his tour must finish at A. To reach this conclusion, we assumed, let us recall, that he did not start at A. We see, then, that if the inspector does have a route, it must either begin or end at A.

By similar reasoning (concentrating his attention on one town at a time), the reader can easily show that the inspector's route must also begin or end at B; that it must begin or end at C; and that it must begin or end at D. Thus if the highway inspector does have a route, then that route must have four ends. But, as we all know, a route cannot have more than two ends. With this analysis, we know that the highway inspector can find no route for this system.

Our insight suggests that the number of sections joining one town to other towns is quite important in studying the inspector's problem. *We will call the* **degree** *of a town the number of sections having an end at that town.* For example, a town at a dead end has degree 1. The same reasoning that we applied to town A in the system just considered proves

THEOREM 1. *If a town has odd degree, then the inspector must either begin or end his tour of inspection at that town.*

And, in the same way that we showed the above system to have no route for the inspector, we can prove

THEOREM 2. *If there are more than two towns of odd degree in a system, then the inspector has no route (taking him over each section exactly once).*

Theorem 2 is not one to please the inspector. There may still be a chance to please him, however, if we look at highway systems containing no more than two towns of odd degree. There are three cases to consider: systems with no town of odd degree; systems with one town of odd degree; and systems with two towns of odd degree. (The reader might try some examples of his own and guess what we will discover for the inspector.)

We will first prove that the second of the three cases cannot occur.

THEOREM 3. *There is no highway system with exactly one town of odd degree.*

PROOF. We shall prove that a system containing a town of odd degree must contain at least one other town of odd degree. To do so, let *T* be a town of odd degree, and imagine starting a vacation trip at *T*. We shall travel quite at random, except that we agree *never to use the same section of highway twice.* Each time we pass through a town we are free to choose as an exit any of the sections over which we have not already traveled.

Let us now make such a journey, beginning at *T*. If we are unlucky, the journey could be quite short. With luck, we could have a long journey. But since there is a limit to the number of sections, our vacation must end in some town, which we will call *E*, for "end."

Could *E* simply be *T*? Observe that, since we started at *T*, an even number of sections at *T* remained unused; hence each time we entered *T* subsequently, we had an escape route. Thus *E* is not *T*.

If *E* were of even degree, then each time we entered it we could have found an exit. But since our trip ended at *E*, the degree of *E* must be odd. This proves the theorem.

Only two cases remain before we have a complete solution to the inspector's problem: systems with no town of odd degree, and systems with two towns of odd degree. Treating first the case in which there is no town of odd degree, we will prove

THEOREM 4. *If a highway system has no town of odd degree, then the in-spector can find a route that will take him over each section exactly once. (Moreover, he can begin his inspection at any town; his tour must end where it starts.)*

Before we begin the proof, the reader should draw a highway system with no town of odd degree and show that it has a route for the inspector and that it ends at the town where it begins.

We should also mention something that we have up to now tacitly assumed in all our highway systems; namely, that they are connected. *A system is* **connected** *if it is possible to travel on its highways from any town to any other town.* For example, the highway system of the United States is, in all likelihood, connected.

Now we are ready for the

PROOF OF THEOREM 4. Not only will we prove that the inspector can find a route through any (connected) highway system with no town of odd degree, but we will show him how to find it.

Select any town T in the system. We will prove that the inspector has a route that begins at T and covers all the sections (clearly this route must end at T).

Here is a recipe for discovering such a route. Get into a car at T, and travel about at random as in the proof of Theorem 3. That is, go over no section twice, and end your journey in a town from which you cannot escape.

Since the highway system has a limited supply of sections, this random trip must end. Where must it end? Since all towns are of even degree, it must end at T. This whimsical trip probably fails to cover all the sections. If so, we will enlarge the trip with a vacation excursion in the following manner.

If the trip did not pass through all the sections, then there must be a town on the trip that is a terminus of one of the sections not covered (since the system is connected). Call this town U. Start a random side trip at U that takes us over no section we have already covered and that, in addition, covers no section twice. Such a side trip will have to end at U. We can combine the first trip and this side trip into one journey by starting at T, traveling along the first trip until reaching U, taking the side trip from U to U, and then continuing on our original trip back to T.

We can continue adding more side trips, forming them into bigger and bigger routes, until finally we obtain a route that uses all the sections. Such a route begins at T, takes the inspector over each section once, and deposits him at T. The inspector has a route in any highway system with no town of odd degree, and he has a way of finding it—by piecing together side trips. Thus Theorem 4 is proved.

The method provided in the proof of Theorem 4 is quite easy to use. For example, let us watch the inspector find a route over this highway system, which has no town of odd degree:

First, he chooses a town for his headquarters and takes a random journey until he is blocked. Perhaps this is the journey:

Then he tosses in an excursion from one of the towns he passed through on his first journey:

These two trips he can combine into one trip:

Since he has still not covered all the sections, he makes another excursion over sections he has not covered:

Now he has covered all the sections and can combine his first trip and the two side trips into one route that carries him over each section once:

Of course on a more complicated system the inspector might have to use more side trips before he reaches a route that covers the whole system.

The only case remaining is covered by

THEOREM 5. *If a highway system has two towns of odd degree, then the inspector can find a route taking him over each section exactly once. (Moreover, he must begin his inspection at one of the two towns of odd degree and must end it at the other.)*

The proof of this, similar to that of Theorem 4, is left to the reader.

We have completely solved the inspector's problem. With a quick count of the towns of odd degree we can tell whether there is a route; if there is, we have a way of finding it. But the inspector is still not happy.

"On these narrow roads I can inspect both lanes at the same time. But soon I will be promoted and will have to inspect the superhighways, which sometimes have the two directions of traffic far apart. How will I be able to tell whether I can find a route then?"

The inspector has raised a new problem. After all, so far we have not bothered about the direction he chose to travel in covering a section. We have been able to think of a section as a line rather than as a one-way arrow. Now we must replace each section by two sections, each furnished with an arrow indicating the permitted direction of travel. For example, instead of a highway system such as this,

we have this one, which consists of one-way roads:

Though we might expect the new problem to be harder than the one we already solved, it turns out to be quite simple. Observe that the number of one-way roads entering a particular town is equal to the number of one-way roads leaving that town. Not only is every town of even degree, but every time the inspector enters a town (other than his headquarters) he can leave it (legally). The reader may use the same kind of reasoning that proved Theorem 4 to prove

THEOREM 6. *If for each town in a system of towns and one-way roads there are as many roads entering as there are leaving, then the inspector has a route that enables him to inspect each one-way road exactly once. (Moreover, he can choose any town as his headquarters. His tour must end where it begins.)*

The proof of this is almost identical to the proof of Theorem 4, and is left to the reader. Actually, Theorem 6 is more than the inspector requires. It includes a system such as:

(Note, for example, that the towns labeled *A* and *B* are joined by a single one-way road.)

Theorem 6 would also apply to systems with loops, such as:

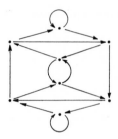

Note that as many one-way routes enter a town as leave it.

In the next chapter we will make use of Theorem 6. In particular, we will be using systems with loops, such as the one just drawn, to analyze an ancient word used in India as an aid for remembering certain rhythmic patterns.

Though we have satisfied the inspector, we have done nothing for the salesman, who wants to know when he can find a route that will take him through each town exactly once. This problem, proposed by W. R. Hamilton in 1859, is still unsolved. Perhaps there is no general way of deciding whether a highway system has a salesman's route other than by simply trying to find one. The inspector will just have to count the towns of odd degree. If there is no such town, or if there are two such towns, he will then know that he has a route; in all other cases, he will know that he has no route. If there is a solution to the salesman's problem, it will probably be much more complicated.

We have previously met pairs of problems that are similar in their formulation but quite different in their difficulty. It was easy to show that there is only one prime that is one less than a square, but nobody knows how many primes are one more than a square (see E 1 and E 2 of Chapter 3). It was fairly easy to prove that there is no end to the primes; but nobody knows whether there is an end to the twin primes. It is very easy to see that if a triangle is cut into triangles and the dots labeled A, B, and C with an odd number of AA edges on the border, then there must be a triangle with duplicated A's (simply take any triangle with an AA edge on the border); but it was much harder to prove that if there is an odd number of AB edges on the border, then there must be at least one ABC triangle. It was easy to prove that every special number is prime; but it was not easy to prove the converse—that every prime is special. The contrast between the problems posed by the inspector and the salesman will play a role in the next chapter.

Exercises

1. Does the salesman have a route in this system? Does the inspector?

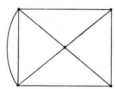

2. Does the salesman have a route in this system? Does the inspector?

3. (a) Count the towns of odd degree in several highway systems.
   (b) Count the towns of even degree in several highway systems.
   (c) Make a conjecture.

4. Using the method we used to prove that there cannot be just one town of odd degree, prove that in an ordinary highway system (with a limited supply of sections) the number of odd towns is even.

5. Devise an example of a highway system with exactly one town of odd degree (but with an *unlimited* collection of sections and towns of even degree).

6. (a) Prove that when a section is deleted from a highway system the number of towns of odd degree changes by an even number.
   (b) Use (a) to prove that the number of towns of odd degree is even.

7. In a given highway system let $T(d)$ be the number of towns of degree d. Thus, for example, $T(1)$ is the number of dead-end towns.
   (a) By a bookkeeping of the way in which sections are contributed by towns, prove that
   $$1T(1) + 2T(2) + 3T(3) + 4T(4) + \cdots$$
   is equal to twice the number of sections.
   (b) Use (a) to prove that the number of towns of odd degree is even.

8. How many inspectors are necessary to inspect a highway system with four towns of odd degree if none of them is to inspect a section more than once? There is no restriction on the number of towns of even degree.
   (a) Carry out three experiments.
   (b) Make a conjecture.
   (c) Prove your conjecture.

9. Prove Theorem 5.

10. Prove Theorem 6.

11. The problem of the inspector was solved in 1735 by Euler, who wrote, "In the town of Koenigsberg there is an island called Kneiphof, with two branches of the river Pregel flowing around it. There are seven bridges crossing the two branches. The question is whether a person can plan a walk in such a way that he will cross each of these bridges once but not more than once···. On the basis of the above I formulated the following very general problem for myself: Given any configuration of the river and the branches into which it may divide, as well as any number of bridges, to determine whether or not it is possible to cross each bridge exactly once."

   This is a diagram of the seven bridges of Koenigsberg:

   Can a person plan a walk that will take him across each bridge exactly once?

12. Can a person find a path in this house that will take him through each door exactly once?

13. Can a person find a path in this house that will take him through each door exactly once?

14. Can a salesman visit each of the towns of this system exactly once?

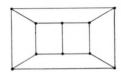

15. Can a salesman visit each of the towns of this system exactly once?

16. Prove that, in any connected system in which all the towns are of degree 2, both the inspector and the salesman have a route.

17. From a highway system in which each town is of even degree we can obtain a system—not necessarily a connected system—in which each town is of degree 2, by replacing every town of degree $2N$ by N nearby towns of degree 2 (for example, a town of degree 6, such as ✕, would be replaced by ⤜).

   Combine this with E 16 to obtain a new proof of the fact that the inspector has a route over a system in which all of the towns are of even degree.

18. Using the technique provided by the proof of Theorem 4, find a route for the inspector of this system:

19. Using the technique provided in the proof of Theorem 4, find a route for the inspector of this system:

20. A highway system consists of three towns, each two of which are joined by a single one-way road.
    (a) There are essentially two such systems. Draw them.
    (b) Show that in both of them the salesman has a route.

21. Using E 20, prove that in any system of four towns in which a one-way road connects each two towns, there is a route for the salesman.

22. (a) Using E 21, prove that any system of five towns, with a one-way road between each two towns, has a route for the salesman.
    (b) Extend the result to any number of towns.

23. In a round robin volleyball tournament, each of 673 teams played each other once. There were no tie games. Prove that it is possible to label the teams $T_1, T_2, T_3, \cdots,$ T_{672}, T_{673} in such a way that T_1 defeated T_2, T_2 defeated T_3, T_3 defeated T_4, and so on. *Hint:* Relate to E 22 (b).

24. A "circuit" in a highway system is a route that begins at some town and, without using any section twice, returns to that town. A "tree" is a highway system without circuits. (The system need not be connected.)
    (a) Draw a tree.
    (b) Remove a path joining two dead ends.
    (c) From the tree that now remains, remove a path joining two of its dead ends.
    (d) Continue till all the sections are removed.
    (e) Count the number of paths you removed.
    (f) Repeat the process on the same tree (possibly using different paths), and count the number of paths you removed.
    (g) Count the number of odd towns in your tree.
    (h) Make a conjecture.

25. Prove that the number of paths used in E 24 is always half the number of towns of odd degree.

26. Using E 25, prove that a tree with s sections and t towns of odd degree must have a path with at least $2s/t$ sections. (Of course the number of sections in a path is always a natural number. Perhaps it would be better to say: "There is a path whose number of sections is at least as large as $2s/t$.")

27. A tree was defined in E 24. Let t be the number of towns and s the number of sections in a connected tree.
    (a) Find s and t for three connected trees.
    (b) Conjecture a relation between s and t for any connected tree.

28. Prove your conjecture of E 27.

29. Draw a connected highway system that is not a tree (one that has circuits). The police want to put up roadblocks in the middle of some sections in such a way that racing around any circuit will be impossible but it will still be possible to travel from any town to any other town without passing a roadblock. In short, the police want to make some cuts in the system to turn it into a connected tree.
    (a) Show (in the highway system you drew) some of the various ways in which the police can set up their road blocks.
    (b) Count the number of roadblocks in each case.
    (c) Make a conjecture.
    (d) Test your conjecture on another highway system.

30. (a) In a highway system, set up roadblocks as in E 29. Count t, the number of towns; s, the number of sections, and b, the number of blocks.
    (b) Do this for three more highway systems.
    (c) Make a conjecture linking s, t, and b.

31. Prove the conjecture of E 30 (c). (Use E 28.)

32. Were a chemist to look at our maps, he might think of the towns as atoms, the sections as bonds between atoms, and the whole highway system as a molecule. What we call the "degree of a town" he would call "the valence of an atom." The valence of hydrogen is 1; the valence of oxygen is 2. Thus the water molecule H_2O corresponds, in our language, to the tree H—O—H. Prove that any molecules that can be formed of hydrogen and oxygen must be a tree.

33. See terms of E 32. The valence of a carbon atom is 4. Let a molecule have c carbon atoms, h hydrogen atoms, a oxygen atoms, and b bonds.
    (a) Prove that $4c + 2a + h = 2b$.
    (b) If the molecule is a tree, prove, using E 27, that

    $$c + a + h - 1 = b.$$

    (c) Combining (a) and (b), prove that in a tree of carbon, hydrogen, and oxygen atoms,

    $$h = 2c + 2.$$

34. See E 33.
    (a) Assemble 4 carbon atoms, 4 oxygen atoms, and 4 hydrogen atoms into a single molecule.

(b) Prove that any molecule formed of 4 carbon atoms, 4 oxygen atoms, and 4 hydrogen atoms must have exactly one circuit. (See E 30.)

Reference

1. J. R. Newman, *The World of Mathematics*, vol. 1, Simon and Schuster, New York, 1956. (Euler's solution of the inspector's problem is presented on pp. 573–580.)

Chapter **9**

MEMORY WHEELS

Mathematics, like every branch of knowledge, is the product of the interplay between past and present, between accumulated knowledge and curiosity, between an autonomous structure and the tastes and needs of the time. What one age considers a pressing question, another may not ask at all. The pure mathematics of one era may be applied in another, perhaps centuries later. Pushing into the unknown, the mathematician is an explorer who is likely to find what he did not seek and who cannot predict how others will use his discoveries.

A problem on which I once worked illustrates these aspects of the growth of knowledge, and its solution captures the flavor of mathematical research. This particular adventure began when the composer George Perle told me about an elaborate theory of rhythm that had been developed in India perhaps some thousand years ago. "While reading about this theory," he said, "I learned my one and only Sanskrit word: *yamátárájabhánasalagám.*" I asked him what it meant.

"It's just a nonsense word invented as an aid in remembering the names of certain rhythms."*

"If a person can remember that," I replied, "he can remember anything."

"There is a lot in those ten syllables," said Perle. "As you pronounce the word you sweep out all possible triplets of short and long beats. The first three syllables, *ya má tá*, have the rhythm short, long, long. The second through the fourth are *má tá rá:* long, long, long. Then you have *tá rá ja:* long, long, short. Next there are *rá ja bhá:* long, short, long. And so on."

I wrote down the word and saw that what Perle said is true. Each successive triplet of syllables displays a different pattern, and the whole word displays all eight possible patterns, giving each once and only once. As a mathematician I was fascinated to find that such a sequence could exist.

That night I returned to the ancient word. To strip it of irrelevancies I replaced

---

* S. V. Arya of Kharagpur informs me that this word is still used in the study of medieval Indian poetry. Perle learned of the word in R 2.

the syllables with digits, letting 0 stand for a short beat and 1 for a long beat. In this notation *yamátárájabhánasalagám* became 0111010001.

After staring at the simplified string for a while, I noticed a lovely thing. The first two digits are the same as the last two; if I bent the string into a loop, it would look like a snake swallowing its own tail. That is, the last 01 could be placed over the first 01, and the two pairs of digits would merge into a single pair. Instead of a line of ten digits I now saw a circle of eight.

I could begin anywhere on this "memory wheel" and move around it in either direction, sweeping out triplets of 0's and 1's. Starting at the top and reading counterclockwise, for example, gave 011, 111, 110, 101, 010, 100, 000, and 001.

The next thing that occurred to me, as it would automatically to any mathematician, was to generalize what I had found. Is there a "word" for listing all quadruplets of 0's and 1's once and only once? For quintuplets? For groups of any size? And if so, does the snake always swallow its tail?

Before attacking the problem for quadruplets I decided to go back and look at couplets. Is there a word that lists each of the four couplets 00, 01, 10, and 11 exactly once? Does it close up on itself? Writing down the sequence 0011, I saw that I already had the three couplets 00, 01, and 11. Adding one more 0, to form 00110, gave the final couplet: 10. I noted that, since the first and last digits are 0's, the snake does swallow its tail. The five-digit word could be bent into this four-digit wheel containing each couplet once and only once.

Now I was ready to take on the quadruplets. I began methodically by listing all the possible groups of four digits composed of 0's and 1's. To do this I first wrote down the eight triplets and placed a 0 in front of each. This gave me all the quadruplets beginning with 0. Then I repeated the triplets and placed a 1 before each, obtaining the quadruplets beginning with 1.

0000	1000
0001	1001
0010	1010
0011	1011
0100	1100
0101	1101
0110	1110
0111	1111

Since the list contained 16 quadruplets, I saw that any memory word that would sweep out each of them once (if any exists) would have to have 19 digits. The first four digits make one quadruplet, and each of the next 15 numbers completes another.

Somewhere in the word I was seeking, I knew there would have to be a string of four 1's and, somewhere, four 0's. Why not put them together and see what would happen? I wrote down the eight symbols 11110000. Then I checked off my list the five quadruplets it contained: 1111, 1110, 1100, 1000, and 0000. So far so good. To avoid getting 0000 twice, I next had to add a 1, which gave 111100001. I checked off 0001 on the list. Adding 010 produced three more quadruplets, all new, and brought the sequence to 111100001010.

From here I proceeded one digit at a time, checking the list to make sure there were no duplications. At each of the next three positions the choice was clear: one of the digits would form a quadruplet already checked; the other would not. I had then reached the 15-symbol word: 111100001010011.

Only four to go. Considering the next digit, I found that neither 1 nor 0 provided a duplication. But a 1 would lead to trouble in the next position, where either 0 or 1 would produce a duplication. I was afraid I might not be able to reach 19 symbols after all. It turned out, however, that a 0 in the sixteenth position involved no such difficulty, and the last three positions presented unambiguous choices. I had found my word of 19 symbols—a word containing each of the 16 quadruplets precisely once: 1111000010100110111.

As soon as I had finished, I looked at the first three symbols and the last three. They were the same. This snake, too, could swallow its tail. This 19-symbol word could be bent into a wheel of 16 symbols:

Inspired by this success, I decided that there must be memory words for quintuplets, sextuplets, and so on. Furthermore, I felt sure they would all close up into wheels. It was time to stop experimenting, however, and look for a proof of the conjecture.

Grappling with the problem, I began to look at the Indian memory word in a slightly different way, concentrating on the eight overlapping triplets it contains:

011
111
110
101
010
100
000
001

In this light, the word appeared as a means of arranging the triplets such that the last two symbols of one are the same as the first two of the next. Suppose the word had not been invented. How would one have gone about finding it? I decided to spread the triplets over a piece of paper and connect the appropriate pairs with arrows. That is, I drew an arrow from one triplet to another whenever the last two symbols of the former were the same as the first two symbols of the latter; for example, 001 —→ 010 and 001 —→ 011. After moving the triplets and arrows around a little to make a simple pattern, I obtained this diagram:

As I gazed at the configuration, I suddenly saw it as a map in which the arrows were one-way roads and the triplets were towns. The problem of arranging the eight triplets into a memory word could now be stated in the terms of our traveling salesman of Chapter 8, who is looking for a route over the one-way roads that will take him through each town just once. With the help of the Indian memory word, I traced one possible route. As this illustration shows, the "town" in which the journey ends is adjacent to the one in which it starts.

There is a section of road that will take the salesman from the finishing point back to the start. This, of course, reflects the fact that the memory word closes into a wheel.

Clearly the same scheme would apply to overlapping couplets, to quadruplets, or to groups of any size. The general problem had been translated into a new language. The question "Is there always a memory word?" now read "Is there always a route for the salesman?" The question "Does every memory word close up on itself?" now read "Does the salesman always finish his trip in a town adjacent to the town in which his trip began?"

Unhappily, the translation did me no good. I had absolutely no luck in solving either of the salesman problems. There was (and still is) no known general technique, other than trying all paths, to tell whether a highway system has a route passing just once through every town (see Chapter 8). And I did not see why these special highway systems arising from overlapping strings of 0's and 1's should have a route for the salesman. After several days without progress, I put the matter aside. A few months later, as I was leafing through the 1946 volume of *The Journal of the London Mathematical Society*, I saw a diagram that resembled my highway system. It appeared in a paper entitled "Normal Recurring Decimals," by I. J. Good. Quite a different topic had brought Good to a consideration of the memory wheel problem—and he had solved it. He was chiefly interested in showing how to produce an endless string of 0's and 1's in which each of the possible sextuplets of 0's and 1's appears with equal frequency. His solution was perfectly general, and applied to groups of any size. He noted further that "··· the result has an application to the construction of teleprinters that use alphabets whose letters consist of a finite number (usually five or six) of 0's and 1's."

Good had also recognized that the problem is related to a highway system, but his system was different from mine. I had seen the triplets (or groups of any other size) as towns, and the roads between them as overlaps. Good saw the problem the other way around: he saw the triplets as roads, and the couplets— the overlapping portions of the triplets—as towns.

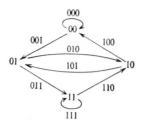

For example, the highway 011 runs from the town 01 to the town 11. To put it another way, there are four towns: 00, 01, 10, and 11. One of these is joined to another if the last digit of the former is the same as the first digit of the latter (01 is joined to 11 by 011).

Now each road represents a triplet, and every incoming triplet overlaps every outgoing triplet for every town. This means that if a person—say, an efficient highway inspector—could find a route taking him over each road just once, he would, in effect, trace a memory wheel. For example, suppose the inspector began at town 01. He could follow a route consisting of highways 011, 111, 110, 101, 010, 100, 000 and 001. The trip is, of course, exactly the one given by *yamátárájabhánasalagám*. Notice also that the last highway, 001, leads into the first one, 011.

A glance at the diagram makes it clear that two roads lead into, and two lead out of, every town. Thus, as we saw in the last chapter, the highway inspector can always find a route over such a highway system (Theorem 6 of Chapter 8). Hence it was no accident that he could find a route over the diagram constructed to find a memory word for triplets.

The same reasoning works just as well on Good's highway system associated with quadruplets. In this case a triplet is a town, and a quadruplet is a one-way road that goes from the first triplet to the last triplet of the town:

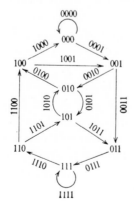

Again, notice that two roads enter each town and that two roads leave. Thus, by Theorem 6 of Chapter 8, the inspector has a route; that is, there is a memory wheel for quadruplets. Similarly, there is a memory wheel for quintuplets, and so on.

Since the salesman's problem for my highway systems is equivalent to the inspector's problem for Good's systems, the salesman also has a route, and his journey must end in a town adjacent to the one in which he starts. As it turns out, I had quite unintentionally come upon a special class of highway systems for which the salesman has a route.

The story does not end here. Through *Mathematical Reviews* I learned that other mathematicians in various parts of the world had been involved with the memory-wheel problem in one guise or another. Twelve years before Good had published his paper, M. H. Martin had solved the problem in a completely different way; he had been led to it by a problem in dynamics. Another mathematician, D. Rees, seeking a more constructive technique than Good's, solved the problem by considering certain divisors of polynomials of the type $X^n - 1$. In 1951, N. M. Korobov, who was studying the fractional part of multiples of numbers, described an entirely different technique for constructing memory wheels. A Dutch engineer, K. Posthumus, working on the theory of telephone circuits, posed another question about memory wheels: How many different wheels are there for couplets, triplets, quadruplets, and so on? He found that there is one for couplets and that there are two for triplets, 16 for quadruplets, 2048 for quintuplets; and he guessed at a general formula for groups of any size (*n*-tuplets): 2 raised to the power $2^{n-1} - n$. In 1946, N. G. de Bruijn proved the conjecture.

I learned that memory wheels have found technological applications. A computer made in Czechoslovakia employs a memory wheel of 1024 symbols to search through an equal number of storage locations on a memory drum. And in the Damodar Valley near Calcutta (the wheel of fate has now made a full turn) a memory wheel in a central office scans automatically transmitted reports from 64 rain gauges. Memory wheels are also used in constructing error-correcting codes for communication theory.

Only after publishing an article on memory wheels (based on an early version of this chapter) in the *Scientific American* of May, 1961 did I learn that the modern history of these wheels goes back to the French telegraph engineer Émile Baudot, who in 1882 used quintuplets of 0 and 1 to transmit information. In a letter appearing in the July, 1961, issue of the *Scientific American*, D. A. Kerr, an engineer working on printing telegraphy, writes, "$\cdots$ (It) appears in a Western Electric tape teletypewriter used very early in this century $\cdots$, and it is known here as the combination-wheel and seeker mechanism. The combina-

WHO	WHERE	WHEN	WHY
Poets	India	A.D. 1000 (?)	Used memory word for triplets of short and long beats.
Émile Baudot	France	1882	Used memory wheel for the 32 quintuplets of telegraphy (for the 26 letters, idle condition, space, line feed, carriage return, shift to regular alphabet, shift to numbers).
M. H. Martin	U.S.A.	1934	Interested in a problem in dynamics; provided simple algorithm for making memory wheels.
K. R. Popper	Austria	1934	Constructed random sequences for probability theory with memory wheels.
I. J. Good	Great Britain	1946	Proved existence of memory wheels in answering a question concerning decimal representation of numbers.
N. G. de Bruijn	Holland	1946	Answered question raised in Telephone engineering; found number of memory wheels.
D. Rees	Great Britain	1946	Stimulated by Good's work, proved existence of memory wheels by using divisors of the polynomials $X^n - 1$.
N. M. Korobov	Russia	1951	Interested in properties of the decimal representation of numbers, devised way of constructing all memory wheels (generalizing Martin's technique).
E. N. Gilbert	U.S.A.	1953	Constructed memory wheels for Bell Telephone Laboratories using methods illustrated in E 12, 13, 14, 15, 16.
R. L. Goodstein	Great Britain	1956	Interested in servomechanisms; independently rediscovered Martin's technique, for which he gave a proof using congruences.
L. R. Ford, Jr.	U.S.A.	1957	Constructed memory wheels to imitate the binomial distribution of probability theory; independently rediscovered Martin's technique, for which he gave a new proof.
S. Golomb and Lloyd Welch	U.S.A.	1957	Extended Gilbert's technique, examined various formulas for producing memory wheels, gave new proof of de Bruijn's theorem.
T. E. Stern and B. Friedland	U.S.A.	1959	Interested in error-correcting codes for communication theory; independently rediscovered Rees's technique.
E. B. Leach	U.S.A.	1960	Constructed certain sequences for probability theory by memory wheels, which he devised in a new way (out of a wheel for n-tuplets he constructed a wheel for $(n + 1)$-tuplets).

tion wheel is, of course, a mechanically coded memory wheel, and the seekers form a device for locating the desired quintuplet on its periphery, thus indexing the desired character for printing."

This has been a fable with many morals. It deals with a question that could have been raised a thousand years ago in India, but was not. And little did Euler dream that his work on a puzzle would be of practical use in the twentieth century. Moreover, the variety of applications reflects both the mathematical mood of our time and the fantastic amount of mathematics being created all over the world. The fact that so many of the workers were ignorant of the others' results, and therefore duplicated much effort, points to another problem: how to record the myriad discoveries constantly flowing into man's store of knowledge.

Exercises

1. Is the resemblance between the highway systems of pp. 113 and 115 accidental? If not, explain their relationship.

2. Check that each of the 64 6-tuplets of 0's and 1's appears exactly once in this memory word:

   0000010000110001011111101100111100100110111010101101001010001111000000.

3. Show that there is only one memory wheel for couplets of 0's and 1's.

4. Show that there are exactly two memory wheels for triplets formed of 0's and 1's, and that one of them is just the other read backwards.

5. (a) Count the number of 0's and the number of 1's in three memory wheels.
   (b) Make a conjecture.

6. See E 5.
   (a) Prove that the number of 0's is the same as the number of 1's in any memory wheel for quintuplets. (*Hint:* Do bookkeeping with respect to contributions of 0's and 1's by quintuplets. Observe, for example, that each 0 and each 1 in the memory wheel is part of 5 quintuplets.)
   (b) Do the same for 6-tuplets.

7. If you write down the string 000 and then build up a word by writing down in succession the larger of the digits 0 and 1 that does not lead to a duplicated triplet, show that you obtain a memory word for all triplets.

8. If you write down the string 0000 and then build up a word by writing down in succession the larger of the digits 0 and 1 that does not lead to a duplicated quadruplet, show that you obtain a memory word for all quadruplets.

9. If you write down the string 00000 and then build up a word by writing down in succession the larger of the digits 0 and 1 that does not lead to a duplicated quintuplet, show that you obtain a memory word for quintuplets. (The method of E 7, E 8, and E 9 is due to M. H. Martin, who in R 1 proved that it always works.)

10. Is it necessary in E 7 to start with 000? Could we have started with the triplet 010 or the triplet 111?

11. Prove directly, without using the notion of highway systems, that each memory word for sextuplets of 0's and 1's must close up into a memory wheel. (Your argument should apply to couplets, triplets, and so on.)

12. Another method of producing a string of quadruplets that fit together to form a memory wheel is used by the Bell Telephone Laboratories. Given a quadruplet Q, form the next quadruplet this way. If the first two digits of Q are the same, write a 0 to the right of Q. If the first two digits of Q are not the same (that is, if one of them is 1 and the other 0), write a 1 to the right of Q. Erase the first digit of Q from the quintuplet just formed. We are left with a quadruplet that overlaps Q in such a way that the two quadruplets might possibly be part of a memory wheel for quadruplets. (This method applied to 1111 gives 1110. When applied to 1101, it gives 1010. When applied to 1010, it gives 0101.)
    (a) Applying this technique repeatedly, manufacture all quadruplets except 0000. (You may start with any quadruplet other than 0000.)
    (b) Using (a) build a memory wheel of 15 digits for the 15 quadruplets other than 0000.
    (c) Insert a 0 in the wheel built in (b) so as to obtain a wheel for the 16 quadruplets.

13. Show that the method of E 12, when applied to the triplet 111, produces all triplets except 000. Use it to form a memory wheel for triplets.

14. Show that the method of E 12, when applied to 11111 (or any other quintuplet except 00000) does *not* produce the 31 quintuplets other than 00000.

15. Show that the method of E 12, when applied to 111111, produces the 63 6-tuplets other than 000000.

16. Show that the method of E 12, when applied to the 7-tuplet 1111111, produces the 127 7-tuplets other than 0000000. (Combining E 12, E 13, E 14, E 15, and E 16, we see that this method can be used to make memory wheels for N-tuplets, $N = 3, 4, 6$, and 7 but not for $N = 5$. It also works for $N = 15$. It is not known, in general, for which N it works.)

17. Is it necessary to start with 111111 in E 15?

18. This is how E. B. Leach, in R 13, devises a memory wheel for quadruplets out of one for triplets: He writes out the wheel of 8 symbols on the line; for example, 11010001. He then forms a string of 8 symbols by first writing below the left digit of the given string the digit 0. Below the second digit he writes a 0 if the first digit of the given string and the string he is building are the same; otherwise he writes a 1. In the example, he writes 1. Below the third digit he writes a 0 if the second digit of the string he is forming and the second digit of the given string are the same; otherwise he writes a 1. Continuing in this manner, he builds the string 01001111. Then he obtains a second string by interchanging 0's with 1's in the string he has just formed. This gives him 10110000.
    To assemble the two strings

$$01001111 \qquad \text{and} \qquad 10110000$$

into a string of length 16, first form the second string into a wheel. Then read this wheel, beginning with the first triplet, 010, of the first string, and write out the result, 01011000. Place the latter string to the right of the string 01001111, and obtain a string of length 16,

$$0100111101011000,$$

which, when placed on a wheel, forms a memory wheel for quadruplets.
    Check that it does.

19. Using the method of E 18, construct a memory wheel for quintuplets.

20. Check that this wheel lists each of the nine possible couplets formed of 0, 1, and 2:

21. Devise a memory word for listing without duplication each of the 27 triplets formed of 0, 1, and 2. Show that it can be pulled around to form a memory wheel.

22. Prove that there is a memory wheel for quadruplets formed of 0, 1, and 2. (*Hint;* Use the same reasoning as Good did, and notice that three roads enter, and that three leave, each town.)

23. Draw the highway system of 9 towns and 27 one-way roads that would be of use in proving that a memory wheel for triplets of 0, 1, and 2 exists. (The towns are the couplets formed with 0, 1, and 2; the roads are the triplets formed with 0, 1, and 2.)

References

1. *M. H. Martin, A problem in arrangements, *Bulletin of the American Mathematical Society*, vol. 40, 1934, pp. 859–864.

2. C. Sachs, *Rhythm and Tempo*, Norton, New York, 1953, pp. 98–101.

3. K. R. Popper, *The Logic of Scientific Discovery*, Basic Books, New York, 1959. (In particular, pp. 162–163, 292.)

4. *N. G. De Bruijn, A combinatorial problem, *Akadamie van wetenschappen*, Amsterdam, vol. 8, 1946, pp. 461–467.

5. *I. J. Good, Normal recurring decimals, *Journal of the London Mathematical Society*, vol. 21, 1946, pp. 167–169.

6. *D. Rees, Note on a paper by I. J. Good, *ibid.*, pp. 169–172.

7. *N. M. Korobov, Normal periodic sequences, *American Mathematical Society, Translations*, series 2, vol. 4, pp. 31–58. (Translation of an article published in Russian in 1951.)

8. R. L. Goodstein, A permutation problem, *Mathematical Gazette*, vol. 40, 1956, pp. 46–47. (This uses the language of congruences, discussed in Chapter 10.)

9. *L. R. Ford, Jr., A cyclic arrangement of *n*-tuplets, The Rand Corporation, 1957.

10. *S. Golomb and L. Welch, Nonlinear shift registers, Jet Propulsion Laboratory, California Institute of Technology, Pasadena, 1957.

11. (a) N. M. Blachman, Central European computers, *Association for Computing Machinery* (Communications), vol. 2, 1959, pp. 14–18.
    (b) M. Nadler and A. Sengupta, Unusual applications, *ibid.*, pp. 40–43.

12. *B. Friedland and T. Stern, Applications of modular sequential circuits to single error-correcting P-Nary codes, *IRE Transactions*, vol. IT-5, 1959, pp. 114–123.

13. *E. B. Leach, Regular sequences and frequency distributions, *Proceedings of the American Mathematical Society*, vol. 11, 1960, pp. 566–574.

14. *W. W. Peterson, *Error-correcting Codes*, M.I.T. Press and John Wiley, New York, 1961.

15. S. Stein, The mathematician as an explorer, *Scientific American*, May, 1961, pp. 149–158. (This is essentially the same as the present chapter.)

Chapter **10**

CONGRUENCE

This chapter provides a language or viewpoint in terms of which much of our work of the first five chapters can be stated more compactly, and, in addition, develops machinery that we will need in the next two chapters.

The first two chapters, The Weaver and The Complete Triangle, were based on the duality of odd and even, which in turn is based on the number 2. The number 2 separates the natural numbers into two classes: one class (the evens) is composed of all natural numbers that leave a remainder of 0 when divided by 2; the other class (the odds) is composed of all natural numbers that leave a remainder of 1 when divided by 2. Since the remainder is either 0 or 1 when a natural number is divided by 2, these two classes exhaust the natural numbers.

If instead of 2 we use 3, then we break the natural numbers into 3 classes: those leaving a remainder of 0 when divided by 3 (that is, those natural numbers divisible by 3), those leaving a remainder of 1 when divided by 3 (these are the good numbers of Lagado), and those leaving a remainder of 2 when divided by 3. The first class is composed of 0, 3, 6, 9, 12, $\cdots$; the second, of 1, 4, 7, 10, 13, $\cdots$; and the third, of 2, 5, 8, 11, 14, $\cdots$.

If instead of 3 we use 4, we break the natural numbers into four types, depending on whether their remainder is 0, 1, 2, or 3 when divided by 4. If we use the natural number M (other than zero), we break the natural numbers into M types.

We will replace the long statement, "The natural numbers A and B have the same remainder when divided by M," by the brief phrase, "A and B are congruent* modulo M," which we write simply

$$A \equiv B \,(\text{mod } M).$$

We will call M the modulus (from the Latin, modulus, "little measure"), and M will always be a natural number different from 0. For example, we have:

$5 \equiv 9 \,(\text{mod } 2),\quad 12 \equiv 0 \,(\text{mod } 3),\quad 12 \equiv 0 \,(\text{mod } 12),\quad 7 \equiv 13 \,(\text{mod } 1),$

$7 \equiv 7 \,(\text{mod } 3),\quad 9 \equiv 3 \,(\text{mod } 2),\quad 9 \equiv 3 \,(\text{mod } 3),\quad 9 \equiv 3 \,\,(\text{mod } 6).$

---

* Congruence of natural numbers is not related to geometric congruence.

122

There is another way of looking at this notion of two natural numbers being congruent modulo *M*—a way that does not refer to the remainders. To develop this other viewpoint we shall look closely at the case in which the modulus is 3.

Let us look at those natural numbers that are congruent to 1 modulo 3. They are 1, 4, 7, 10, 13, 16, $\cdots$. Observe that each of these differs from 1 by a multiple of 3. That is, the statement

$$A \equiv 1 \ (\text{mod } 3),$$

means that $A - 1$ is divisible by 3. Similarly, as the reader may check, a natural number is congruent to 2 modulo 3 only if it differs from 2 by a multiple of 3.

This suggests a more direct way of defining congruence. We could say that

$$A \equiv B \ (\text{mod } M)$$

if *M* divides $A - B$. Furthermore, this suggests how we could define congruence between any two integers (positive or negative). We will say that *two integers, A and B, are congruent modulo M if M divides A − B*. For example,

$$-3 \equiv 7 \ (\text{mod } 5),$$

since $(-3) - 7 = -10$ is divisible by 5.

Before we investigate this notion of two integers being congruent modulo *M*, let us use it to restate some of our earlier results.

In Chapter 1 we proved that the number of switches, *S*, in a seamless hatband is even. This now reads: $S \equiv 0 \ (\text{mod } 2)$. In the same chapter we also observed that if *B* is the backward number of one arrangement, and if B' is the backward number of another arrangement, then *S*, the number of switches in going from the first to the second arrangement, is always even if $B - B'$ is even; odd if $B - B'$ is odd. These two assertions are both included in the statement

$$S \equiv B - B' \ (\text{mod } 2).$$

In Chapter 2 (Theorem 2) we proved that if the number of *AB* edges on the border of a triangle is odd, then so is the number of *ABC* triangles. We also proved that if the number of *AB* edges on the border of the triangle is even, then so is the number of *ABC* triangles. Both of these statements are included in this assertion: the number of *AB* edges on the border is congruent to the number of *ABC* triangles (mod 2).

In Chapter 3 our statement that *A* is a divisor of *B* can be translated as $B \equiv 0 \ (\text{mod } A)$. The basic idea behind the Prime-manufacturing Machine can be expressed (for *M* larger than 1) as follows: if *A* is congruent to 0 (mod *M*), then $A + 1$ is not congruent to 0 (mod *M*).

In Chapter 4 we defined a special natural number as one that, whenever it divides the product of two natural numbers, divides at least one of them. In the language of congruences, the natural number *S* is special if

$A \times B \equiv 0 \pmod{S}$ forces $A \equiv 0 \pmod{S}$ or $B \equiv 0 \pmod{S}$.

In Chapter 4 we also met the important theorem: if A and B are natural numbers, then there are integers M and N (one positive and one negative) such that

$$(A, B) = M \times A + N \times B.$$

This can be translated in two different ways into the language of congruences. First, using the modulus A, we could assert: for any natural numbers A, B, there is an integer N such that

$$(A, B) \equiv N \times B \pmod{A}.$$

Secondly, using the modulus B, we could assert: for any natural numbers A, B, there is an integer M such that

$$(A, B) \equiv M \times A \pmod{B}.$$

In Chapter 5 we made use of the fact that if a prime appears, say, h times, when M^2 is written as the product of primes, then

$$h \equiv 0 \pmod{2}.$$

In E 4, E 6, and E 7 of Chapter 8 we proved that the number of towns of odd degree in a highway system is even. Using the language of congruence, we could say then that the number of towns of odd degree is congruent to 0 (mod 2).

But the notion of congruence provides more than just a new language for saying old things. The arithmetic of congruences is useful for dealing with many problems about integers.

Before we apply the notion of congruence we will establish some of its useful properties. Our first theorem will show that the symbol $\equiv$ behaves like the symbol $=$. I suggest that the reader check each of the following theorems with examples before beginning their proofs.

THEOREM 1. (a) $A \equiv A \pmod{M}$.

(b) If $A \equiv B \pmod{M}$, then $B \equiv A \pmod{M}$.

(c) If $A \equiv B \pmod{M}$ and $B \equiv C \pmod{M}$, then $A \equiv C \pmod{M}$.

PROOF. (a) To prove the statement $A \equiv A \pmod{M}$ we must show that M divides $A - A$. But any natural number divides 0; hence M divides $A - A$.

(b) To prove that $A \equiv B \pmod{M}$ implies that $B \equiv A \pmod{M}$ we proceed in this manner. We know that there is an integer Q such that

$$A - B \equiv Q \times M.$$

Multiplying both sides by -1 gives

$$-A + B = (-Q) \times M,$$

and hence

$$B - A = (-Q) \times M.$$

Thus M divides $B - A$. That is,

$$B \equiv A \;(\text{mod } M).$$

(c) If we assume that $A \equiv B \,(\text{mod } M)$ and that $B \equiv C \,(\text{mod } M)$, then there are integers Q_1 and Q_2 such that

$$A - B = Q_1 \times M$$

and

$$B - C = Q_2 \times M.$$

Adding the left sides of these two equations together, we get

$$(A - B) + (B - C) = Q_1 \times M + Q_2 \times M.$$

Since the B's cancel, and since we have

$$Q_1 \times M + Q_2 \times M = (Q_1 + Q_2) \times M,$$

we obtain

$$A - C = (Q_1 + Q_2) \times M;$$

and thus $A \equiv C \,(\text{mod } M)$. This ends the proof.

Furthermore, as the following theorem shows, the symbol $\equiv$ behaves in the same way as does the symbol $=$ with respect to addition and multiplication.

THEOREM 2. *If $A \equiv B$ (mod M) and $a \equiv b$ (mod M), then*

$$a + A \equiv b + B \;(\textit{mod } M).$$

PROOF. We again must go back to the definition of the symbol $\equiv$. We know that there are integers Q_1 and Q_2 such that

$$A - B = Q_1 \times M$$

and

$$a - b = Q_2 \times M.$$

Adding these equations, we get

$$(A - B) + (a - b) = (Q_1 \times M) + (Q_2 \times M).$$

From this it follows that

$$(A + a) - (B + b) = (Q_1 + Q_2) \times M.$$

That is,

$$A + a \equiv B + b \;(\text{mod } M).$$

THEOREM 3. *If $A \equiv B$ (mod M) and $a \equiv b$ (mod M), then $Aa \equiv Bb$ (mod M).*

Before proceeding to the proof, let us illustrate this theorem, which may be more surprising than Theorem 2. For example, it asserts that, since

$$17 \equiv 3 \;(\text{mod } 7)$$

and

$$5 \equiv 12 \;(\text{mod } 7),$$

we will have

$$17 \times 5 \equiv 3 \times 12 \pmod 7,$$

or

$$85 \equiv 36 \pmod 7,$$

a congruence that the reader may check.

Now we will present a

PROOF OF THEOREM 3. Since $A \equiv B \pmod M$ and $a \equiv b \pmod M$, there are integers Q_1 and Q_2 such that

$$A - B = Q_1 \times M$$

and   (1)

$$a - b = Q_2 \times M.$$

Out of these two equations we hope to construct an integer Q such that

$$Aa - Bb = Q \times M.$$

Were we to proceed as in the proof of Theorem 2 (multiplying instead of adding the equations $A - B = Q_1 \times M$ and $a - b = Q_2 \times M$), we would get

$$(A - B) \times (a - b) = (Q_1 \times M) \times (Q_2 \times M),$$

which, multiplied out, expands to give

$$Aa - Ba - Ab + Bb = Q_1 \times Q_2 \times M \times M.$$

This would get us nowhere near a proof of Theorem 2, for there is too great a tangle of A's, a's, b's, and B's.

To avoid this difficulty let us start over, this time first separating A from B and a from b by replacing the opening equations (1) with

$$A = B + (Q_1 \times M)$$

and

$$a = b + (Q_2 \times M).$$

If we multiply these together we obtain

$$Aa = (B + Q_1M) \times (b + Q_2M).$$

Multiplying out the right-hand side gives

$$Aa = Bb + BQ_2M + Q_1Mb + Q_1MQ_2M.$$

This can be rewritten as

$$Aa = Bb + (BQ_2 + Q_1b + Q_1MQ_2) \times M.$$

Thus

$$Aa - Bb = (BQ_2 + Q_1b + Q_1MQ_2) \times M.$$

Now, $BQ_2 + Q_1b + Q_1MQ_2$ is an integer, which we may call Q. We then have $Aa - Bb = QM$; and hence

$$Aa \equiv Bb \pmod M.$$

Now we shall use the machinery represented by Theorems 1, 2, and 3 to prove several other theorems.

The proof in E 21 of Chapter 3, or in Chapter 4 (p. 40) that 2 is special is based on the fact that the product of two odd integers is odd. Let us show that this result is just a special case of Theorem 3.

THEOREM 4. *If A and a are odd, then so is A × a.*

PROOF. We have

$$A \equiv 1 \pmod 2$$

and

$$a \equiv 1 \pmod 2.$$

By Theorem 3,

$$A \times a \equiv 1 \times 1 \pmod 2.$$

Since $1 \times 1 = 1$, we have

$$Aa \equiv 1 \pmod 2.$$

Thus Aa is odd.

In a similar manner we can prove

THEOREM 5. *For any natural number N,*

$$10^N \equiv 1 \pmod 9.$$

PROOF. Since $10^1 = 10$, we see that $10^1 \equiv 1 \pmod 9$. If we apply Theorem 3 to the congruences

$$10 \equiv 1 \pmod 9$$

and

$$10 \equiv 1 \pmod 9,$$

we obtain

$$10 \times 10 \equiv 1 \times 1 \pmod 9.$$

Thus

$$10^2 \equiv 1 \pmod 9.$$

To prove that $10^3 \equiv 1 \pmod 9$ we apply Theorem 3 to the congruences

$$10 \equiv 1 \pmod 9$$

and

$$10^2 \equiv 1 \pmod 9.$$

We could continue in this manner, proving $10^4 \equiv 1 \pmod 9$, $10^5 \equiv 1 \pmod 9$, and so on.

Let us now apply Theorem 5 to explain an arithmetic device—**casting out 9's**—which the reader may have met in grammar school. This method is useful for finding out quickly whether a natural number (usually large) is divisible by 9. We illustrate the rule with the natural number 56,093,742. First we add the digits; $5 + 6 + 0 + 9 + 3 + 7 + 4 + 2 = 36$. The rule then says that since 9 divides 36, 9 divides 56,093,742.

To justify this, and even more, we will prove

THEOREM 6. *When a natural number N is divided by 9 the remainder is the same as that obtained when the sum of the digits of N is divided by 9.*

PROOF. Denote by D_0 the units digit of N. (D_0 is an integer between 0 and 9.) Denote by D_1 the tens digit of N. Similarly, define D_2, D_3, $\cdots$ until we stop at D_d, where d is 1 less than the number of digits in N. (In the example above, $D_0 = 2$, $D_1 = 4$, $D_2 = 7$, $\cdots$, $D_7 = 5$.) Thus

$$N = 10^d D_d + \cdots + 100 D_2 + 10 D_1 + D_0.$$

The sum, S, of the digits of N is

$$S = D_d + \cdots + D_2 + D_1 + D_0.$$

To prove that N and S have the same remainder when divided by 9, we will prove that $N \equiv S \pmod 9$; to prove $N \equiv S \pmod 9$ we will use Theorems 1(a), 2, 3, and 5.

Since $10^1 \equiv 1 \pmod 9$ and $D_1 \equiv D_1 \pmod 9$, we have by Theorem 3 that $10^1 \times D_1 \equiv 1 \times D_1 \pmod 9$; that is, $10 D_1 \equiv D_1 \pmod 9$.

Similarly, $10^2 \equiv 1 \pmod 9$, and $D_2 \equiv D_2 \pmod 9$; thus, by Theorem 3, $10^2 \times D_2 \equiv 1 \times D_2 \pmod 9$; that is, $10^2 D_2 \equiv D_2 \pmod 9$. Continuing in this fashion, we obtain $10^3 D_1 \equiv D_1 \pmod 9$, $\cdots$, and finally, $10^d D_d \equiv D_d \pmod 9$.

With the aid of Theorem 2, which asserts that we can add congruences, we then have

$$10^d D_d + \cdots + 100 D_2 + 10 D_1 + D_0 \equiv D_d + \cdots + D_2 + D_1 + D_0 \pmod 9.$$

That is,

$$N \equiv S \pmod 9.$$

Perhaps we should explain why the rule is called "casting out 9's." If we had erased the 9 before we computed the sum $5 + 6 + 0 + 9 + 3 + 7 + 4 + 2$ we would not have changed the remainder. Similarly, we could have crossed out the 7 and the 2 (which add up to 9) and the 3 and the 6, and the 5 and the 4. Thus the remainder of 56,093,742 when divided by 9 will be the same as the remainder of 0 when divided by 9.

As another example, let us predict the remainder of 4,659,027 when divided by 9. Before adding the digits, we can "cast out" the 4 and the 5, the 9, and the 2 and the 7; thus, before adding the digits, we have 4659027. The sum of the digits left over is 6. The remainder of 6 when divided by 9 is obviously 6.

The reader may check that the remainder of 4,659,027 when divided by 9 is, as predicted, 6.

The next two theorems will be needed in Chapters 11 and 12. If the reader prefers, he may wait till then to examine them.

The resemblance between the symbols $\equiv$ and $=$ is further displayed in

THEOREM 7. *If A and M are natural numbers such that $(A, M) = 1$, then for any integer B we can find an integer X such that*

$$AX \equiv B \ (mod \ M).$$

What we are saying is that we can generally solve a congruence analogous to an equation $AX = B$. As an example, before proving Theorem 7, let us see if there is an X such that $5X \equiv 7$ (mod 11). If we experiment with $X = 1, 2, 3, 4, 5, 6,$ or 7, we see that none of them satisfies the demand $5X \equiv 7$ (mod 11). But $5 \times 8 \equiv 7$ (mod 11), as the reader may check. We now give a

PROOF OF THEOREM 7. Since $(A, M) = 1$, we know by Lemma 4 of Chapter 4 that there are integers P and Q such that

$$1 = P \times A + Q \times M.$$

(We call them P and Q instead of M and N because the letter M is already being used to name the modulus.)

Multiplying our equation by B produces

$$B = (B \times P) \times A + (B \times Q) \times M.$$

Thus $B \equiv (B \times P) \times A$ (mod M). Hence $B \times P$ serves as the desired X.

Once we have one solution to a congruence such as $AX \equiv B$ (mod M), we can easily manufacture more by adding (as often as we please) the modulus M to the solution already found. For example, we saw above that 8 is a solution to $5X \equiv 7$ (mod 11). Suppose that C is obtained from 8 by adding 11 to 8 one or more times. Then $C \equiv 8$ (mod 11) and hence, by Theorem 3, $5C \equiv 5 \times 8$ (mod 11). Theorem 1(c) then yields $5C \equiv 7$ (mod 11), thus C is also a solution to $5X \equiv 7$ (mod 11).

Conversely, if C is any solution of $5X \equiv 7$ (mod 11), then, necessarily, $C \equiv 8$ (mod 11). This follows from

THEOREM 8 (Cancellation Theorem). *If A and M are natural numbers such that $(A, M) = 1$, and if C and D are integers satisfying*

$$AC \equiv AD \ (mod \ M),$$

then

$$C \equiv D \ (mod \ M).$$

Before beginning the proof, let us consider what is involved. We know that M divides $AC - AD$, which is equal to $A(C - D)$. We wish to prove that M divides $C - D$. This resembles the assertion that if a prime divides the product of two natural numbers, then it divides at least one of them (Theorem 3 of Chapter 4). The reader will find that the proof we now give of Theorem 8 is similar to the one we gave for Theorem 3 of Chapter 4.

PROOF OF THEOREM 8. Since $(A, M) = 1$, we know by Lemma 4 of Chapter 4 that there are integers P and Q such that

$$1 = P \times A + Q \times M.$$

Multiplying both sides of this equation by $C - D$ gives

$$C - D = P \times A \times (C - D) + Q \times M \times (C - D).$$

Since M divides the right side of this equation, it divides $C - D$.

Theorem 8 justifies "cancellation" in congruences under certain circumstances. If we remove the restriction $(A, M) = 1$, then the conclusion of Theorem 8 need not hold. For example,

$$2 \times 1 \equiv 2 \times 3 \ (\text{mod } 4),$$

yet it is *not* true that 1 is congruent to 3 modulo 4.

The arithmetic of congruences has its own multiplication table and addition table, which are much simpler than those we had to memorize in grammar school for ordinary multiplication and addition. (Of course, since it is harder to learn, the multiplication table is given greater publicity in grammar school. But it is important to memorize sums up to $9 + 9$, and sometimes a table is made for them.)

Let us illustrate this with the modulus 4. The set of integers congruent modulo 4 to a particular integer, A, we will denote $[A]$, *and we will call it a* **residue class** *modulo 4*. Thus $[5]$ consists of

$$\cdots, -15, -11, -7, -3, 1, 5, 9, 13, \cdots.$$

Note that $[-7] = [-3] = [1] = [5]$. Perhaps the best name for this particular residue class would be $[1]$, since this class consists of precisely those integers leaving a remainder of 1 when divided by 4.

Since there are four possible remainders (0, 1, 2, or 3) upon division by 4, there are four residue classes modulo 4: $[0]$, $[1]$, $[2]$, and $[3]$.

We can add two residue classes $[A]$ and $[B]$ by defining their sum to be the residue class containing $A + B$. This new addition we will denote by $\oplus$ (a symbol which, incidentally, is a letter in the Etruscan alphabet). For example,

$$[2] \oplus [3] = [5] = [1].$$

Similarly, we can define a multiplication $\otimes$ (another Etruscan letter) by

$$[A] \otimes [B] = [A \times B].$$

Thus, for example,

$$[2] \otimes [3] = [6] = [2].$$

The table for $\oplus$ is:

$\oplus$	[0]	[1]	[2]	[3]
[0]	[0]	[1]	[2]	[3]
[1]	[1]	[2]	[3]	[0]
[2]	[2]	[3]	[0]	[1]
[3]	[3]	[0]	[1]	[2]

(mod 4)

It will be convenient to omit the brackets and write the table simply as:

$\oplus$	0	1	2	3
0	0	1	2	3
1	1	2	3	0
2	2	3	0	1
3	3	0	1	2

(mod 4)

The multiplication table for $\otimes$, with the brackets omitted, is:

$\otimes$	0	1	2	3
0	0	0	0	0
1	0	1	2	3
2	0	2	0	2
3	0	3	2	1

These tables can be thought of as a record of how remainders of two natural numbers (when divided by 4) determine the remainder of their sum and product. For example, the entry, 1, for $2 + 3$,

$\oplus$			3
2			1

records the following: if A leaves a remainder of 2 when divided by 4, and B leaves a remainder of 3 when divided by 4, then $A + B$ leaves a remainder of 1 when divided by 4.

We can make such tables not only for the modulus 4 but for any modulus. For the modulus 5 we have these two tables:

$\oplus$	0	1	2	3	4
0	0	1	2	3	4
1	1	2	3	4	0
2	2	3	4	0	1
3	3	4	0	1	2
4	4	0	1	2	3

(mod 5)

$\otimes$	0	1	2	3	4
0	0	0	0	0	0
1	0	1	2	3	4
2	0	2	4	1	3
3	0	3	1	4	2
4	0	4	3	2	1

(mod 5)

In Chapters 11 and 12 we will study tables that, like the addition tables above, have no duplications in any row or column. Such tables are used in the design of experiments; furthermore, they will help us increase our understanding of our usual addition and multiplication. In those same chapters, we will find our arithmetic of congruences useful on several occasions.

Exercises

1. Show that each of these statements is true: $4 \equiv 12$ (mod 8), $4 \equiv 12$ (mod 1), $4 \equiv 12$ (mod 2), $4 \equiv 12$ (mod 4).

2. Show that each of these statements is true: $5 \equiv 21$ (mod 4), $5 \equiv 21$ (mod 8), $5 \equiv 21$ (mod 16), $5 \equiv 21$ (mod 2), $5 \equiv 21$ (mod 1).

3. Show that each of these statements is true: $-3 \equiv 7$ (mod 5), $57 \equiv 0$ (mod 19), $1 \equiv 1$ (mod 17).

4. Show that each of these statements is true: $8 \equiv -6$ (mod 7), $5 \equiv 5$ (mod 8), $117 \equiv 0$ (mod 39).

5. Translate these statements into the language of congruences:
   (a) The sum of two even integers is even.
   (b) The sum of an even integer and an odd integer is odd.
   (c) The sum of two odd integers is even.

6. Translate these statements into the language of congruences:
   (a) The product of an even integer and any integer is even.
   (b) The product of two odd integers is odd.

7. With congruences it is easy to prove that 3 is special as follows. Assume that A and B are natural numbers, with $A \times B \equiv 0$ (mod 3). Then, to show that at least

one of $A \equiv 0 \pmod 3$ or $B \equiv 0 \pmod 3$ holds, rule out one by one the following four cases:
(a) $A \equiv 1 \pmod 3$ and $B \equiv 1 \pmod 3$,
(b) $A \equiv 1 \pmod 3$ and $B \equiv 2 \pmod 3$,
(c) $A \equiv 2 \pmod 3$ and $B \equiv 1 \pmod 3$,
(d) $A \equiv 2 \pmod 3$ and $B \equiv 2 \pmod 3$.
(*Hint:* Use Theorem 3.)

8. Using the method of E 7, prove that (a) 5 is special, (b) 7 is special.

9. Using the method of E 7, prove that 11 is special.

10. Prove, using congruences, that a natural number is congruent to its units digit mod 2. How does this give a test for divisibility by 2?

11. That a natural number has the same remainder as does the sum of its digits when divided by 9 can be proved without congruences. Notice that $10^N - 1$ is divisible by 9 since all its digits are 9. From this observation, write out a detailed proof, without using the language of congruences, for the rule of casting out 9's. (That is, prove Theorem 6 without using the symbol $\equiv$.)

12. Using Theorem 3, prove that $10 \equiv -1 \pmod{11}$, $100 \equiv 1 \pmod{11}$, $1000 \equiv -1 \pmod{11}$, $10^4 \equiv 1 \pmod{11}$, $10^5 \equiv -1 \pmod{11}$, and so on.

13. With the aid of E 12, justify the following test for divisibility by 11: A natural number is divisible by 11 if the units digit minus its tens digit plus its hundreds digit minus its thousands digit, and so on, is divisible by 11. (For example, 3564 is divisible by 11, since $4 - 6 + 5 - 3$ is divisible by 11.)

14. (a) In the proof of Theorem 5 what was the important property of 9 that we used?
   (b) Prove that remainders can be predicted for division by 3 in a manner similar to that for division by 9.

15. Without using congruences, prove E 14 (b).

16. (a) Using Theorem 3, prove that the remainder of $A \times B$ when divided by 9 is congruent modulo 9 to the product (remainder of A when divided by 9) $\times$ (the remainder of B when divided by 9).
   (b) Use (a) to show that 73×65 is *not* equal to 4645.
   (c) Compute 73×65.
   (This exercise shows how we can use the rule of casting out 9's as a check on our multiplication.)

17. Using E 16 (a), show that
   (a) 141×625 is not equal to 88025,
   (b) 58×73 is not equal to 4244.

18. (a) Show by computing the product correctly that 172×251 is not equal to 41372.
   (b) Does the rule of casting out 9's show that 172×251 is not 41372?

19. Using Theorem 8, prove that an even natural number divisible by 3 is divisible by 6. With this test, show that 213042 is divisible by 6.

2). Give three solutions in natural numbers to each of these congruences:
   (a) $X \equiv 1 \pmod 2$,

(b) $3X \equiv 2 \pmod 5$,

(c) $2X \equiv 3 \pmod 9$.

(A natural number, N, is a solution of a congruence if a true statement results when X is replaced by N.)

21. Give three solutions in natural numbers to each of these congruences:

(a) $X \equiv 7 \pmod 2$,

(b) $2X \equiv 3 \pmod 5$,

(c) $3X \equiv 1 \pmod 8$.

22. Prove that there is no solution in integers to the congruence $2X \equiv 3 \pmod 8$.

23. Prove that there is no solution in integers to the congruence $6X \equiv 8 \pmod{15}$.

24. Make the addition and multiplication tables that correspond to these moduli:

(a) 3,   (b) 2,   (c) 6.

25. Make the addition and multiplication tables that correspond to these moduli:

(a) 7,   (b) 8.

26. Theorem 8 implies that if A is 1, 2, 3, or 4, then $AC \equiv AD \pmod 5$ implies $C \equiv D \pmod 5$. What does this mean about the multiplication table for the modulus 5?

27. Theorem 8 implies that if A is 1, 2, 3, 4, 5, or 6, then $AC \equiv AD \pmod 7$ implies $C \equiv D \pmod 7$. What does this mean about the multiplication table for the modulus 7?

28. The congruence $3X \equiv 2 \pmod 5$ has an endless supply of solutions: $\cdots$, -6, -1, 4, 9, 14, $\cdots$ [in fact, any integer congruent to 4 (mod 5)]. But the congruence $3X \equiv 2 \pmod 5$ has only one solution if we demand that a solution be between 0 and 4. Assuming that we place this same restriction on solutions, show how many solutions there are of

(a) $3X^2 \equiv 2 \pmod 5$,   (b) $3X^2 \equiv 1 \pmod 5$.

29. Show how many solutions there are between 0 and 7 of

(a) $X^2 \equiv 1 \pmod 8$,   (b) $X^3 \equiv 3 \pmod 8$,   (c) $X^2 \equiv 0 \pmod 8$.

30. Using the congruence $5 \equiv -1 \pmod 6$, predict the remainder when 5^{100} is divided by 6.

31. Using $7 \equiv -1 \pmod 8$, predict the remainder when (a) 7^{50} is divided by 8, (b) 7^{75} is divided by 8.

32. (a) For each natural number A from 2 through 5, find the natural number B between 1 and 6 such that $A \times B \equiv 1 \pmod 7$. (For example, if A is 2, then B is 4.)

(b) Using (a), show that $1 \times 2 \times 3 \times 4 \times 5 \times 6 \equiv 6 \pmod 7$.

33. (a) For each natural number A from 2 through 9 find the natural number B between 1 and 10 such that $A \times B \equiv 1 \pmod{11}$. (For example, if A is 3, then B is 4.)

(b) Using (a), show that

$$1 \times 2 \times 3 \times 4 \times 5 \times 6 \times 7 \times 8 \times 9 \times 10 \equiv 10 \pmod{11}.$$

34. In the proof of Theorem 3 of Chapter 3 we defined $N!$ as the product of all natural numbers from 1 through N. In E 24 of Chapter 3 it was shown that, for composite N larger than 4,

$$(N - 1)! \equiv 0 \pmod{N}.$$

   (a) Show that E 32 (b) proves that $6! \equiv -1 \pmod 7$.
   (b) Show that E 33 (b) proves that $10! \equiv -1 \pmod{11}$.
   (c) Using the ideas of E 32 and E 33, prove that if P is prime, then

$$(P - 1)! \equiv -1 \pmod P.$$

35. In E 12 it was proved, for example, that $10^2 \equiv 1 \pmod{11}$, $10^3 \equiv -1 \pmod{11}$, $10^4 \equiv 1 \pmod{11}$ and $10^5 \equiv -1 \pmod{11}$. Check each of these congruences by dividing 11 into the appropriate difference of two integers.

36. Solve E 7 (b) of Chapter 8 by using congruences.

37. Translate the technique of E 12, Chapter 9, into the language of congruence modulo 2.

38. Predict the remainder when $16 \times 15 \times 22 \times 29 \times 31$ is divided by 7 by using congruences and Theorem 3.

39. (a) What is the remainder of 9546 when divided by 9?
    (b) What is the remainder of 4965 when divided by 9?
    (c) The remainders in (a) and (b) are equal. Prove that whenever we rearrange the digits of a number, we do not change its remainder relative to division by 9.

40. (a) Is the analogue of E 39 true for remainders relative to division by 2?
    (b) Is the analogue of E 39 true for remainders relative to division by 3?

41. Prove that a natural number is divisible by 4 if the number formed by the last two digits of this number is divisible by 4. (*Hint:* Notice that 4 is a divisor of 100 and all higher powers of 10.)

42. Obtain a test for divisibility by 8. (*Hint:* E 41 may give a clue.)

43. (a) Fill out the multiplication table for the modulus 6.
    (b) Do the same for the modulus 7.

44. Fill out the multiplication table for the modulus 9.

45. (a) Which of the multiplication tables constructed in E 43 and E 44 and in this chapter for the modulus 4 or 5 have the property that 0 appears only in boxes of the top row or left column?
    (b) What property of the modulus is involved in (a)?

References

1. R. Courant and H. Robbins, *What is Mathematics?*, Oxford University Press, New York, 1960. (Congruences, pp. 31–40.)

2. I. Niven and H. S. Zuckerman, *An Introduction to the Theory of Numbers*, Wiley, New York, 1960. (Congruences, pp. 20–33.)

3. O. Ore, *Number Theory and its History*, McGraw-Hill, New York, 1948. (Congruences, pp. 209–233.)

4. G. Birkhoff and S. MacLane, *A Survey of Modern Algebra*, Macmillan, New York, 1953. (Congruences, pp. 23–29.)

Chapter 11

STRANGE ALGEBRAS

If we never travel, we may get into the habit of thinking that our way of life, with all its idiosyncrasies and peculiar customs, is the best and only reasonable way, and that all other peoples behave quite oddly. We may be like that child in Robert Louis Stevenson's *A Child's Garden of Verses*, who offers this sympathy to foreign children:

> You have curious things to eat,
> I am fed on proper meat;
> You must dwell beyond the foam,
> But I am safe and live at home.

In some lands the calendar presents the weeks vertically instead of horizontally; the American traveler must cock his head to read it. Even after years in such a land, he may still feel that the weeks should be horizontal. It is not easy to question the world we knew when we were children.

In this chapter we will visit algebras quite different from the one we met in grammar school. When we return to our own algebra, we will appreciate virtues in our system that we might never have noticed had we not made this journey. And, if we travel with an open mind, we might admit that the other systems have their own advantages.

Our journey begins in the countryside, with a problem suggested by agriculture. In these days of scientific farming, it is very important that a farmer get as great a return from his investment as possible. Thus a good number of experimental studies are made to find the best diet for each crop. How much water? How much nitrogen? How much potassium? In many small doses or in a few large ones?

Let us design an experiment for comparing the effect of four different doses of water on tomato plants. We might arrange four plants in a straight line and give each plant one of the four doses *A*, *B*, *C*, and *D*.

But scientists have observed that arranging plants in a line frequently introduces a bias that makes the experiment worthless. The statistician R. A. Fisher warns,

In many fields there is found to occur either a gradient of fertility across a whole area, or parallel strips of land having a higher or lower fertility than the average····. Such soil variations may be due in part to the past history of the field, such as the lands in which it has been lain up for drainage producing variations in the depth and present condition of the soil, or to portions of it having been manured and cropped otherwise than the remainder.

As a precaution, we follow the advice and practice of the scientists, and instead of working with four plants in a straight line we devise without much effort a square arrangement of sixteen plants to which we distribute the four treatments like this:

A	*C*	*D*	*B*
D	*B*	*A*	*C*
B	*D*	*C*	*A*
C	*A*	*B*	*D*

A horizontal line of plants we shall call a **row**; *a vertical line of plants we shall call a* **column.** Each row contains each of the treatments once, as does each column.

We may think of the arrangement as a crossword puzzle in four-letter words, or perhaps we are reminded of the problem of forming memory words by making certain strings of 0's and 1's overlap in a special way. But what we should observe is the resemblance this agricultural experiment bears to the usual multiplication table.

The multiplication table that we all once memorized looks like this:

	1	2	3	4	5	6	7	8	9
1	1	2	3	4	5	6	7	8	9
2	2	4	6	8	10	12	14	16	18
3	3	6	9	12	15	18	21	24	27
4	4	8	12	16	20	24	28	32	36
5	5	10	15	20	25	30	35	40	45
6	6	12	18	24	30	36	42	48	54
7	7	14	21	28	35	42	49	56	63
8	8	16	24	32	40	48	56	64	72
9	9	18	27	36	45	54	63	72	81

Actually, the multiplication table does not stop at 9 by 9. It goes on to the right and downward without end. But with knowledge of the 9 by 9 table, together with the rules for carrying and adding, we can compute larger products, such as 193×64.

Both tables are square. The little table lacks a guide row and a guide column. These we can put in alphabetically and make of the tomato experiment a miniature and exotic algebra:

(*1*)

	A	*B*	*C*	*D*
A	*A*	*C*	*D*	*B*
B	*D*	*B*	*A*	*C*
C	*B*	*D*	*C*	*A*
D	*C*	*A*	*B*	*D*

In such a miniature table, let us name each column by the guide letter above it. Thus column *C* is

$$D$$
$$A$$
$$C$$
$$B$$

Similarly, we shall name each row by the guide letter to its left. Thus row *B* is

$$D \quad B \quad A \quad C$$

The letter that appears in the box where row *B* meets column *C* we shall denote by

$$B \circ C.$$

(We may read this "*B* circle *C*").

In our little table,

$$B \circ C = A.$$

In any such table, *what appears in the box where row X meets column Y, we shall denote by X ∘ Y.* Pictorially, it looks like this:

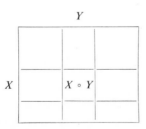

When we use our ordinary multiplication table, we write $X \times Y$ instead of $X \circ Y$. Similarly, in the usual addition table, we write $X + Y$ instead of $X \circ Y$.

Now let us leave our ordinary arithmetic and algebra far behind. Let us roam through various miniature arithmetics and, when we are done, compare them with our own.

A "table" will be a square arrangement of symbols without duplication in any row or in any column. (On occasion, the table might be of unlimited extent.) That is, for any X, Y, and Z, with Y different from Z, we have

$$X \circ Y \text{ different from } X \circ Z$$

and

$$Y \circ X \text{ different from } Z \circ X.$$

The fact that row X has no duplications is expressed by the requirement that $X \circ Y$ be different from $X \circ Z$:

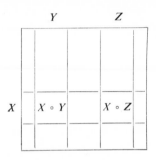

The fact that column X has no duplications is expressed by the requirement that $Y \circ X$ be different from $Z \circ X$:

The letters used in the guide row will be the same as those used in the guide column; and they will be written in the same order in both. *Each box of the table will contain one of the letters that appear in the guide row.*

The number of rows (or the number of columns) of a table we will call its **order.** Looking at our little table of order 4, we observe that

$$A \circ A = A, \qquad B \circ B = B, \qquad C \circ C = C, \qquad D \circ D = D.$$

These four equations can be summarized in the brief assertion: for all X we have $X \circ X = X$. The phrase "for all X" is short for "whenever X is replaced by one of the letters of the table."

A table satisfying the rule "$X \circ X = X$ for all X" we call **idempotent** (from the Latin *idem*, self; *potens*, power). It is very easy to see whether a table is idempotent: the diagonal stretching from the upper left corner down to the lower right should read the same as the guide row (or guide column). *Henceforth let us call this diagonal the* **main diagonal.**

Neither our ordinary multiplication nor our addition is idempotent. For example, 5×5 is not 5, nor is $5 + 5$ equal to 5. We are certainly far from our usual daily routine.

But our ordinary multiplication and addition satisfies a rule that the little table of order 4 disobeys. In learning the multiplication table, once we had memorized a product, such as $6 \times 9 = 54$, we had the product 9×6 without further effort. We did not have to memorize 9×6 separately because ordinary multiplication satisfies the rule:

$$X \times Y = Y \times X \qquad \text{(for all } X \text{ and } Y\text{).}$$

This is the so-called *commutative rule*. Ordinary addition and multiplication are both commutative. But the little table of order 4 is not; for example,

$$A \circ B = C,$$

whereas

$$B \circ A = D.$$

It is almost as easy to check pictorially whether a table is commutative as it is to see whether it is idempotent. A table is commutative if it is symmetric with respect to the main diagonal. That is, the table can be made by first filling in the triangle above the main diagonal and then flipping it over that diagonal.

Here, for example, is a commutative table of order 4:

(2)

	A	B	C	D
A	A	B	C	D
B	B	A	D	C
C	C	D	A	B
D	D	C	B	A

So far, we have visited miniature arithmetics only of order 4. But it is a simple matter to devise tables of other orders. Here are some tables of orders 1, 2, and 3:

	A
A	A

(3)

	A	B
A	A	B
B	B	A

(4)

	A	B	C
A	C	A	B
B	B	C	A
C	A	B	C

(5)

The table of order 1 is the dullest arithmetic possible; nevertheless, we might acknowledge that it is idempotent and commutative. The table of order 2 is not idempotent, but it is commutative. Table (5), of order 3, is neither commutative nor idempotent.

With a little effort, such as we might use in solving a crossword puzzle, we can devise a commutative table of order 3:

(6)

	A	B	C
A	A	B	C
B	B	C	A
C	C	A	B

Indeed, in the chapter on congruences we found a way of producing commutative tables of all orders. Let us illustrate the technique by producing a commutative table of order 5. Instead of the letters A, B, C, D, and E, we will use the numbers 0, 1, 2, 3, and 4. In the box where row X meets column Y we will place the remainder of $X + Y$ when divided by 5. For example, $3 \circ 4$ will be 2. Since ordinary addition is commutative, so will this table be commutative. Filling in the 25 boxes we obtain

(7)

	0	1	2	3	4
0	0	1	2	3	4
1	1	2	3	4	0
2	2	3	4	0	1
3	3	4	0	1	2
4	4	0	1	2	3

Observe that since there are no duplications in any row or column, (7) is a table. We could translate it into letters by replacing 0 by A, 1 by B, 2 by C, 3 by D, and 4 by E. If we do so we obtain this table:

(8)

	A	B	C	D	E
A	A	B	C	D	E
B	B	C	D	E	A
C	C	D	E	A	B
D	D	E	A	B	C
E	E	A	B	C	D

Tables (7) and (8) really represent the same system. After all, if we had obtained a new table from (7) by painting all the numbers red, we would still think of it as the same table in disguise. The basic thing is that Tables (7) and (8) have the same *form* (just as, in Chapter 7, it was discovered that certain electrical networks and tilings of a rectangle by rectangles have the same underlying form). *Two tables, obtainable from each other by simply renaming all the letters (or all the numbers, as the case may be) we will call* **isomorphic** (from the Greek *iso*, same; *morph*, form).

The same technique that gave us Table (7) can be used for any order. Thus we have

THEOREM 1. *There are commutative tables of all orders.*

Having discovered that there are commutative tables of all orders, let us extend our journey by finding out whether there are tables of all orders that are both commutative and idempotent.

We have already noticed that the table of order 1 is both commutative and idempotent. Let us try to build a table of order 2 that is both commutative and idempotent. Since it is to be idempotent, we can begin by filling in the main diagonal:

(9)

	A	*B*
A	*A*	
B		*B*

But what can we put in the box where row *A* meets column *B*? That is, what shall we have for the value of *A* ∘ *B*? We see that *A* ∘ *B* cannot be *A*, for then row *A* would have a duplication. Nor can *A* ∘ *B* be *B*, for then column *B* would have a duplication. This information we record in

THEOREM 2. *There is no commutative and idempotent table of order 2. (In fact, there is no idempotent table of order 2.)*

Theorem 2, asserting that we cannot do something, is an example of an "impossibility" theorem. We shall meet a much more surprising "impossibility" theorem in Chapter 16.

Let us attack order 3. Starting with the main diagonal we must have

(10)

	A	*B*	*C*
A	*A*		
B		*B*	
C			*C*

What can we define $A \circ B$ to be? Not A, for row A already has an A. Not B, for column B already has a B. We have no choice. We must set $A \circ B = C$. By commutativity, we must then have $B \circ A = C$. Continuing in this fashion, we obtain this idempotent and commutative table of order 3:

(11)

	A	B	C
A	A	C	B
B	C	B	A
C	B	A	C

Let us attack order 4. Is there an idempotent and commutative table of order 4? The main diagonal must be:

(12)

	A	B	C	D
A	A			
B		B		
C			C	
D				D

We have two choices for $A \circ B$: either C or D. Let us choose C first and follow up the consequences. If the table is to be commutative we must also have $B \circ A = C$. Thus, with the choice of $A \circ B = C$, we would have:

(13)

	A	B	C	D
A	A	C		
B	C	B		
C			C	
D				D

What will $A \circ C$ be? Since A and C already appear in row A, $A \circ C$ cannot be A or C. If we made $A \circ C = B$, then we would be forced to have $A \circ D = D$ (since D has to appear in row A). But D is already present in column D. So the only possibility for $A \circ C$ is D. Then, by commutativity, $C \circ A = D$. Since row A must have B somewhere, we must then have $A \circ D = B$. By commutativity, $D \circ A = B$. Let us record all the boxes already filled in (with the only free choice being $A \circ B = C$).

(14)

	A	B	C	D
A	A	C	D	B
B	C	B		
C	D		C	
D	B			D

Where can D appear in row B? Since D already appears in column C, we cannot have $A \circ C = D$, and since it already appears in column D, we cannot have $A \circ D = D$. We are blocked. And, as the reader may easily check, we would be blocked eventually if we had made the other choice at the beginning; namely, $A \circ B = D$. Thus there is no idempotent commutative table of order 4.

For orders 1 and 3 there are idempotent commutative tables; for orders 2 and 4 there are none at all. This suggests that we are once again involved with the duality of the odd and even natural numbers. The next two theorems show that this suspicion is justified.

THEOREM 3. *There are idempotent commutative tables of all odd orders.*

PROOF. Let N be an odd natural number. We will construct a table of order N that is both idempotent and commutative. It will be convenient to build it on the numbers $0, 1, 2, 3, 4, \cdots, N - 1$, just as Table (7) was built on numbers rather than letters. Our method will be a variation of the one we used to make Table (7).

Where row X meets column Y we will put the natural number Z (less than N) that satisfies the equation

$$2Z \equiv X + Y \ (\mathrm{mod}\ N).$$

(The reader is strongly urged at this point to fill out a table of order 5 by the method just given.)

That the Z of the equation can be found is guaranteed by Theorem 7 of Chapter 10 [note that, *since N is odd*, $(2, N) = 1$]. That only one such Z can be found is guaranteed by Theorem 8 of Chapter 10 (the Cancellation Theorem).

Thus we have specified how we will fill in all the boxes. Now we must check that this construction provides an idempotent and commutative table of order N.

We have defined $X \circ Y$ by the demand

$$2(X \circ Y) \equiv X + Y \ (\mathrm{mod}\ N).$$

Is $X \circ X$ always X? We know that

$$2(X \circ X) \equiv X + X \,(\text{mod } N).$$

Since $2X \equiv X + X \,(\text{mod } N)$ and $2(X \circ X) \equiv X + X \,(\text{mod } N)$ we see, by Theorem 8 of Chapter 10 (the Cancellation Theorem), that

$$X \circ X \equiv X \,(\text{mod } N).$$

But two natural numbers that are both less than N and congruent modulo N must be equal; that is, $X \circ X = X$. The table is idempotent.

Is $X \circ Y$ always equal to $Y \circ X$? What we do know is that

$$2(X \circ Y) \equiv X + Y \,(\text{mod } N)$$

and that

$$2(Y \circ X) \equiv Y + X \,(\text{mod } N).$$

Since ordinary addition is commutative, $X + Y$ is equal to $Y + X$. Thus we see that

$$2(X \circ Y) \equiv 2(Y \circ X) \,(\text{mod } N).$$

Again, using the Cancellation Theorem (Theorem 8 of Chapter 10), we conclude that

$$X \circ Y \equiv Y \circ X \,(\text{mod } N).$$

But $X \circ Y$ and $Y \circ X$ are both less than N. Hence $X \circ Y = Y \circ X$. Therefore our system is commutative.

Finally, *is it a table?* We must show that there are no duplications in any row or column. Let us look at a typical row, say, row X. We must prove that if Y_1 is different from Y_2, then $X \circ Y_1$ is different from $X \circ Y_2$. Suppose, on the contrary, that $X \circ Y_1 = X \circ Y_2$. Then

$$2(X \circ Y_1) = 2(X \circ Y_2),$$

and from this we conclude that

$$X + Y_1 \equiv X + Y_2 \,(\text{mod } N).$$

Hence

$$Y_1 \equiv Y_2 \,(\text{mod } N).$$

But Y_1 and Y_2 are both less than N; therefore $Y_1 = Y_2$. Since this is a contradiction, our original assumption must be wrong. Thus $X \circ Y_1$ is different from $X \circ Y_2$, and so we have proved that there are no duplications in any row.

Similarly, there are no duplications in any column. (In a commutative table, row X and column X look alike.) Thus our way of filling in the boxes indeed produces a table.

We shall next show that there is no idempotent commutative table of any even order. Our proof will be in the same spirit as the one proving that it is impossible to find two natural numbers whose quotient is $\sqrt{2}$, or to find solutions to certain Fifteen puzzles. We will prove that if there were such a table, then a certain natural number would have to be both odd and even. Theorem 4 will be another "impossibility" result.

THEOREM 4. *There is no idempotent commutative table of even order.*

PROOF. Let N be an even natural number larger than 0. We will prove that there is no idempotent commutative table of order N. Suppose, on the contrary, that there does exist such a table. We will examine the boxes of this table that are occupied by the letter A and obtain a contradiction.

Since the table is commutative, the number of boxes occupied by A and not on the main diagonal is even. Since the table is idempotent, there is exactly one box on the main diagonal occupied by the letter A. Thus the number of boxes occupied by A is one more than an even number. That is, the number of boxes occupied by A is *odd*.

On the other hand, since A appears exactly once in each of the N rows, A must occupy an *even* number of boxes. This contradiction proves Theorem 4.

There are algebras stranger than those that are idempotent and commutative. Indeed, there are algebras, as yet unnamed, that satisfy the rule

$$X \circ (X \circ Y) = Y \circ X \qquad \text{(for all } X \text{ and } Y\text{)}.$$

Table (*1*), which was used to arrange the sixteen tomato plants, is an example of such a weird algebra. To show that Table (*1*) does satisfy the rule $X \circ (X \circ Y) = Y \circ X$, we must make 16 checks, since there are four choices for Y and, for each choice of Y, four choices of X. Let us carry out just two of these 16 checks.

Does $A \circ (A \circ C) = C \circ A$? To answer this we must compute both sides of the equation in question and see whether they are equal. Before we can compute $A \circ (A \circ C)$ we have to find $A \circ C$. Looking at Table (*1*) we see that $A \circ C = D$. Thus $A \circ (A \circ C) = A \circ D$. But we have still not finished the computation of $A \circ (A \circ C)$; we must compute $A \circ D$. Looking again at Table (*1*) we see that $A \circ D = B$. Thus $A \circ (A \circ C) = B$. Next, we compute the other side of the equation we are checking; namely, the expression $C \circ A$. Looking at Table (*1*), we see that $C \circ A = B$. Since both $A \circ (A \circ C)$ and $C \circ A$ are B, we see that $A \circ (A \circ C) = C \circ A$. This completes only one of the 16 checks that are to be made.

Another of the 16 checks would be, for example, to show that the rule $X \circ (X \circ Y) = Y \circ X$ is satisfied when X and Y are both replaced by D; that is, to show that

$$D \circ (D \circ D) = D \circ D.$$

Glancing at Table (*1*) we see that $D \circ D = D$. Hence both sides of this equation in question are equal to D. Thus the equation $X \circ (X \circ Y) = Y \circ X$ is valid in this case too. The reader is invited to make a few more checks for himself.

Most of what is known about tables that satisfy the rule $X \circ (X \circ Y) = Y \circ X$ is reported in the following two theorems:

THEOREM 5. *Any table that satisfies the rule* $X \circ (X \circ Y) = Y \circ X$ *for all* X *and* Y *is idempotent.*

PROOF. Since $X \circ (X \circ Y) = Y \circ X$ for all X and Y, we have, when Y and X coincide,

$$X \circ (X \circ X) = X \circ X.$$

Since row X has no duplications, $X \circ X$ must be the same as X.

THEOREM 6. *Any table that satisfies the rule* $X \circ (X \circ Y) = Y \circ X$ *has the property that distinct letters do not commute. That is, if* X *is different from* Y, *then* $X \circ Y$ *is different from* $Y \circ X$.

PROOF. Let U and V be any two distinct letters in a table satisfying the rule $X \circ (X \circ Y) = Y \circ X$. We will prove that $U \circ V$ must be different from $V \circ U$.

Assume for the moment that $U \circ V = V \circ U$. We will obtain a contradiction. Indeed, since $U \circ V = V \circ U$, we have

$$U \circ (U \circ V) = U \circ (V \circ U).$$

Next, since the table satisfies the rule $X \circ (X \circ Y) = Y \circ X$, we see in particular that $U \circ (U \circ V) = V \circ U$. Thus we have

(15) $$V \circ U = U \circ (V \circ U).$$

Theorem 5 tells us that our table is idempotent. Thus

(16) $$V \circ U = (V \circ U) \circ (V \circ U).$$

From equations (15) and (16) we obtain

(17) $$U \circ (V \circ U) = (V \circ U) \circ (V \circ U).$$

Since column $V \circ U$ has no duplications, we see from (17) that

(18) $$U = V \circ U.$$

On the other hand, since our table is idempotent,

(19) $$U = U \circ U.$$

Equations (18) and (19) tell us that

(20) $$U \circ U = V \circ U.$$

Since column U has no duplications, we conclude from Equation (20) that

$$U = V,$$

contradicting the fact that U and V are distinct.

Theorems 5 and 6 help us a little in deciding which orders are possible for tables satisfying the rule $X \circ (X \circ Y) = Y \circ X$. First, there can be none of order 2, since there is no idempotent table of order 2. Secondly, there can be none of order 3, since any idempotent table of order 3 must be commutative, as the reader may easily check. But no one knows in general for which orders there are tables satisfying the rule $X \circ (X \circ Y) = Y \circ X$. This is quite a contrast to the complete solution we found for the rules $X \circ X = X$ and $X \circ Y = Y \circ X$ (Theorems 3 and 4).

Though there are many other exotic tables, which satisfy other strange rules, we must now end our journey and come back to our own arithmetic and look at it with the fresh viewpoint of the returning traveler.

First of all, we are glad that our addition and multiplication are commutative, for once we memorize $X \times Y$ and $X + Y$ we also know $Y \times X$ and $Y + X$.

But there is a deeper virtue in our addition and multiplication. Observe that when we compute $3 \times 6 \times 7$ we can proceed in two ways. We can either consider it as $(3 \times 6) \times 7$, in which case 3×6 is computed first and the result then multiplied by 7; or we can consider it as $3 \times (6 \times 7)$, in which case 6×7 is computed first and the result then multiplied by 3. Both methods give the same final result, 126. A similar remark can be made about addition.

Consider someone who must work with the arithmetic of Table (*1*). If he were to write down $A \circ B \circ C$ he would be in trouble. If he interprets it as $(A \circ B) \circ C$ he would first compute $A \circ B$, which is C, and then $C \circ C$, which is C. Therefore $(A \circ B) \circ C$ is C. On the other hand, as the reader may check, $A \circ (B \circ C)$ is A. Parentheses are important in computing with Table (*1*), since their omission would cause confusion.

We can omit parentheses when working with multiplication because multiplication satisfies the rule

$$X \times (Y \times Z) = (X \times Y) \times Z \qquad \text{(for all } X, Y, \text{ and } Z).$$

Any table satisfying this rule is called **associative**—it does not matter whether Y is "associated" with X or with Z. Since $X + (Y + Z) = (X + Y) + Z$ (for all X, Y, and Z), addition is also associative.

But let us not get the impression that we have the only associative arithmetics, the only systems in which parentheses can be dropped. Table (*2*) is associative, as the reader may check (a complete check would require testing 64 equations, since there are four choices for each of X, Y, and Z). Table (*7*) is also associative.

An associative table is called a **group.** Groups have been studied by mathematicians for over a century, and what is now known about them fills thousands of pages. Among the many results we will mention only two: Any group whose order is a prime or the square of a prime is commutative. Any group has exactly one row that reads the same as the guide row and exactly one column that reads the same as the guide column; moreover, the row and column referred to have the same name.

It is not easy to tell at a glance whether a table is associative. There is no nice pictorial interpretation of associativity. Associativity is best thought of in terms of "dispensing with parentheses." If a system is associative, we do not have to use parentheses, even when we have four or more letters (or numbers) to work with.

For example, there are five ways of placing parentheses in $A \circ B \circ C \circ D$ meaningfully:

$$A \circ (B \circ (C \circ D)), \quad A \circ ((B \circ C) \circ D), \quad (A \circ B) \circ (C \circ D),$$
$$(A \circ (B \circ C)) \circ D, \quad ((A \circ B) \circ C) \circ D.$$

But if the table is a group, then all five of these computations lead to the same value.

To see why, observe that, since $B \circ (C \circ D) = (B \circ C) \circ D$, the first two of the five have the same value. Similarly, the last two have the same value. Also, by associating C with D and then with $A \circ B$, we have

$$(A \circ B) \circ (C \circ D) = ((A \circ B) \circ C) \circ D;$$

thus, the third and the fifth expressions have the same value. Also, by associating B with $C \circ D$ and then with A, we have

$$A \circ (B \circ (C \circ D)) = (A \circ B) \circ (C \circ D);$$

thus the first and the third expressions have the same value.

Combining these observations, we obtain

THEOREM 7. *In a group, no matter how we parenthesize $A \circ B \circ C \circ D$ to describe a computation, the result will be the same.*

The reader is invited to show that the fourteen ways of parenthesizing $A \circ B \circ C \circ D \circ E$ all lead to the same value if the table is a group. It can be proved that Theorem 7 holds for any number of letters, not just four or five. Thus in a group no ambiguity is caused by omitting the parentheses.

In ordinary arithmetic we need parentheses when working with expressions that involve both addition and multiplication. For example, were we to omit parentheses from $3 \times (6 + 7)$, we would not know whether to compute $(3 \times 6) + 7$ or $3 \times (6 + 7)$. As the reader may check, the two results are quite different.

As a matter of fact, there is a general agreement that when parentheses are omitted in an expression involving both multiplication and addition, we should multiply first, then add. Omission of the multiplication sign helps us carry out this agreement. Thus $ab + 1$ is short for $(a \times b) + 1$. We abided by this agreement, for example, in Chapter 4 where we wrote $Q \times A + R$ and $4ab + 2a + 2b + 1$.

Now we see that our algebra is one of many possible algebras, just as our planet is one of several planets. We are glad that our addition and multiplication are commutative and associative. But perhaps we envy the hypothetical beings who work with small tables and fascinating rules. And if, as in the next chapter, one of these exotic algebras should turn out to be of use to us (in designing experiments more complicated than the one described at the beginning of this chapter), we will not hesitate to exploit it. We will not cock our heads and complain, "this is not proper meat."

Exercises

1. Prove that every idempotent table of order 3 is commutative.

2. Prove that every table of order 2 is commutative.

3. (a) Make a table of order 2.
   (b) Make the eight checks necessary to prove that it satisfies the rule $X \circ (Y \circ Z) = (X \circ Y) \circ Z$ for all X, Y, and Z (and thus is a group).

4. Use the method we used to make Table (7) to produce a commutative table of order 6.

5. Make four of the 27 checks necessary to prove that Table (6) is a group.

6. Use the method we used to make Table (7) to produce a commutative table of order 3.

7. Is the table you made in E 6 isomorphic to Table (6)?

8. Is Table (5) isomorphic to Table (6)?

9. We showed that Table (12) could not be filled in so as to be idempotent and commutative if we made the choice $A \circ B = C$. Prove that the choice $A \circ B = D$ also fails to produce such a table.

10. In the proof of Theorem 3 we used this fact: if A and B are natural numbers, both less than N, and if $A \equiv B \pmod{N}$, then A must be B. Prove that this assertion is valid.

11. What theorem on congruences allowed us to say, "Thus we see that $2(X \circ Y) \equiv 2(Y \circ X) \pmod{N}$"? (From the proof of Theorem 3.)

12. Prove that every letter appears exactly once on the main diagonal of a commutative table of odd order.

13. Make the 16 checks necessary to prove that Table (1) satisfies the rule $X \circ (X \circ Y) = Y \circ X$.

14. (a) In the proof of Theorem 6, did we use the fact that a row has no duplications?
    (b) Prove that, if a square is filled in to satisfy the rule $X \circ (X \circ Y) = Y \circ X$ and if no column has a duplication, then no row has a duplication.

15. Show that Table (7) does *not* satisfy the rule $X \circ (X \circ Y) = Y \circ X$.

16. Show that Table (6) does *not* satisfy the rule $X \circ (X \circ Y) = Y \circ X$.

17. Using the letters A, B, C, D, and E, construct a table of order 5 that satisfies the rule $X \circ (X \circ Y) = Y \circ X$. (To simplify your bookkeeping as you gradually fill in the 25 boxes, be sure to use Theorems 5 and 6.)

18. Make four of the 64 checks necessary to prove that Table (2) is associative (that is, is a group).

19. Make four of the 125 checks necessary to prove that Table (7) is associative (that is, is a group).

20. Prove that Table (7) is associative, not by making the 125 checks, but by making use of the original definition of the table:
    (a) First prove that $X \circ (Y \circ Z) \equiv X + (Y + Z) \pmod 5$.
    (b) Next prove that $(X \circ Y) \circ Z \equiv (X + Y) + Z \pmod 5$.
    (c) Using the fact that $+$ is associative, deduce that $X \circ (Y \circ Z) \equiv (X \circ Y) \circ Z$ $\pmod 5$.
    (d) Finally, prove that $X \circ (Y \circ Z) = (X \circ Y) \circ Z$.

21. Using the method of E 20, prove that there are groups of all orders, 1, 2, 3, 4, $\cdots$.

22. Prove that in a group $(A \circ B) \circ ((C \circ D) \circ E) = (A \circ (B \circ C)) \circ (D \circ E)$.

23. (a) Prove that, in a group, $(A \circ (B \circ C)) \circ (D \circ E) = A \circ ((B \circ (C \circ D)) \circ E)$.
    (b) Prove that, in a group, $((A \circ B) \circ (C \circ D)) \circ E = A \circ ((B \circ C) \circ (D \circ E))$.

24. List the 14 different ways there are of parenthesizing $A \circ B \circ C \circ D \circ E$ so as to describe a sequence of computations.

25. (a) Prove that, in a commutative group, $B \circ (C \circ A) = (C \circ B) \circ A$.
    (b) Prove that, in a commutative group, $(A \circ B) \circ C = (C \circ A) \circ B$.
    (c) Make a conjecture.

26. (a) Prove that, in a commutative group, $(A \circ (C \circ B)) \circ D = B \circ (D \circ (C \circ A))$.
    (b) Prove that, in a commutative group, $(A \circ B) \circ (C \circ D) = (A \circ C) \circ (B \circ D)$.
    (c) Make a conjecture.

27. (a) In Table (5), what are the two possible interpretations of A^3?
    (b) What rule assures us that in our usual arithmetic 5^3 has only one value?
    (c) What rule assures us that in our usual arithmetic 5^4 has only one value?

28. Build a table of order 5 on the numbers 0, 1, 2, 3, and 4 by defining $X \circ Y$ to be the remainder when $4X + 2Y$ is divided by 5.
    (a) Fill in the 25 boxes.
    (b) Check that no row or column has duplications.
    (c) Check that the table satisfies the rule $X \circ (X \circ Y) = Y \circ X$ by using the definition of the table and the congruences (not by checking the 25 cases).

29. Show that the tables you constructed in E 17 and E 28 are isomorphic.

30. Build a table of order 11 on the numbers 0, 1, 2, 3, 4, 5, 6, 7, 8, 9, and 10 by defining $X \circ Y$ to be the remainder when $9X + 3Y$ is divided by 11.
    (a) Compute $3 \circ 3$.
    (b) Compute $4 \circ 8$.
    (c) Without filling in the 121 boxes of the table, prove by using congruences that no row or column has duplications.
    (d) Without filling in the table, prove that it satisfies the rule $X \circ (X \circ Y) = Y \circ X$.

31. Prove that an idempotent group must have order one.

32. Prove that Table (*1*) satisfies the rule $(X \circ Y) \circ (Y \circ X) = X$ for all X and Y.

33. Prove that in a table satisfying the rule $(X \circ Y) \circ (Y \circ X) = X$ for all X and Y, distinct letters do not commute.

34. Prove that Table (*1*) satisfies the rule $X \circ (Y \circ X) = (X \circ Y) \circ X$ for all X and Y.

35. Prove that any table satisfying the rule $X \circ (X \circ Y) = Y \circ X$ for all X and Y must also satisfy the rule
$$X \circ (Y \circ X) = (X \circ Y) \circ X.$$

36. Let the symbol $\circ$ denote the operation of ordinary subtraction. For example, $4 \circ 5 = -1$, and $7 \circ 2 = 5$. Prove that the operation $\circ$
    (a) is not commutative.
    (b) is not associative.
    (c) is not idempotent.
    (d) does satisfy the rule $X \circ X = Y \circ Y$.
    (e) does satisfy the rule $X \circ (X \circ Y) = Y$.
    (f) does satisfy the rule $(X \circ Y) \circ (Z \circ W) = (X \circ Z) \circ (Y \circ W)$.

37. Let the symbol $\circ$ denote ordinary division. For example, $6 \circ 2 = 3$, and $3 \circ 4 = \frac{3}{4}$. Prove that statements (a) through (f) of E 36 hold for this operation.

38. Prove that
$$X + Y = X - ((X - X) - Y).$$

This equation shows that addition can be expressed in terms of a combination of several subtractions. (Of course, $X + Y$ is also equal to $X - (-Y)$, but the second minus in $X - (-Y)$ has a different meaning from the first one; these two meanings are defined in Appendix A.)

39. Prove that subtraction cannot be expressed in terms of a combination of several additions (compare with E 38).

40. Comparing E 38 and E 39 why might we think that "subtraction is more fundamental than addition"?

41. Prove that $X \times X = X/((X/X)/Y)$. This equation shows that multiplication can be expressed in terms of division (compare with E 38).

42. Prove that division cannot be expressed in terms of a combination of multiplications. In view of E 41, why might we think that "division is more fundamental than multiplication"? (Compare with E 40.)

43. Prove that any table satisfying the two rules

$$X \circ (X \circ Y) = Y \quad \text{and} \quad (Y \circ X) \circ X = X \quad \text{(for all } X \text{ and } Y)$$

must be commutative.

44. Let A be one of the letters in a table for a group. Since A appears somewhere in column A, there is a letter, T, such that $T \circ A = A$.
    (a) Prove that $T \circ X = X$ for any letter X in the group.
    (b) How does row T compare with the guide row?

45. Using the method of E 44, prove that any group has a column reading the same as the guide column.

46. (a) Prove that the row exhibited in E 44 and the column exhibited in E 45 have the same name, T.
    (b) For ordinary addition of integers, what is T?
    (c) For ordinary multiplication of positive rationals, what is T?

47. Prove that the tables constructed in Theorem 3 satisfy the rule

$$(X \circ Y) \circ (Z \circ W) = (X \circ Z) \circ (Y \circ W) \quad \text{(for all } X, Y, Z, \text{ and } W).$$

48. If A and B are natural numbers other than 0, denote their greatest common divisor $A \circ B$ instead of (A, B). For example, $8 \circ 12 = 4$.
    (a) Prove that the operation $\circ$ is idempotent, commutative, and associative.
    (b) Give an example of A, B, and C such that B is different from C, yet $A \circ B = A \circ C$.

References

1. R. A. Fisher, *The Design of Experiments*, Hafner, New York, 1951. (The warning is quoted from p. 70.)

2. M. J. Weiss, *Higher Algebra for the Undergraduate*, Wiley, New York, 1962. (Group theory, pp. 39–55.)

3. K. S. Miller, *Elements of Modern Abstract Algebra*, Harper and Brothers, New York, 1958. (Group theory, pp. 1–14.)

Chapter 12

ORTHOGONAL
TABLES

"A very curious question, which has exercised for some time the ingenuity of many people," wrote Euler in 1779 (in a paper called "On a New Type of Magic Square") "has involved me in the following studies, which seem to open a new field of analysis, in particular in the study of combinations. The question revolves around arranging 36 officers to be drawn from 6 different ranks and at the same time from 6 different regiments so that they are also ranged in a square so that in each line (both horizontal and vertical) there are 6 officers of different ranks and different regiments."

If the "very curious question" had asked instead for an arrangement of 9 officers in a 3 by 3 square, such that in each row and in each column the 3 officers were from different ranks and different regiments, then it would be (as Euler himself noted) a simple matter to give a solution. If we call the three regiments a, b, and c, and the three ranks A, B, and C, then one possible arrangement would be

(1)

aA	bC	cB
bB	cA	aC
cC	aB	bA

Let us look for a moment at this arrangement of 9 officers. The regiments a, b, and c themselves form the table

(2)

a	b	c
b	c	a
c	a	b

This is of the type met in the last chapter—in each row and in each column each letter appears exactly once. Looking at the arrangement of the ranks A, B, and C, we have the table

A	C	B
B	A	C
C	B	A

(3)

again of the type met in the last chapter.

Thus the problem of selecting 9 officers is the same as that of making two tables like (2) and (3) such that, after placing one on top of the other, we may look down on them and see each of the 9 pairs aA, aB, aC, bA, bB, bC, cA, cB, and cC exactly once. In perspective we can think of them placed like two trays of muffins in an oven:

(4)

Another way of thinking of the relation between Tables (2) and (3) is this: If one looks at the three boxes of Table (3) that are occupied by officers of rank A, then in the corresponding boxes of Table (2) one finds each of the three regiments a, b, and c.

We will say that two tables, of order N, one of which uses small letters and the other capital letters, are **orthogonal** *if when we put one on top of the other we see all N^2 combinations of small and capital letters.* The problem of the 36 officers now reads: devise a pair of orthogonal tables of order 6. All that we have shown is that there is a pair of orthogonal tables of order 3.

Before considering order 6, let us treat another simpler problem. Is there an orthogonal pair of order 2? Recall that entries on the main diagonal of any table of order 2 are the same; that is, the two shaded boxes must always have the same letter:

From this fact we can see that two tables of order 2 are never orthogonal. If we place one table of order 2 above another and look only at the shaded boxes, we will already see pairs duplicated. Thus we have proved

THEOREM 1. *There are no orthogonal tables of order 2. There are orthogonal tables of order 3.*

It will sometimes be convenient to have numbers instead of letters in the boxes. If we start with the tables

(5)

a	b	c
b	c	a
c	a	b

and

A	C	B
B	A	C
C	B	A

and, throughout, make the replacements 1 for *a*, 2 for *b*, 3 for *c* and 1 for *A*, 2 for *B*, 3 for *C*, we obtain these two tables:

(6)

1	2	3
2	3	1
3	1	2

and

1	3	2
2	1	3
3	2	1

If we put one of these new tables above the other we see that they too ought to be called orthogonal; as we look down we see each of the 9 possible pairings of the numbers 1, 2, 3, with 1, 2, 3: the pairs (1, 1), (1, 2), (1, 3), (2, 1), (2, 2), (2, 3), (3, 1), (3, 2), and (3, 3). For example, the pair (1, 1) appears in the boxes of row 1, column 1 and only there.

We could have replaced *A* by antelope, *B* by bear, and *C* by crocodile without losing information. We would still find ourselves with a pair of orthogonal tables. Or we could have replaced *A* by 1, *B* by 3, *C* by 2 and *a* by 1, *b* by 2, *c* by 3, and found ourselves with this orthogonal pair:

(7)

1	2	3
2	3	1
3	1	2

and

1	2	3
3	1	2
2	3	1

Notice that the top row in each of these tables consists simply of the numbers 1, 2, and 3 in order.

The ideas displayed by this example of order 3 we summarize in

THEOREM 2. *From any two orthogonal tables of order N we can get two orthogonal tables of order N whose boxes are filled with the numbers 1, 2, $\cdots$, N. Moreover, the latter tables can be chosen in such a way that the first row of each consists of the numbers 1, 2, $\cdots$, N in their usual order.*

We shall use Theorem 2 soon.

Before we examine orthogonal tables in greater detail, however, we ought to have a definition of them that does not involve such geometric ideas as "above" and "looking down." To find a better definition, let us look at the orthogonal Tables (7). If we furnish each of them with a guide row and guide column, they become

	1	2	3
1	1	2	3
2	2	3	1
3	3	1	2

and

	1	2	3
1	1	2	3
2	3	1	2
3	2	3	1

(8)   (9)

In Table (8) we denote the entry located where row X meets column Y by $X \circ Y$. For example, $2 \circ 3 = 1$. In Table (9) the entry located where row X meets column Y we must give a different name; say, $X * Y$ (which we can read as "X star Y"). Thus $2 * 3 = 2$.

The fact that Tables (8) and (9) are orthogonal can be expressed as follows: For each of the 9 possible pairs (M, N) formed from the numbers 1, 2, 3, we can find an X and a Y such that the following two equations both hold:

(10) $$X \circ Y = M; \qquad X * Y = N.$$

Equations (10) state that if (M, N) is any one of the 9 pairs formed from the numbers 1, 2, and 3, then M and N appear in a pair of corresponding boxes in Tables (8) and (9). For example, if M is 3 and N is 2, the reader may check that $X = 3$ and $Y = 1$ are solutions (and the only solutions) of equations (10); that is,

$$3 \circ 1 = 3,$$

and

$$3 * 1 = 2.$$

Clearly Equations (10) provide an algebraic criterion for testing whether two tables, furnished with guide row and guide column, are orthogonal. (In E 19, for example, this criterion is useful.)

Let us now try to make a pair of orthogonal tables of order 4. As one table of the pair let us try one of the most orderly tables of order 4:

(11)

a	b	c	d
b	c	d	a
c	d	a	b
d	a	b	c

The challenge is to find a table of order 4 (say, with the letters *A, B, C,* and *D*) that is orthogonal to the first table.

Let us, for a moment, think only of the four boxes that the letter *A* will occupy, and disregard the other twelve boxes. These four boxes will come from four different rows and four different columns. And the four boxes of (*11*) below them will each contain a different one of the letters, *a, b, c,* and *d*.

Let us attack the problem by looking for four boxes in (*11*), no two in the same column, no two in the same row, and no two containing the same one of the letters *a, b, c,* and *d*. *These four boxes may be thought of as a* **sampling** *quartet, in the sense that they sample all the rows, all the columns, and all the letters a, b, c, and d.* The four boxes in which we hope to place *B* will also form a sampling quartet. Similarly for *C* and *D*. Building a table orthogonal to (*11*) is thus the same as grouping the sixteen boxes into four sampling quartets.

If we try to find even a single sampling quartet for this particular table, we will have no luck. To see this, note that Table (*11*) is simply the table

(*12*)

0	1	2	3
1	2	3	0
2	3	0	1
3	0	1	2

in disguise. Put in a guide row and a guide column:

(*13*)

	0	1	2	3
0	0	1	2	3
1	1	2	3	0
2	2	3	0	1
3	3	0	1	2

We see that $X \circ Y$ is just the remainder when the usual $X + Y$ is divided by 4. For example, the remainder is 1 when $2 + 3$ is divided by 4, and $2 \circ 3 = 1$ in the table. The reader may check the other boxes without trouble. Note that $X \circ Y \equiv X + Y \pmod 4$ since any integer is congruent modulo 4 to its remainder when divided by 4.

Let us suppose, now, that we can find a sampling quartet. Then there is some arrangement of the column guide numbers (say, *P, Q, R, S*) such that the four numbers $0 \circ P$, $1 \circ Q$, $2 \circ R$, and $3 \circ S$ are, in turn, some arrangement of the numbers 0, 1, 2, and 3. Then, clearly,

$$(0 \circ P) + (1 \circ Q) + (2 \circ R) + (3 \circ S) = 6.$$

Hence

$$0 \circ P \equiv 0 + P \pmod 4,$$
$$1 \circ Q \equiv 1 + Q \pmod 4,$$
$$2 \circ R \equiv 2 + R \pmod 4,$$
$$3 \circ S \equiv 3 + S \pmod 4.$$

Adding these four congruences we obtain

$$(0 \circ P) + (1 \circ Q) + (2 \circ R) + (3 \circ S)$$
$$\equiv (0 + P) + (1 + Q) + (2 + R) + (3 + S) \pmod 4,$$

and hence

$$6 \equiv 0 + 1 + 2 + 3 + P + Q + R + S \pmod 4.$$

But P, Q, R, S is some arrangement of $0, 1, 2, 3$; therefore $P + Q + R + S = 6$.
Thus

$$6 \equiv 6 + 6 \pmod 4,$$

which is clearly not true.

We see, then, that there is no sampling quartet for Table (11) and that there is no chance of finding a table orthogonal to it. We have proved

THEOREM 3. *There is no table orthogonal to Table (11).*

We are not the first to run into difficulty in building orthogonal tables of order 4. On March 12, 1842, Schumacher, in a letter to Gauss, wrote about orthogonal tables of order N:

··· For $N = 2$ this is impossible, for $N = 3$, easy, and I believed to have understood earlier from you, that it is also impossible for $N = 4$··· but I must have been wrong since Clausen brought me this solution···:

(14)

a	b	c	d
c	d	a	b
d	c	b	a
b	a	d	c

D	A	B	C
A	D	C	B
B	C	D	A
C	B	A	D

May I ask, as long as the investigation costs you no effort, for which values of N is it impossible?

Three weeks later, April 2, 1842, Gauss replied:

I could devote only a few minutes to the question of your last letter. That I at any time should have asserted that the problem in question was impossible for $N = 4$, I can hardly believe since one sees on first glance that Clausen has not even imposed the most stringent demands. One can even add this demand: that in both diagonals all of the *a*, *b*, *c*, *d* and all of the *A*, *B*, *C*, *D* occur; the diagrams you sent me do not satisfy this condition. But here is an example:

(15)

a	b	c	d
c	d	a	b
d	c	b	a
b	a	d	c

D	A	B	C
C	B	A	D
A	D	C	B
B	C	D	A

(The question: "for which values of *N* is it impossible?" Gauss did not answer. We will soon consider it.)

Evidently neither Schumacher nor Gauss was familiar with Euler's work of 1779, for he had already found these three tables, any two of which are orthogonal:

(16)

a	b	c	d
b	a	d	c
c	d	a	b
d	c	b	a

A	C	D	B
B	D	C	A
C	A	B	D
D	B	A	C

A	D	B	C
B	C	A	D
C	B	D	A
D	A	C	B

This suggests new questions, but let us concentrate first on the problem of seeking just two orthogonal tables.

For the next order, 5, we can obtain an orthogonal pair by flipping the table

(17)

A	C	D	E	B
D	B	E	C	A
E	A	C	B	D
B	E	A	D	C
C	D	B	A	E

upside down along the axis of its main diagonal, which gives

(18)

A	D	E	B	C
C	B	A	E	D
D	E	C	A	B
E	C	B	D	A
B	A	D	C	E

Tables (17) and (18) are orthogonal, as the reader may verify.

So far, then, we have managed to find orthogonal tables of orders 3, 4, and 5, and have shown that order 2 is impossible. Before we tackle the next order, 6, let us read what Euler, writing in 1779, had to say about the problem it presents:

> I have examined a very great number of tables $\cdots$ and I do not hesitate to conclude that one cannot produce an orthogonal pair of order 6 and that the same impossibility extends to the orders 10, 14, $\cdots$ and in general all the orders which are twice an odd number.

In the year 1900, Gaston Tarry, assisted by his brother Herbert Tarry, by a careful and laborious listing of all tables of order 6, proved that no two of them are orthogonal. This method was criticized for failing to show *why* the problem could not be solved; what was the mysterious property of 6? For the order 2 (which also is twice an odd number) we had an insight; but for the order 6 there was just a long list. Anyway, by the year 1900 it was certain that there are no orthogonal tables of order 2 or 6. Orders 10, 14, 18, $\cdots$ (doubles of odd numbers) remained a mystery.

Although mathematicians failed to find a solution to the problem, they nevertheless raised a more general question. They asked: How long a list of tables of order N can be found such that any two tables in the list will be orthogonal?

We shall call such a list simply *a list of orthogonal tables*. For order 4 we have, for example, Euler's list of three orthogonal tables. For orders 2 and 6, since there are no orthogonal pairs whatsoever, we will say that the list must stop with just one table. (We use "one" rather than "zero" to record the fact that there is a table of order 6.) Euler conjectured that any list for orders twice an odd number must stop at one.

Some restraint is put on the length of such lists, for a fixed order N, by

THEOREM 4. *For any given order N, it is impossible to make a list of N orthogonal tables.*

PROOF. For simplicity let us take as a specific example the order 5. We will show that it is impossible to find a list of 5 orthogonal tables of order 5. Our reasoning will work not only for 5, but for any order.

Picture the 5 tables as 5 muffin trays in an oven, stacked one above the other. Using Theorem 2, we will first, if need be, relabel the muffins on these trays such that the muffins in the first row of each tray will be numbered 1, 2, 3, 4, 5, in order.

Our oven looks like this:

(*19*)

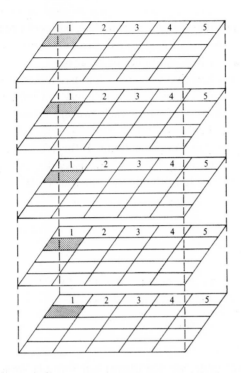

Although the remaining twenty muffins on each tray are numbered in some way or another, let us consider just the five muffins found in the first box of the second row in each tray [shaded in (*19*)]. Since in each tray there is already a muffin labeled 1 in column 1, none of the five muffins under consideration can be labeled 1, which means that we have five muffins and only four labels: 2, 3, 4, and 5. By the "pigeonhole principle" (discussed in the introduction to E 37), at least two of these five muffins must have the same number. But then the two trays carrying these two muffins with the same label could not be orthogonal; for, looking down on the first row of these two trays, we already see the five pairs (1, 1), (2, 2), (3, 3), (4, 4), and (5, 5), in which the two numbers are the same. Thus there is no list having five orthogonal tables of order 5. Since similar reasoning applies to any order N, the theorem is proved.

Theorem 4 says, for example, that we can never find four tables of order 4 of which each pair is orthogonal. But we already have an example of a list of three orthogonal tables of order 4. Thus the longest list for order 4 has three tables.

Theorem 4 says also that we can never find six tables of order 6 of which each two are orthogonal. As mentioned above, the Tarry brothers proved that we cannot find even two orthogonal tables of order 6.

Theorem 4 says, further, that we cannot find five tables of order 5, of which each two are orthogonal. But, using the machinery of Chapter 11, we can easily build four tables of order 5 of which each two are orthogonal. Here is how:

Number the rows and columns 0, 1, 2, 3, and 4. One table is made by placing in the box formed by row X and column Y the remainder when $X + Y$ is divided by 5. Calling this entry $[X + Y]$, we have, for example, $[3 + 4] = 2$. Filling in all 25 boxes, we have the first of our four tables:

	0	1	2	3	4	
0	0	1	2	3	4	
1	1	2	3	4	0	
2	2	3	4	0	1	$[X + Y]$
3	3	4	0	1	2	
4	4	0	1	2	3	

To get the second table, we will distort our formula somewhat. In the box of row X, column Y, let us *not* put $[X + Y]$, but rather $[X + 2Y]$; that is, the remainder when $X + 2Y$ is divided by 5. For example, in the box of row 3 and column 4 we place $[3 + (2 \times 4)] = [3 + 8] = [11] = 1$ (the remainder when 11 is divided by 5). Here is our second table:

	0	1	2	3	4	
0	0	2	4	1	3	
1	1	3	0	2	4	
2	2	4	1	3	0	$[X + 2Y]$
3	3	0	2	4	1	
4	4	1	3	0	2	

In the box where row X meets column Y, the third table will have $[X + 3Y]$; the fourth table $[X + (4Y)]$. If we stack all four of these muffin pans in the oven, we can check that the four trays are orthogonal:

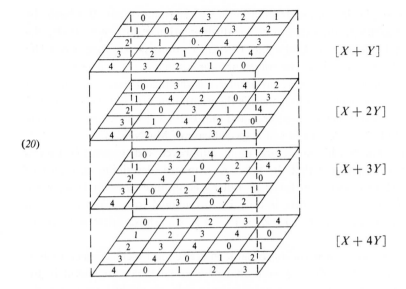

The same method can be used to prove

THEOREM 5. *If N is a prime, then there is a list of N − 1 orthogonal tables of order N.*

If N is not a prime this method fails to produce a list of $N − 1$ orthogonal tables of order N. Indeed, some of the square arrangements that it produces for such an N will have duplications in some rows. (As an example, the reader might take N to be 6, fill in the arrangement given by the formula $[X + 2Y]$, and see why duplications occur.)

In order to summarize what we have learned about lists of orthogonal tables, let us denote by $L(N)$ the largest number of tables of order N that can be orthogonal to each other. This is what we have seen about $L(N)$:

$$L(2) = 1, \quad L(3) = 2, \quad L(4) = 3,$$
$$L(5) = 4, \quad L(6) = 1, \quad L(N) = N − 1$$

for any prime N; and finally, Euler's conjecture of 1779, $L(N) = 1$ if N is twice an odd integer.

In 1923, H. F. MacNeish wrote an article in which he did three things. He proved that whenever N is a power of a prime, $L(N) = N − 1$ [for example, $L(27) = 26$. Theorem 4 tells us only that $L(27)$ is less than 27]. Next, he gave an incorrect proof of Euler's conjecture. Finally, he made this more general conjecture: $L(N)$ can be computed by (1) writing N as the product of powers of distinct primes, and then (2) subtracting 1 from the smallest of these powers.

As an example, let us use his conjecture to compute $L(36)$. We begin by writing 36 as the product of powers of distinct primes: $36 = 4 \times 9$. (By the Fundamental Theorem of Arithmetic, this can be done in only one way.) The smaller of these powers is 4. The conjecture implies that $L(36) = 4 - 1$; that is, $L(36) = 3$. Similarly, the conjecture implies, as the reader may compute, that $L(9)$ is 8 (in agreement with MacNeish's theorem), that $L(6)$ is 1, that $L(10)$ is 1 (in agreement with Euler's conjecture), and that $L(21)$ is 2. The reader may easily show that Euler's conjecture is just a special case of MacNeish's.

In a sense, MacNeish's conjecture, though unproved, did suggest that Euler's conjecture was right and that the latter was, indeed, describing only part of the truth. More evidence in favor of Euler's conjecture came in 1944, when H. B. Mann proved that there is no table orthogonal to a group (that is, a table satisfying the rule $X \circ (Y \circ Z) = (X \circ Y) \circ Z$), whose order is twice an odd integer.

More and more mathematicians became interested in Euler's conjecture after R. A. Fisher, in the 1920's, showed that orthogonal tables are useful in the design of certain kinds of experiments. For example, we might want to test the effect on tomato plants of various doses of water combined with various doses of nitrogen fertilizer. The orthogonal tables (2) and (3) show how to apply the doses a, b, and c of water and A, B, and C of nitrogen on nine plants arranged in a square. Each of the nine possible combinations is represented once. As a result of this new use for orthogonal tables, many research papers devoted to them appeared in the mathematical and statistical journals in the following decades.

In 1958, to the surprise of the mathematical world, MacNeish's conjecture was shown to be false. Using group theory and finite geometries, E. T. Parker constructed a list of three orthogonal tables of order 21, contradicting MacNeish's conjecture that $L(21) = 2$. But Euler's conjecture still remained.

A few months later, the statisticians Bose and Shrikhande, putting a new twist in Parker's technique, constructed two orthogonal tables of order 22, which is twice an odd number. Euler's conjecture, which had stood for 180 years, was proved false. After a furious correspondence, the three mathematicians together proved that the only orders for which Euler's conjecture is true are 2 and 6.

In 1960, Sade noticed that a technique he had invented in 1950 for constructing a table of order $a + bc$ out of tables of orders a, b, $a + b$, and c behaves well with respect to orthogonality. In particular, it yields orthogonal tables of order $22 (= 1 + 3 \times 7)$ and thus, again disproves Euler's conjecture.

Now that the two conjectures have been shown to be false, mathematicians face the more difficult question: what is $L(N)$ for each N? The first unsolved case is $L(10)$, which is at least 2 and at most 9. Work is being done on this problem. Also, using techniques of number theory, Chowla, Erdös, and Strauss proved that when N gets large, $L(N)$ is larger than $\sqrt[91]{N}$ and hence becomes (and remains) large. If there is a formula for computing $L(N)$, it is probably much more complicated than the one MacNeish had conjectured.

One question may still be troubling the reader: why did Euler title his paper, "On a New Type of Magic Square"? Let us answer that question. By a "magic square of order N" we mean an arrangement of the N^2 natural numbers from 1 to N^2 in a square array of N^2 boxes such that the sums of the entries in each row, each column, and each of the two diagonals are the same.

Euler showed how to construct magic squares from two orthogonal tables if these tables have no duplications in any one of their four diagonals. For example, let us construct a magic square of order 4 starting with the orthogonal tables (15) given by Gauss.

Replace a, b, c, d by 1, 2, 3, 4 and A, B, C, D by 0, 4, 8, 12. Then form the sums of entries in corresponding boxes:

(21)

$1 + 12$	$2 + 0$	$3 + 4$	$4 + 8$
$3 + 8$	$4 + 4$	$1 + 0$	$2 + 12$
$4 + 0$	$3 + 12$	$2 + 8$	$1 + 4$
$2 + 4$	$1 + 8$	$4 + 12$	$3 + 0$

This is clearly a magic square, since each row, column, and diagonal adds up to $1 + 2 + 3 + 4 + 0 + 4 + 8 + 12$. Written out in a manner that conceals its origin, it is

(22)

13	2	7	12
11	8	1	14
4	15	10	5
6	9	16	3

Just as Euler did not foresee that his work on the Koenigsberg bridge problem would some day be applied to telegraphy and electronic computers, he did not foresee that his work on the problem of the 36 officers would be applied to the design of statistical experiments.

The assertion he made at the end of his memoir is thus partly right and partly wrong:

> · · · Leaving it to geometers to see whether there are ways of achieving an enumeration of all possible cases—that which appears to provide a vast field for new and interesting research—I place an end here to my thoughts on a question which, although itself of little use, has led us to important observations both in the theory of combinations and the general theory of magic squares.

Exercises

1. Find a sampling quartet for this table

a	b	c	d
c	d	a	b
d	c	b	a
b	a	d	c

2. Find as many sampling quartets as you can for the table of E 1.

3. Prove that this table has no sampling sextet.

0	1	2	3	4	5
1	2	3	4	5	0
2	3	4	5	0	1
3	4	5	0	1	2
4	5	0	1	2	3
5	0	1	2	3	4

4. The second table of (14) provides 4 sampling quartets for the table of E 1. What are they? Are they on the list you made for E 2?

5. Find the 3 sampling triplets for the table

a	b	c
b	c	a
c	a	b

determined by each of the letters *A*, *B*, and *C* of the following table orthogonal to it:

A	C	B
B	A	C
C	B	A

Are there any more sampling triplets for the first table?

6. Each of the letters *a*, *b*, and *c* in E 5 determines a sampling triplet for the second table of E 5. Find these triplets. Are there any more sampling triplets for this table?

7. Replace Tables (*14*) with tables of the same form, but built on the integers 1, 2, 3, and 4 instead of letters, and in such a way that the top row of both tables reads 1, 2, 3, 4 in the usual order.

8. The right pair of tables in (*16*) are both orthogonal to the left table of (*16*). Indicate the 8 sampling quartets that the right pair determines in the left table.

9. (a) Replace all the letters in the three tables of (*16*) by 1, 2, 3, 4 in order that the top row of each table will read 1, 2, 3, 4 in the usual order.
   (b) Check that each two of the three tables constructed in (a) are orthogonal.

10. How many sampling quartets does the left table of (*16*) have?

11. (a) The bottom three tables of (*20*) provide 15 sampling quintets for the top table of (*20*). Find and list them.
    (b) Does the top table of (*20*) have any sampling quintets not listed in (a)?

12. Prove that table (*17*) satisfies the rule $X \circ (X \circ Y) = Y \circ X$ for all X and Y.

13. Prove that if a table satisfies the rule $X \circ (X \circ Y) = Y \circ X$, then it is orthogonal to the table obtained by rotating it about the axis of its main diagonal. Compare this with the relation between (*17*) and (*18*).

14. Can a table that is orthogonal to the table obtained by rotating it about its main diagonal be commutative?

15. If a table is orthogonal to the table obtained by rotating it about its main diagonal, what must be true about its main diagonal?

16. Of which of the tables of (*15*) and (*16*) can it be said that the table is orthogonal to the table obtained by rotating it about its main diagonal?

17. We proved Theorem 4 for order 5.
    (a) Prove it for order 12.
    (b) Prove it for any order.

18. Show that table $[X + 3Y]$ of (*20*) is orthogonal to table $[X + 2Y]$ of (*20*) by finding the 5 sampling quintets that the second table determines for the first.

19. Show that table $[X + 3Y]$ of (*20*) is orthogonal to table $[X + 2Y]$ of (*20*) by proving that, for any integers M and N from 0 through 4, the equations

$$[X + 3Y] = M$$

and

$$[X + 2Y] = N$$

can be solved for X and Y. *Hint:* Using congruences, replace the above equations by the equations

$$X + 3Y \equiv M \ (\text{mod } 5)$$

and

$$X + 2Y \equiv N \ (\text{mod } 5).$$

First solve for Y by subtracting one congruence from the other, and then find X (indicate which theorems about congruences you are using).

20. Using congruences, prove that each of the tables in (*20*) has no duplication in any row or in any column. What property of the number 5 is important here?

21. Construct a list of 6 orthogonal tables of order 7.

22. A square of order 9 is filled in with the numbers 0 through 8 by letting $X \circ Y$ be $[X + 4Y]$, the remainder when $X + 4Y$ is divided by 9. Prove that there are no duplications in any row or column.

23. A square of order 9 is filled in as in E 22, except that $X \circ Y$ is $[X + 3Y]$, the remainder when $X + 3Y$ is divided by 9. Do any rows have duplications? Do any columns have duplications?

24. Using the method of E 22, construct two tables of order 9 by using $[X + 2Y]$ and $[X + 5Y]$. Prove that neither of these two tables of order 9 has duplications in any row or column. Are they orthogonal?

25. Can a scientist figure out a way of applying 4 doses of water, 4 doses of fertilizer, and 4 doses of sunlight to 16 tomato plants arranged in a square such that
    (a) each dose of each factor is applied to 4 plants, of which no two come from the same row or column;
    (b) each of the 16 combinations of water and fertilizer is represented;
    (c) each of the 16 combinations of water and sunlight is represented; and
    (d) each of the 16 combinations of fertilizer and sunlight is represented?
    If so, show how it can be done.

26. Show how the four tables in (*20*) can be used for testing the effect of combinations of water, sunlight, potassium, and nitrogen on tomato plants.

27. Prove that if MacNeish's conjecture had been correct, then Euler's conjecture would also have been correct.

28. Is it possible to design an experiment that will test the effects of 6 doses of water in combination with 6 doses of nitrogen on 36 plants arranged in a square?

29. We constructed the magic square (*22*) from (*15*) by replacing letters by numbers in a certain way. What magic square results if we replace a, b, c, and d by 3, 1, 2, and 4, respectively; and A, B, C, and D by 4, 0, 12, and 8, respectively?

30. See E 29. Construct still another magic square from (*15*) by making a replacement with a different order of 1, 2, 3, 4 and 0, 4, 8, 12.

31. Use the middle two squares of (*20*) to produce a magic square of order 5. (Note that neither contains duplications in the diagonals.)

32. *Let us call an arrangement of the N^2 natural numbers from 1 through N^2 an* **almost-magic square** *if all the rows and columns have the same sum (we disregard the*

diagonals). Construct an almost-magic square of order 3 by using the orthogonal tables (*2*) and (*3*).

33. Construct an almost-magic square (see E 32) of order 4 by using the orthogonal tables (*14*).

34. Construct an almost-magic square (see E 32) of order 4 by using the left two orthogonal tables of (*16*).

35. Show that this almost-magic square (see E 32) comes from a pair of orthogonal tables of order 4. (*Hint:* Write each entry as the sum of one of 0, 1, 2, 3 and one of 0, 4, 8, 12).

13	2	7	12
3	16	9	6
8	11	14	1
10	5	4	15

36. Show that this magic square does not come from a pair of orthogonal tables.

16	3	2	13
5	10	11	8
9	6	7	12
4	15	14	1

INTRODUCTION TO E 37 THROUGH E 49

In the proof of Theorem 4 we used the fact that if we have 5 muffins, each labeled with 1, 2, 3, or 4, then at least two of the muffins must have the same label. This is an application of the "pigeonhole principle": if one has more letters than pigeonholes, then when one places the letters in the pigeonholes, at least one pigeonhole will contain more than one letter. The following exercises can be solved easily if the pigeonhole principle is employed; these exercises are otherwise unrelated to the chapter.

37. See the preceding introduction. Prove that in a crowd of 400 people at least two people celebrate their birthday the same day.

38. See the introduction preceding E 37.
    (a) Prove that if 12 natural numbers are given, there must be among them a pair with the same remainder when divided by 11.
    (b) Using (a), prove that there are two different natural numbers M and N such that
    $$2^M \equiv 2^N \pmod{11}.$$
    (c) Using (b), prove that there is a natural number A, bigger than 0, such that
    $$2^A \equiv 1 \pmod{11}.$$
    (d) Find an example of such an A.

39. (a) Using the ideas of E 38 prove the following

THEOREM. *If P is a prime (other than 2), then there is a natural number A, bigger than 1, such that*
$$2^A \equiv 1 \ (mod \ P).$$

(b) Find an example of such an A for $P = 5$, for $P = 7$, and for $P = 13$.

40. (a) Must the modulus in E 39 be prime?
    (b) Must the number being raised to a power be 2?
    (c) Generalize the theorem of E 39 as far as possible.

41. Prove that if five pins are stuck into a piece of cardboard cut in the form of an equilateral triangle of side 2, then at least two of the pins must be within a distance

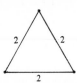

1 of each other. (*Hint:* Break up the triangle into four smaller congruent triangles, and apply the pigeonhole principle.)

42. See E 41. Prove that if 17 pins are stuck into a piece of cardboard cut in the form of an equilateral triangle of side 2, then at least two of the pins are within a distance $\frac{1}{2}$ of each other.

43. (a) See E 41. Prove that if five pins are stuck into a piece of cardboard cut in the form of a 2 by 2 square, then at least two of the pins are within a distance of $\sqrt{2}$ of each other.
    (b) Show that nine pins can be stuck into the square described in (a) without any two of the pins being closer than 1 to each other.

44. (a) See E 43. How close must some pair of pins be if 17 pins are stuck into a rectangle of dimensions 4 by 4?
    (b) Show that 25 pins can be stuck into the square described in (a) without any two of the pins being closer than 1 to each other.

45. (a) Exhibit 100 natural numbers, in the range from 1 to 200, none of which is a divisor of any of the other 99.
    (b) Prove that any list of 101 natural numbers, in the range from 1 to 200, must contain at least two natural numbers such that one of them divides the other. (*Hint:* Write every number in the list as an odd number times a power of 2, and apply the pigeonhole principle to these odd numbers.)

46. In Chapter 1 we studied arrangements of natural numbers and backward pairs. Let us define backward triplets, backward quadruplets, $\cdots$ and forward triplets, forward quadruplets, $\cdots$. For example, a backward triplet (or 3-tuplet) is an arrangement ABC of three different natural numbers with A bigger than B and B bigger than C. Within the arrangement

$$3, 8, 4, 1, 5, 6, 2, 7, 9$$

we have, for example, the backward triplet 8 5 2, the forward 4-tuplet 3 4 5 6, the forward 6-tuplet 3 4 5 6 7 9, and so on. A natural number by itself is regarded as both a backward and a forward 1-tuplet.

Prove that any nonrepetitious arrangement of the first N natural numbers that has no backward couplet must be a forward N-tuplet (pigeonhole principle not needed).

47. Exercise 46 shows that an arrangement that is not at all backward is completely forward. This is a special case of a more general theorem, which we now state.

THEOREM. *Let B and F be natural numbers bigger than 1, and let N be a natural number bigger than the product $(B - 1) \times (F - 1)$. Then any nonrepetitious arrangement of the numbers $1, 2, 3, \cdots, N - 1, N$ that has no backward B-tuplet must have a forward F-tuplet.*

We outline a proof:

(a) Assume that there are no backward B-tuplets and no forward F-tuplets.
(b) For each natural number m in the arrangement let b_m be the number of natural numbers in a longest backward tuplet whose right member is m; let f_m be the number of natural numbers in a longest forward tuplet whose left member is m.
(c) Show for each m that b_m is no more than $B - 1$ and no less than 1, and that f_m is no more than $F - 1$ and no less than 1.
(d) Let us call b_m the "given name of m" and f_m the "family name of m." Prove that no two m's have both the same given name and family name.
(e) Compare (c) and (d), and show that the pigeonhole principle has been violated. Why does this prove the theorem?

48. (a) Using the result of E 47, prove that any arrangement of 10 (or more) natural numbers must have a backward 4-tuplet or a forward 4-tuplet.
   (b) Devise an arrangement of the natural numbers 1, 2, 3, 4, 5, 6, 7, 8, and 9 that has no backward quadruplet or forward quadruplet.

49. Show that E 46 is a special case of E 47.

References

1. *New York Times*, April 24, 1959, p. 1. (News story on the work of Bose, Parker, and Shrikhande.)

2. *A. Seidenberg, A simple proof of a theorem of Erdös and Szekeres, *Journal of the London Mathematical Society*, vol. 34, 1959, p. 352. (This is the basis of E 46 and E 47.)

3. M. Gardner, Mathematical games, *Scientific American*, November, 1959, pp. 181–188. (An article on the disproof of Euler's conjecture.)

4. W. W. Rouse Ball, *Mathematical Recreations and Essays*, Macmillan, New York, 1947. (Chapter 7 describes several other ways of constructing magic squares.)

5. R. A. Fisher, *The Design of Experiments*, Hafner, New York, 1951. (See p. 86, where orthogonal tables are used to find a defective bobbin in a cotton mill.)

6. *R. C. Bose, S. S. Shrikhande, and E. T. Parker, Further results in the construction of mutually orthogonal Latin squares and the falsity of Euler's conjecture, *Canadian Journal of Mathematics*, vol. 12, 1960, pp. 189–203.

7. *S. Chowla, P. Erdös, and E. G. Strauss, On the maximal number of pairwise orthogonal Latin squares of a given order, *ibid.*, pp. 204–208.

Chapter 13

MAP COLORING

The squares of a checkerboard can be colored with only two colors in such a way that any two squares sharing an edge will be of different colors. As the reader may easily check, we can color this map of sixteen countries in two colors such that countries sharing an edge have different colors.

(1)

But we cannot do so with this map:

(2)

The reader may make some experiments of his own and discover for himself a simple rule for checking whether a map can be colored in two colors.

For the sake of brevity, we will say that "a map can be colored in two colors" or that "a map has a two-coloring" if we can color the countries with only two colors in such a way that countries sharing at least one edge have different colors. Similarly, later in the chapter, we will speak of "coloring a map in three colors" or of "a five-coloring." We will always mean, whatever the coloring, that countries sharing an edge have different colors.

Let us think of (*1*) and (*2*) as maps of islands divided into countries. *All vertices not on the shore of the island we shall call* **dry vertices.** A map of an island that has a dry vertex of odd degree cannot be colored in two colors, since the colors must alternate as we run through the countries meeting at a

175

dry vertex. Recall that the degree of a vertex is the number of edges that meet at that vertex. We thus have

THEOREM 1. *If the countries of an island can be colored in two colors, then each dry vertex is of even degree.*

We would hope that the opposite (or converse) would also be true; namely, that if each dry vertex were of even degree, then the countries of the island could be colored in two colors. As an example, consider this map, in which each dry vertex is even:

(3)

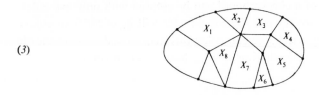

If we color one of the countries red (say, country X_1), one of its neighbors black (say country X_2), and continue to alternate colors along a typical journey (say X_1, X_2, X_3, X_4, X_5, X_6, X_7, X_8) until we return to a neighbor of X_1, we find that X_1 and X_8 fortunately have different colors. Though we worried only about coloring each country different from its predecessor at each step, we encountered no trouble when we returned to the first country. That we never will run into this trouble is guaranteed by

THEOREM 2. *If each dry vertex is of even degree, then the countries of an island can be colored in two colors.*

PROOF. Stick a tack into each country. Select one of the tacks, and call it Rome. Consider the (typical) tack T indicated below:

(4)

To simplify our reasoning it will be convenient to place Rome such that no straight line from Rome to any other tack crosses a vertex.

The reader, traveling on the island from tack T to Rome, and passing over no vertex, will notice that each such trip crosses an even number of edges.

(Of course, for another tack the number of crossings might be odd.) For example, this trip has ten crossings,

whereas the most direct trip has two crossings:

To see why each trip from T to Rome must have an even number of crossings, let us consider such a trip and trace out its course with a taut elastic, taping the latter to the map along the way (we suppose that one end of the elastic is tied to T; and the other end, to Rome). Now we remove the tape from the elastic; when we do this, the elastic contracts until it forms a straight line joining T and Rome.

Watch what happens to the number of crossings as the shrinking elastic passes a vertex:

(5)

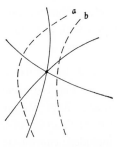

In particular, consider the number of crossings in the vicinity of the vertex shown in (5) as the elastic shrinks from position (a) to position (b). In position (a) there are four crossings; in position (b), after the elastic passes the vertex, there are two crossings (a change by an even number). Why will this change always be even at each vertex? The answer is simple: the number of crossings near the vertex in position (a) plus the number of crossings near the vertex in position (b) equals the degree of the vertex, which is even. (If

two integers have an even sum, then their difference must also be even, as
the reader may easily check.)

Thus, as the contracting elastic passes a vertex, the number of crossings
changes by an even number. Furthermore, as the contracting elastic frees
itself of a border in this manner,

the change is again even.

Finally, the elastic forms the direct straight line trip from T to Rome.
Since this direct trip has an even number of crossings, so must the original
trip, which we had turned into rubber.

Thus any trip from T to Rome has an even number of crossings. *We will
call any tack with this property* **even.** In particular, Rome itself is even (since
we can travel from Rome to Rome on a path that crosses no edge at all).
On the other hand, consider a tack T' whose direct trip to Rome has an odd
number of crossings. Then, in view of the above discussion, it is clear that
any trip from T' to Rome must also have an odd number of crossings. *We
will call any tack with this property* **odd.**

Now observe that if two tacks are adjacent in the sense that we can travel
from one to the other with just one crossing, then, clearly, one of them is
odd and the other even. It follows that we can obtain a two-coloring of the
island by coloring the countries with even tacks red and the countries with
odd tacks blue. Theorem 2 is proved.

In order to avoid the necessity of distinguishing dry vertices from shoreline
vertices we shall from now on insist that the ocean also be colored. That is, we
will treat the ocean as just another country. We can think of the ocean, together
with all the countries, as covering the surface of the earth.

Figure (*1*), with the ocean included, cannot be colored in two colors (since
some of the dots on the shore are of odd degree). Figure (*6*), however, can be
colored in two colors:

(*6*)

The same technique that we used to prove Theorem 2 provides a proof of

THEOREM 3. *If each vertex is of even degree, then the ocean and the countries on an island can be colored in two colors.*

Theorem 3 is more elegant than Theorem 2 because it does not have o dis-tinguish the dry vertices from the wet. However, it has seemingly complicated matters by distinguishing between the ocean and the countries on the island. But this distinction is quite artificial. After all, if we were to draw our map on a ball instead of on a flat paper, the ocean would look just like another country. Theorem 3 really should be replaced by the still more revealing

THEOREM 4. *If the surface of a sphere is divided into countries,* and if each vertex is of even degree, then these countries can be colored in two colors.*

We have completely solved the two-color problem. That is to say, we have discovered a simple test for determining when a map can be colored in only two colors: simply check that all the vertices are of even degree.

From Theorem 4 we can obtain (for later use) this

LEMMA. *If the surface of a sphere is divided into countries such that each country has an even number of edges, then the vertices can be colored red or blue in such a way that the two vertices of each edge have different colors.*

PROOF. Consider, for example, such a map as this one, which represents eleven countries covering the sphere:

Each country (including the "ocean") has an even number of edges. We obtain from this map a new map on the sphere by placing a dot in each of the eleven countries and joining two dots if their countries share an edge (if two countries share k edges, we join the corresponding dots by k lines):

---

* If the reader is concerned about the disappearance of the ocean, he can think of maps of a dry sphere, such as the moon.

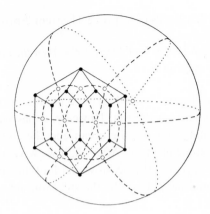

(For the sake of clarity the maps are now drawn in perspective as they appear on a sphere.)

The number of vertices in the new map formed of broken lines is the same as the number of countries in the original map. Each vertex of this new map has even degree because each country of the old map has an even number of edges.

Theorem 4 then tells us that the new map can be colored in two colors. This incidentally provides a coloring of the vertices of the original map, of the type promised in the lemma. A similar argument proves the lemma in general.

Let us turn next to the problem of determining which maps can be colored in three colors. The results in this direction are quite incomplete. In 1941, R. L. Brooks proved

THEOREM 5. *If the entire surface of a sphere is divided into countries, each of which shares its borders with three neighboring countries, then the countries can be colored in three colors or less.*

Though we will not prove Theorem 5, we suggest that the reader check it on some examples, including the following:

(7)

Note that when the ocean is drawn on a sphere, it also becomes a country bordering three countries. Be sure to color the ocean also.

Another three-color result, found by Kempe in 1880, is

THEOREM 6. *If the surface of a sphere is divided into countries, each of which has an even number of edges, and if three countries meet at each vertex, then this map can be colored with exactly three colors.*

An illustration of Theorem 6 is Figure (8), which, as the reader may check, can be colored with three colors.

(8)

Note that the ocean also has an even number of edges. It is to be colored along with all the other countries.

If we start to color (8) by coloring one of the countries, then we must alternate the two other colors as we run through the countries that border the original country. Since there are an even number of countries bordering that country, we have no trouble. If we were to color a country with the color *A*, then we would color the countries adjacent to this coun'ry *B* and *C*, as in this diagram:

(9)

$$\begin{array}{ccc} & C \mid B & \\ B & A & C \\ & C \mid B & \end{array}$$

But being able to color in the vicinity of each country does not, of course, assure us that we can color the whole map with three colors.

Though we will not prove Theorem 6 in detail, we will describe the technique for coloring such maps. The first step consists in placing at each vertex either a

clockwise circle ( ) or a counterclockwise circle ( ) in such a way that the two vertices at the ends of each edge are furnished with one clockwise and one counterclockwise circle. (That this can be done is guaranteed by the lemma proved after Theorem 4.) Doing this for figure (8), we obtain

(10)

Next, using the colors *A*, *B*, and *C*, we shall color the edges in the following manner. First we choose an edge and color it *A* [as in Figure (10)]. The two edges that meet this edge at one of its ends we color *B* and *C* in such a way that the direction of turning (starting with the edge colored *A*, then the edge colored *B*, then the edge colored *C*) will be the same as the direction given by the little circle where the three edges meet. For example if we have

then the edges are to be colored

If we have

then the three edges are to be colored

As we travel along the edges we continue coloring uncolored edges such that the turning direction *A*, then *B*, and then *C* always agrees with the little circle.

We get this coloring for the edges of (8):

(11)

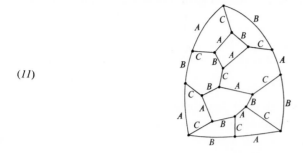

The reader may check that at each vertex the direction given by *A, B, C* is the same as that given by the arrowed circle of (*10*). Note that the borders of each country (including the ocean) have only two colors. Now we color each country with the color that does not appear on its border. Neighboring countries will, of course, receive different colors. Thus the map can be colored in three colors.

Theorems 5 and 6 cover most of what is known about the three-color problem. No one has discovered a general rule for determining which maps can be colored in three colors.

The problem of coloring maps with four colors has a long history. The experience of map makers indicated that any map on the globe could be colored with four (or fewer) colors. Möbius mentioned it in a lecture in 1840; de Morgan discussed it in 1850; and Cayley remarked, in 1878, that he could not prove it. In 1880 Kempe published an erroneous proof in a paper that contained these remarks:

> Some inkling of the nature of the difficulty of the question, unless its weak point be discovered and attacked, may be derived from the fact that a very small alteration in one part of a map may render it necessary to recolor it throughout. After a somewhat arduous search, I have succeeded, suddenly, as might be expected, in hitting upon the weak point, which proved an easy one to attack. The result is, that the experience of the map makers has not deceived them, the maps they had to deal with, viz: those drawn on a [sphere] can in every case be painted with four colors.

The flaw in Kempe's proof was exposed in 1890 in a paper by P. J. Heawood, which began:

The Descriptive-Geometry Theorem that any map whatsoever can have its divisions properly distinguished by the use of but four colors, from its generality and intangibility, seems to have aroused a good deal of interest a few years ago when the rigorous proof of it appeared to be difficult if not impossible, though no case of failure could be found. The present article does not profess to give a proof of this original Theorem; in fact its aims are so far rather destructive than constructive, for it will be shown that there is a defect in the now apparently recognized proof····.

In the same paper Heawood showed that Kempe's technique could be used to prove that every map on the sphere can be colored with five (or fewer) colors. We shall divide this proof into several lemmas.

Before we begin, let us point out three assumptions that have so far been taken for granted. The first assumption is that the border of a country can be thought of as a single piece of string in the form of a loop that does not meet or cross itself. Thus a country looks like this:

Note that the following figures are *not* countries:

(12)

(Nor is the whole surface of the sphere itself a country.) Without this assumption, Lemmas 2 and 3, which follow, would not always hold. We will also assume that an edge in a map has two different ends (that is, does not close up to form a loop). Thus the border of a country is divided into at least two edges, and hence has at least two vertices. Furthermore, we will assume that any map in question has a finite number of countries.

As we did for the proof of the Fundamental Theorem of Arithmetic, we now supply a diagram showing how the six lemmas leading up to the Five-color Theorem fit together. All these lemmas refer to maps on a sphere.

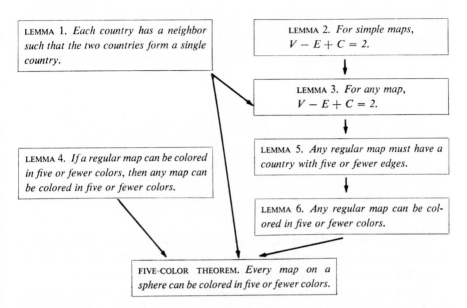

In any map on a sphere, let V be the number of vertices, E the number of edges, and C the number of countries (including the ocean, if the map is drawn on a flat piece of paper). A list of V, E, and C for some of the maps we have met in this chapter is given in this table (which the reader is invited to check):

MAP	V	E	C
(1)	16	31	17
(2)	10	18	10
(3)	13	23	12
(4)	9	20	13

(13)

Inspection of this table shows that, in each case,

$$V - E + C = 2.$$

That is, the sum of the number of vertices and the number of countries is two more than the number of edges. That $V - E + C = 2$ is true for any map on a sphere was proved first by Descartes in 1640 and was later proved independently by Euler in 1752. Before we can prove Descartes' theorem, we will need

LEMMA 1. *In any map (with more than two countries) that covers a sphere, each country has a neighbor such that when their common border is erased, the resulting region forms a country.*

Before we begin the proof, observe that if two of the countries, say, X and Y, meet in exactly one arc, then (since there are more than two countries on the map) X and Y form a single country when their common border is erased. On the other hand, if X and Y meet in more than just a single arc, then X and Y must surround at least one island. The latter situation is illustrated by the following examples:

With these observations in mind, we begin the

PROOF OF LEMMA 1. Let X_1 be any one of the countries. Suppose that, contrary to the assertion of the lemma, X_1 has no neighbor Y such that X_1 and Y form a single country when their common border is erased.

Let X_2 be a country that meets X_1 along at least one edge. Then, applying the observations made immediately above, we see that X_2 meets X_1 along more than just one edge, and, consequently, X_1 and X_2 surround at least one island. Consider one such island. Among the countries on this island there must be at least one that meets X_1 along at least one edge; pick one such country, and call it X_3. Arguing just as before, we can show that X_1 and X_3 surround at least one island. Again consider one such island, and note that there is at least one country on this island that meets X_1 along at least one edge; pick one such country, and call it X_4. If we continue in this manner, we will, of course, obtain an unending list

$$X_1, X_2, X_3, X_4, \cdots$$

of distinct countries. But since there is only a limited supply of countries on the map, we have arrived at a contradiction, which proves Lemma 1.

As indicated by the diagram that shows the order of the lemmas, we will need Lemma 1 twice.

LEMMA 2. *If a map has just two countries, then $V - E + C = 2$.*

PROOF. We may think of the two countries as two hemispheres meeting on the equator. On the equator, there appear exactly as many vertices (all of degree 2) as edges (V spokes divide a rim into V arcs), thus $V = E$. Since $C = 2$, we have $V - E + C = 2$.

Now it will be easy to prove

LEMMA 3. *For any map covering the sphere,* $V - E + C = 2$.

PROOF. Choose any map on the sphere, and let K denote the number $V - E + C$. We wish to prove that $K = 2$. To do so we are going to change the given map into a map with only two countries by repeatedly

(1) deleting any vertex of degree 2,
(2) deleting the edge shared by two countries that, together, form a country.

If we delete a vertex of degree 2, we obtain a map having the same countries, but with two short edges replaced by one longer edge. (The reader should provide a picture for this.) Let V', E', and C' be the number of vertices, edges, and countries in this new map. We have

$$V' = V - 1,$$

and (since two edges merge into one when a dot is removed)

$$E' = E - 1.$$

Since there is no change in the number of countries,

$$C' = C.$$

Thus

$$V' - E' + C' = (V - 1) - (E - 1) + C.$$

But

$$(V - 1) - (E - 1) + C = V - E + C = K,$$

hence

$$V' - E' + C' = K.$$

Now let us see what happens if, instead, we delete an edge (but not its two ends). In the new map, $V' = V$, $E' = E - 1$, and $C' = C - 1$, as the reader may check. Thus, we again have

$$V' - E' + C' = K.$$

By repeated applications of (1) and (2), we can go from the original map to a map with just two countries. The preceding remarks show that, after each step,

(*14*) (number of vertices) $-$ (number of edges) $+$ (number of countries) $= K$.

In particular, (*14*) holds for the final map, which has just two countries. Thus by Lemma 2, $K = 2$, and Lemma 3 is proved.

We will need Lemma 3 in the proof of Lemma 5.

LEMMA 4. *If we can color in five or fewer colors every map on the sphere whose vertices are all of degree 3, then we can color any map on the sphere in five or fewer colors.*

PROOF. Place a small country over each vertex whose degree is more than 3. For example, let us replace a vertex such as

by several vertices of degree 3:

Since each vertex in the new map is of degree 3, then by our assumption the map can be colored in five or fewer colors. If we remove the patches and color the little regions thus exposed the same as the countries to which they belong, we will obtain a coloring of the original map in five or fewer colors.

Maps having every vertex of degree 3 will play an important role in the following lemmas. *For convenience we name them* **regular maps.**

LEMMA 5. *A regular map on the sphere must have at least one country with five or fewer edges.*

PROOF. Let C_2 be the number of countries with two edges, C_3 the number of countries with three edges, and so on. When n is sufficiently large, C_n is 0. Note that

(15) $$C_2 + C_3 + C_4 + C_5 + C_6 + C_7 + \cdots = C.$$

We wish to prove that not all four numbers C_2, C_3, C_4, and C_5 can be 0.

To do so we shall do some bookkeeping much in the spirit of Chapter 2.

Let us consider any vertex; we place a little red mark close to it on each of the three edges that meet at that vertex. We do this for each vertex. All told, we make $3V$ red marks on the edges. But each edge will have two such marks, one near each of its two ends. Thus

(16) $$3V = 2E.$$

Next, let us consider any country; we place a blue mark on each of its edges. We do this for every country. Each of the C_2 countries that have two edges contributes two such marks. Thus the countries with two edges contribute, all told, $2C_2$ marks. Similarly, the C_3 countries with three edges contribute, all told, $3C_3$ marks. Thus the total number of blue marks is

$$2C_2 + 3C_3 + 4C_4 + 5C_5 + 6C_6 + 7C_7 + \cdots .$$

But each edge will have two blue marks, since each edge is on the border of two countries. Thus we have

(17) $$2C_2 + 3C_3 + 4C_4 + 5C_5 + 6C_6 + 7C_7 + \cdots = 2E.$$

Note also that, by Lemma 3,

(18) $$V - E + C = 2.$$

Using only (16), (17), and (18) we will be able to complete the proof of Lemma 5. The idea is to obtain an equation involving only C_2, C_3, $\cdots$ (but not the V and the E).

From (16) we have $V = \frac{2}{3}E$. This we replace in (18) and obtain an equation involving only the E and the C:

(19) $$\frac{2}{3}E - E + C = 2.$$

In order to avoid fractions, we multiply (19) by 3 and obtain

$$2E - 3E + 3C = 6,$$

which reduces to

$$-E + 3C = 6.$$

To avoid the minus sign, we add E to both sides and get the simpler equation

(20) $$3C = 6 + E.$$

Next we shall use (17) to eliminate the E in (20). In order to do so as simply as possible, we first multiply (20) by 2 and get

(21) $$6C = 12 + 2E.$$

Combining (17) and (21) we obtain the desired equation:

(22) $$6C = 12 + 2C_2 + 3C_3 + 4C_4 + 5C_5 + 6C_6 + 7C_7 + \cdots ,$$

an equation without V and E.

We shall now examine (22) and see why at least one of the four numbers C_2, C_3, C_4, and C_5 must be larger than 0.

Recalling that

$$C = C_2 + C_3 + C_4 + C_5 + C_6 + C_7 + \cdots ,$$

we learn from (22) that

(23) $$6(C_2 + C_3 + C_4 + C_5 + C_6 + C_7 + \cdots)$$
$$= 12 + 2C_2 + 3C_3 + 4C_4 + 5C_5 + 6C_6 + 7C_7 + \cdots .$$

Multiplying out the left side of (23) we have

(24) $6C_2 + 6C_3 + 6C_4 + 6C_5 + 6C_6 + 6C_7 + \cdots$

$$= 12 + 2C_2 + 3C_3 + 4C_4 + 5C_5 + 6C_6 + 7C_7 + \cdots.$$

We collect C_2's, C_3's, C_4's, and C_5's on the left, and C_7's, C_8's, C_9's, $\cdots$ on the right (note that the $6C_6$'s cancel):

(25) $4C_2 + 3C_3 + 2C_4 + C_5 = 12 + C_7 + 2C_8 + 3C_9 + \cdots.$

Since the right side of (25) is not zero (in fact, it is at least 12), the left side of (25) cannot be 0. Hence at least one of the four numbers C_2, C_3, C_4, C_5 must be larger than 0. This proves Lemma 5.

With the aid of Lemma 5 we can easily prove

LEMMA 6. *Any regular map on a sphere can be colored in five (or fewer) colors.*

PROOF. Clearly, if a map has at most five countries, then it can be colored with five or fewer colors. Now, let C be a natural number, and let us assume that any regular map with at most C countries can be colored with five colors. On the basis of this assumption we shall show that any regular map with $C + 1$ countries can be colored with five colors.

Let us consider a regular map with $C + 1$ countries. By Lemma 5 there is at least one country present with five or fewer edges. We shall divide the argument into two cases:

Case 1: There is a country X having four or fewer edges. By Lemma 1, there is a country Y bordering X such that X and Y together form a country. If we erase the border between X and Y, together with its end vertices, we obtain a new regular map with only C countries. (The reader should draw a picture of this.) By our assumption, this map with only C countries can be colored in five colors. If we now replace the border we find that X and Y have the same color. But we can erase the color of X, and give X a different color from those of its neighbors. (Since X has at most four neighbors, and we have five colors available, this is possible.)

Case 2: There is a country X having exactly five edges. This time, we do not have enough colors to use the same argument as in Case 1. However, as the reader may check, X has two neighboring countries Y and Z such that Y and Z do not meet and such that X, Y, and Z together form a country. For example:

If we delete the border between X and Y, the border between X and Z, and also the end vertices of these borders, we obtain a regular map with $C - 1$ countries (two less than the original $C + 1$ countries). By assumption, this map with $C - 1$ countries is colorable with at most five colors (since $C - 1$ is less than C).

Next we put the deleted borders (and vertices) back. When we do so, we see that the countries X, Y, and Z all have the same color. Since Y and Z do not meet, we do not need to change their color. But the color of X must be changed. Since Y and Z have the same color, no more than four different colors will appear in the countries bordering X. But since we have five colors available, we can select one to give X a color different from those of its neighbors. This completes the argument for Case 2.

Since we can color any map that has five or fewer countries with five or fewer colors, the argument just given (for $C = 5$) tells us that we can color any regular map that has six countries. Applying the argument again (with $C = 6$), we see that we can color any regular map that has seven countries with five or fewer colors. Finally, using this argument as many times as necessary, we see that any regular map can be colored with five or fewer colors, which proves Lemma 6.

Combining Lemmas 4 and 6, we obtain

THE FIVE-COLOR THEOREM: *Every map on a sphere can be colored with five or fewer colors.*

It has also been proved in recent years that any map with fewer than 37 countries can be colored with four or fewer colors. No one knows whether there is a map on a sphere that requires five colors.

If we consider maps on a doughnut or inner tube, instead of maps on a sphere, then the coloring problem is completely solved. Heawood proved that any map on an inner tube can be colored with seven or fewer colors. Moreover, there are maps on an inner tube that require seven colors (see E 30). That the coloring problem on an inner tube is easier than that on a sphere seemed odd to Heawood, who remarks in his introduction (which we interrupted in order to prove the Five-color Theorem):

> $\cdots$[my] main object is to contrast with that simple proposition [the four-color conjecture] some remarkable generalizations of it, of which strangely the rigorous proof is much easier.

In spite of the work of many mathematicians since 1840, the original question: "Can every map on a sphere be colored in four colors?" still remains unanswered.

Exercises

1. Give an example of a map of an island that requires four colors.

2. (a) Draw a map of an island such that every vertex, dry or wet, is of even degree.
   (b) Color the countries on your island in two colors.
   (c) Check that there are an even number of edges along the coast line.
   (d) Using Theorem 3, prove that the number of edges in (c) must be even.

3. Let us assume that all the edges of the maps satisfying the hypothesis of Theorem 3 are straight.
   (a) Place a lighthouse in each country and in the ocean in such a way that no lighthouse lies on the line determined by any edge.
   (b) Assume that the rotating beam from each lighthouse always has one ray of light.
   (c) Prove that, for a given lighthouse, the rotating beam is always directly above an even number of edges or else is always directly above an odd number of edges.
   (d) How can such lighthouses be used to give another proof of Theorem 3 (at least when the edges are straight)?

4. If a map on the sphere consists only of triangles, then, when it is drawn on a flat piece of paper, exactly three countries have a coastline.
   (a) Draw a map in which each country shares its border with three neighbors (we take the ocean as a neighbor) and in which the ocean borders three countries.
   (b) Color it in three colors.
   (c) Does this map agree with Theorem 5?

5. See E 4. Draw a map of your own that illustrates Theorem 5.

6. In the map below, each country (including the ocean) has an even number of edges.
   (a) Prove that this map cannot be colored in three colors.
   (b) Does this map contradict Theorem 6?

7. (a) Draw a map in which every vertex is of degree 3 and in which each country (including the ocean) has an even number of edges.
   (b) Place at each vertex a clockwise or counterclockwise circle, alternating the circles as in the informal proof of Theorem 6.
   (c) Using these circles, color the edges in three colors.
   (d) From the coloring of the edges, obtain a coloring of the map in three colors.

8. Do E 7 (a), (b), (c), and (d) for still another map of your choice.

9. Draw three different maps, and check for each that $V - E + C = 2$. (*Hints:* Be

sure to count the ocean as a country; to help avoid errors, number each vertex, edge, or country as you count it.)

10. In the proof of Lemma 3 we indicated that any map on a sphere can be gradually reduced to a map with just two countries by using steps (1) and (2).
    (a) Draw a map with seven countries (on a flat piece of paper the ocean represents a country).
    (b) Reduce this map to one with just two countries by repeatedly applying steps (1) and (2).

11. The same as E 10 for a map with ten countries (again count the ocean as a country).

12. As in Chapter 2, dots are drawn on the surface of a sphere and are then used to divide the surface into triangles (with curved sides, of course). Prove this

    THEOREM. *If each dot is of even degree, then the dots can be labeled with the letters A, B, and C such that each of the triangles has all three of the letters.*

    (*Hint:* If you draw in countries whose capitals are the dots, then this becomes an immediate consequence of Theorem 6.) Compare to E 15 of Chapter 2.

13. Twelve wires are put together to form the edges of a cube. A light bulb is put inside this cube, and the cube is put inside a sphere. The shadows of the wires can be thought of as edges of a map on the sphere. Each of the six faces of the cube corresponds to a country. Thus any theorem we have proved about coloring maps on the surface of the sphere will apply to coloring each of the faces of the cube such that faces meeting along a wire have different colors.
    (a) Color the faces of the cube in as few colors as you can (such that adjacent faces have different colors).
    (b) Show that the cube illustrates Theorem 6.

14. See E 13. A tetrahedron is a pyramid having four triangular faces:

    (a) Color the faces of the tetrahedron with as few colors as possible (such that adjacent faces have different colors).
    (b) Show that the tetrahedron illustrates Theorem 5.

15. See E 13. An octahedron has eight triangular faces with four meeting at each vertex:

(a) Color the faces of the octahedron with as few colors as possible.

(b) Show that the octahedron illustrates Theorem 3.

16. Cut out of paper twelve circles all of the same diameter (at least three inches). Inscribe in each a regular pentagon like this:

Fold up the five flaps on each circle, and glue the twelve pieces of paper along the flaps in such a way that they form a surface in which three pentagons meet at each vertex (the flaps can show, or can be glued inside, as you prefer). This surface is called a dodecahedron.

(a) Prove that the dodecahedron cannot be colored in two colors.

(b) Prove that it cannot be colored in three colors.

(c) Color it in four colors.

17. The instructions are similar to those of E 16: Cut out twenty circles all of the same diameter, and inscribe in each an equilateral triangle. Then fold up the flaps, and glue the twenty pieces of paper together such that five triangles meet at each vertex. The resulting twenty-sided figure is called an icosahedron.

(a) Prove that the twenty triangles cannot be colored in two colors.

(b) What theorem assures us that we can color them in three colors?

(c) Color them in three colors.

18. Draw a map consisting of several countries, one of which, contrary to our agreement, has a hole in it. Color this map with as few colors as possible.

19. See E 18.

(a) Using the Five-color Theorem, prove that even if we allow one country to have holes (such that it surrounds islands made up of other countries), we can still color any such map on the sphere with five colors. (*Hint:* Show that a country with a hole creates two "simpler" coloring problems: one for the countries in the hole, and one for the countries outside.)

(b) The same as (a), but allow two countries to have holes.

20. The surfaces described in E 13, E 14, E 15, E 16, and E 17 are **regular polyhedra.** *A regular polyhedron is a polyhedron whose faces all have the same number of edges and whose vertices all have the same degree.* Prove that there is no regular polyhedron for which each vertex is of degree 3 and each face has six sides. (*Hint:* Look at Lemma 5.)

21. Prove that there is no map covering the surface of a sphere such that each vertex has degree 4 and each country has six edges. (*Hint:* Prove that $4V = 2E$ and that $6C = 2E$; combine these facts with $V - E + C = 2$ to obtain a contradiction.)

22. See E 20 and E 21. Prove that there is no map covering the surface of the sphere such that all vertices are of the same degree (larger than 2) and all countries have six edges.

23. See E 22. Prove that there is no map covering the sphere such that all vertices are of the same degree, d (larger than 2), and all countries have the same number of edges, p, and for which p is at least six.

24. The surface of a ball is cut up into countries such that each country has five edges and each vertex is of degree 3. Prove that there must be exactly twelve countries. (See the hint in E 21, but, instead of seeking a contradiction, prove that $C = 12$.)

25. The surface of a ball is cut up into countries such that each country has three edges and each vertex is of degree 5. Prove that there must be exactly twenty countries. (See the hint in E 24.)

26. The surface of a sphere is cut up into countries such that each country has three edges and all the vertices have the same degree Q. Prove that Q must be either 2, 3, 4, or 5. How many countries are there in each case? (See E 22, E 23, E 24, and E 25.)

27. The surface of a sphere is cut into countries such that each country has four edges and all the vertices have the same degree Q. Prove that Q is either 2 or 3. How many countries are there in each case?

28. The surface of a sphere is cut into countries such that each country has five edges and all the vertices have the same degree Q. Prove that Q is either 2 or 3. How many countries are there in each case?

29. The dressmaker's pattern for an inner tube is

If the edges marked c are sewn together such that A and D coincide and B and C coincide, we obtain a pipe. Sewing the edges marked d together joins the ends of the pipe to form an inner tube. This pattern enables us to represent an inner tube on a flat piece of paper.

Check that this diagram, drawn on the dressmaker's pattern for an inner tube, represents seven countries on the tube, each of which shares a border with the other six countries. (This map is due to P. Ungar, 1953.)

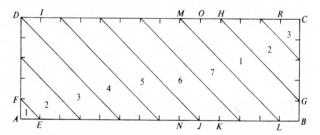

For example, country 1 borders country 2 on EF and GH, 3 on $LB = RC$, 4 on $AE = DI$, 5 on $MO = NJ$, 6 on $JK = OH$, and 7 on LM. If this map is drawn on an inner tube, then each country will twist like this:

30. (a) Why does the map of E 29 require seven colors?

    (b) Draw the map of E 29 on an inflated inner tube. First draw a circle on the inner tube, as indicated below, and then mark off on this circle fourteen regularly spaced divisions to serve as a guide.

31. Show that in the map of E 29, $V - E + C = 0$.

32. Assume that for any map covering the inner tube we have $V - E + C = 0$. Following our reasoning for Lemma 5 as closely as possible, prove that any map covering the inner tube and having each vertex of degree 3 must have a country with six or fewer edges.

33. See E 32. Prove that any map covering the inner tube and having each vertex of degree 3 must have a country with at least six edges.

34. If a hole is made in a (very elastic) inner tube, then it can be turned inside out:

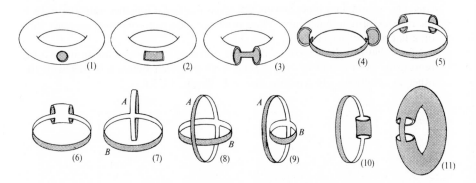

From (1) to (7) we shrink the tube. To go from (7) to (8) we turn band A inside out without moving any part of band B (this is easy to do if you make a paper model, or simply use a belt, to represent A). From (8) to (9) we shrink band B. From (9) to (11) we stretch the tube. Comparison of (11) and (3) shows that we have turned the inner tube inside out. (This exercise is not related to coloring problems.)

35. In the year 1880 Tait offered what he called a "very simple solution of the problem of map-coloring with four colors." We describe Tait's technique for coloring regular maps in (a) and (b) below:

   (a) Label the edges 1, 2, and 3 in such a way that the three edges meeting at each vertex have all three numbers.

   (b) First color one of the countries with the color A, and then color the remaining countries with colors A, B, C, and D in accordance with the following rules: Any edge labeled 1 is to separate countries colored either A and B or C and D; any edge labeled 2 is to separate countries colored either A and C or B and D; and any edge labeled 3 is to separate countries colored either A and D or B and C.

   (c) Draw a map in which each vertex is of degree 3. Does Tait's technique work for your map (including the ocean)? (See E 36.)

   (d) Prove that if Tait's technique always works, then any map on the sphere (regular or not) can be colored in four or fewer colors.

36. See E 35. Regrettably, Tait's proof that the edges can always be numbered as he required in E 35 (a) was false. Prove that if a regular map can be colored with the colors A, B, C, and D, then the edges can be numbered 1, 2, and 3 in such a way that at each vertex all three numbers are represented. (*Hint:* Use the rule of E 35 (b) in the reverse direction.) Comparing E 35 and E 36, show that the problem of coloring the edges of a regular map, as in E 35 (a), is equivalent to the four-color problem.

37. A flat island has one hundred towns. Some pairs of towns are joined directly by roads; we call such towns "adjacent." Two or more roads may meet at a town, but none cross outside of towns. Prove that it is possible for each town to offer exactly one of these five services: hospital, library, radio station, newspaper, and school in such a way that no two adjacent towns offer the same service.

38. Kempe, in the same 1879 paper that contains his imperfect proof of the four-color theorem, observed:

   If we lay a sheet of tracing paper over a map and mark a point on it over each district and connect the points corresponding to districts which have a common boundary, we have on the tracing paper a diagram of a "linkage," and we have as the exact analogue of the question we have been considering, that of lettering the points in the linkage with as few letters as possible, so that no two directly connected points shall be lettered with the same letter.

   In our terminology, a linkage is a system of towns and highways. Let us even allow a linkage to have bridges, in order that we can connect as many towns as we wish directly to each other. (Kempe's linkages have no bridges.) Draw a linkage of eight towns, of which any two are adjacent. Clearly this linkage could not be "colored" (that is, lettered) in fewer than eight colors.

39. See E 38. An "n-cage" in a linkage consists of n towns, named A_1, A_2, $\cdots$, A_n, and paths in the linkage between each two of the n towns such that no two paths meet except at the n towns. (That the paths might pass through other towns in the linkage does not concern us.) Thus (a) is a 2-cage (with 1 path), (b) is a 3-cage (with 2 paths), (c) is a 4-cage (with 6 paths), and (d) is a 5-cage (with 10 paths):

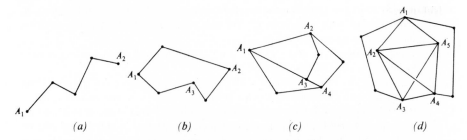

(a)   (b)   (c)   (d)

(Note that in (d), because of the bridge, the path from A_3 to A_5 does not meet the path from A_2 to A_4.) Prove that if there is no 2-cage in a linkage, then the towns of the linkage can be colored with just one color. (*Hint:* Show that there are no highways at all.)

40. See E 39. Prove that if a linkage contains no 3-cage, then it can be colored in two colors. (*Hint:* First show that the linkage is a tree.)

41. See E 39 and E 40. Dirac proved in 1952 that if a linkage contains no 4-cage, then it can be colored in three colors. Draw a linkage containing a 3-cage but no 4-cage, and check Dirac's theorem for your linkage.

42. See E 39, E 40, and E 41. (a) Show by a few experiments that any linkage that can be drawn on a flat piece of paper without the use of bridges has no 5-cage.
    (b) What theorem (like those of E 39, E 40, and E 41) would you like to be true?
    (c) Why would such a theorem prove the four-color theorem for countries on an island or on a sphere?

43. (a) Draw a map in which each vertex is of degree 3.
    (b) Place the number 1 or the number -1 at each vertex in such a way that the sum of the labels you meet as you go around each country is a multiple of 3.
    (c) Replace each 1 by a clockwise circle and each -1 by a counterclockwise circle.
    (d) Using the technique employed in the informal proof of Theorem 6, obtain a labeling of the edges with the numbers 1, 2, and 3 such that the three edges meeting at each vertex carry all three numbers.
    (e) Using the technique of E 35, color the map in four colors.
    No one has been able to prove that step (b) can always be made.

44. On a sphere are placed 100 dots. There are many maps, all of whose countries have three edges and whose vertices are the given 100 dots. Prove that any two such maps with 100 vertices have the same number of countries.

45. Explain why all the maps in E 25 of Chapter 2 have the same number of triangles. (See E 44.) (*Hint:* Take two (elastic) copies of the big triangle, and glue these copies together along their borders. Stretch the resulting figure until it becomes a sphere and compare with E 44.)

46. By an inspection of equation (25) prove that any regular map on the sphere must have at least three countries with five or fewer edges.

47. What is the similarity between the proof of Lemma 1 of the present chapter and the proof of Theorem 8 of Chapter 6?

References

1. H. S. M. Coxeter, Map coloring problems, *Scripta Mathematica*, vol. 23, 1957, pp. 11–25.

2. W. W. Rouse Ball, *Mathematical Recreations and Essays*, Macmillan, 1947. (Especially Chapters 5 and 8.)

3. P. Franklin, The four-color problem, *Scripta Mathematica* Library, Number 5.

4. H. Weyl, *Symmetry*, Princeton University Press, 1952. (In particular, pp. 75–76 discuss the regular polyhedra. Part of this book is reprinted in J. R. Newman, *The World of Mathematics*, Simon and Schuster, vol. 1, 1956. The illustrations on p. 721 show the 8-, 12-, and 20-faced polyhedra as they appear in nature.)

5. *R. L. Brooks, On colouring the nodes of a network, *Proceedings of the Cambridge Philosophical Society*, vol. 37, 1941, pp. 194–197.

6. *G. A. Dirac, A property of 4-chromatic graphs and some remarks on critical graphs, *Journal of the London Mathematical Society*, vol. 27, 1952, pp. 85–92.

7. D. Hilbert and S. Cohn-Vossen, *Geometry and the Imagination*, Chelsea, New York, 1952. (Regular polyhedra, pp. 89–93, 289–293; map-coloring problems on various surfaces, pp. 333–340.)

8. M. Gardner, *The Second Scientific American Book of Mathematical Puzzles and Diversions*, Simon and Schuster, New York, 1961. (Regular polyhedra, pp. 13–23.)

9. P. Franklin, The four color problem, *Scripta Mathematica*, vol. 6, 1939, pp. 149–156 and 197–210.

Chapter 14

THE
REPRESENTATION
OF NUMBERS

The basketball scorekeeper, making a mark for each point scored, is using the oldest and most cumbersome method of writing the natural numbers. The number 13, which we write with just two symbols, he would write as

///////////////

or, to make the marks easier to count, perhaps as

₦₦   ₦₦   ///.

Even with this device, his method is still a far from ideal notation for the natural numbers. For a larger number, such as 500, which we can write with just three symbols, he requires 500 marks.

Our system of representing the natural numbers has virtues other than brevity. For example:

1. We can see easily whether one number is larger than another by looking at their representations.

2. If we know the representations of the natural numbers A and B, we can easily compute the representation of $A + B$.

3. If we know the representation of the natural numbers A and B, we can easily compute the representation of $A \times B$.

Once we memorize the addition table for the digits 1, 2, 3, 4, 5, 6, 7, 8, and 9 we can compute any $A + B$. For example, watch this slow motion computation of $57 + 85$. First of all,

$$57 + 85 = (5 \text{ tens} + 7) + (8 \text{ tens} + 5) = (5 \text{ tens} + 8 \text{ tens}) + (7 + 5).$$

Having memorized the addition table up to $9 + 9$, we know that $5 + 8 = 13$ and that $7 + 5 = 12$ ($= \text{ten} + 2$). Thus $57 + 85 = 13 \text{ tens} + 1 \text{ ten} + 2$, or 14 tens $+ 2$. Recalling that 10 tens are one hundred, we have $57 + 85 = 1 \text{ hundred} + 4 \text{ tens} + 2$, which we write as 142. Similarly, once we memorize the multiplication table up to 9×9, we can compute $A \times B$ no matter how large A and B might be.

But let us not conclude that ours is necessarily the best of all possible systems.

200

In our system we express a natural number as the sum of various powers of the natural number 10, each power appearing at most 9 times. For example, 3102 is short for $(10^3 + 10^3 + 10^3) + (10^2) + 10^0 + 10^0$. (Recall that in E 37 of Chapter 3 we defined 10^0 to be 1.) We just do not bother to write the 10^3, 10^2, and 10^0, or the various plus signs. Instead, we record, in a standard order, just the numbers 3, 1, 0, 2, the so-called "coefficients," or "digits" that tell how often the various powers of 10 appear. But there is nothing sacred about this system that depends so heavily on the number 10; it was chosen thousands of years ago when the fingers played a larger role in arithmetic than they do now.

Let us see what would happen if we used the number 2 instead of 10. The question is: Can we write every natural number as a sum of powers of 2 with suitable coefficients? Let us note that the first few powers of 2 are $2^0 = 1$ (see E 37 of Chapter 3), $2^1 = 2$, $2^2 = 4$, $2^3 = 8$, $2^4 = 16$, $2^5 = 32$, $2^6 = 64$, $2^7 = 128$, $2^8 = 256$, $2^9 = 512$, $2^{10} = 1024$, and $2^{11} = 2048$. As an example, let us see if we can write 153 as a sum of powers of 2 with suitable coefficients. Since 153 is between 128 and 256, 2^7 is the largest power of 2 less than 153. We have

$$153 = 2^7 + 25.$$

Now let us work on 25 in a similar manner. Twenty-five is trapped between $2^4 = 16$ and $2^5 = 32$. We have $25 = 2^4 + 9$, and hence

$$153 = 2^7 + 2^4 + 9.$$

Finally, let us work on 9. Nine is trapped between 2^3 and 2^4; in fact, $9 = 2^3 + 1$, which means we can write

$$153 = 2^7 + 2^4 + 2^3 + 1.$$

Thus we have expressed 153 as a sum of powers of 2 (recall that $1 = 2^0$).

If we wish to omit the plus signs, as we do in our usual representation of natural numbers with powers of 10, we proceed as follows. Instead of $2^7 + 2^4 + 2^3 + 1$, we first write

$$(1 \times 2^7) + (0 \times 2^6) + (0 \times 2^5) + (1 \times 2^4)$$
$$+ (1 \times 2^3) + (0 \times 2^2) + (0 \times 2^1) + (1 \times 2^0),$$

and then record just the coefficients:

$$1\ 0\ 0\ 1\ 1\ 0\ 0\ 1.$$

In order to indicate that we are recording powers of 2, not powers of ten, we shall use a subscript "2":

$$153 = 1\ 0\ 0\ 1\ 1\ 0\ 0\ 1_2.$$

Perhaps it would also be wise to indicate that 153 records powers of ten by using the subscript "ten":*

---

* Since one $= 1_2 = 1_{ten}$, we will omit the symbol for the base in the representation of 1.

$$153_{\text{ten}} = 1 \ 0 \ 0 \ 1 \ 1 \ 0 \ 0 \ 1_2.$$

The scorekeeper's $\cancel{||||} \ \cancel{||||} \ \cancel{||||} \ \cancel{||||} \ //$ has the representations 22_{ten} and 10110_2 [since $22_{\text{ten}} = 2^4 + 2^2 + 2^1 = (1 \times 2^4) + (0 \times 2^3) + (1 \times 2^2) + (1 \times 2^1) + (0 \times 2^0)$].

The representation of natural numbers as sums of powers of ten (with coefficients at most 9) is called the representation to the **base ten**, *or the* **decimal system** *of representation* (from the Latin *decem*, ten). *Similarly, the representation of natural numbers as sums of powers of 2 (with coefficients at most 1) is called the representation to the* **base 2**, *or the* **binary system** *of representation* (from the Latin *binarius*, two by two).

The reader may check that in the binary system the first nine natural numbers larger than 0 have these representations: one = 1, two = 10_2, three = 11_2, four = 100_2, five = 101_2, six = 110_2, seven = 111_2, eight = 1000_2, nine = 1001_2.

What are the relative merits of the decimal versus the binary system? The decimal system provides a shorter notation for the natural numbers: compare 22_{ten} to 10110_2. But this is the principal advantage that the decimal system has over the binary.

As for determining which of two numbers is larger, both systems are equally efficient. Working in the binary system, we know, for example, that 1001_2 is larger than 111_2, since 1001_2 is larger than 2^3, whereas 111_2 is less than 2^3. More generally, if A is longer than B when written in the binary system, then A is larger than B. If A and B have the same number of digits in the binary system, then we need only glance at the digits in the place farthest to the left at which they differ. For example, 11101 is larger than 11001. In short, we determine which of two numbers is the larger just as we do in the decimal system. Therefore on this point neither system has the advantage.

But when it comes to computing $A + B$, it is the binary system that is superior. Instead of requiring us to memorize a nine by nine addition table, it asks us to learn only that

$$1 + 1 = 10_2.$$

That is, one plus one equals two. With this knowledge we can easily compute a sum such as $100_2 + 100_2$. The computation is simply

(1)
$$
\begin{array}{r}
100_2 \\
+\ 100_2 \\
\hline
1000_2
\end{array}
$$

Here we have just added the two given numbers together, digit by digit, starting from the right (as in the decimal notation). Note, in particular, that we have used the formula $1 + 1 = 10_2$. To check this computation, observe that 100_2 is simply 2^2, with the result that $100_2 + 100_2 = 2^2 + 2^2 = 2^3$. But $2^3 = 1000_2$.

Now let us turn to the computation of a sum that is not so simple; say,

$1110_2 + 111_2$. This we shall do in detail in order to justify "carrying" in the base 2 (and indirectly to shed light on the "carrying" we do in the decimal system). First we write 1110_2 as the sum $1000_2 + 100_2 + 10_2$, and 111_2 as the sum $100_2 + 10_2 + 1$, in order to have easier numbers to add. We wish to express the sum $1000_2 + 100_2 + 100_2 + 10_2 + 10_2 + 1$ to the base 2; that is, express it as a sum of distinct powers of two. Working first with the smallest repeated numbers, we record $10_2 + 10_2 = 100_2$ and also $100_2 + 100_2 = 1000_2$. Thus our sum of six numbers is replaced by the sum of the four numbers $1000_2 + 1000_2 + 100_2 + 1$. Still, we have a power of 2 appearing twice, namely $1000_2 + 1000_2$; this duplication we can avoid by using the fact that $1000_2 + 1000_2 = 10000_2$. Hence we have the sum of four powers of 2 replaced by the sum of three distinct powers of 2; namely, $10000_2 + 100_2 + 1$. Since $10000_2 + 100_2 + 1 = 10101_2$, we have $1110_2 + 111_2 = 10101_2$, and the sum is computed.

If we wrote all these sums vertically rather than horizontally we would have these steps:

$$
\begin{array}{cccc}
\begin{array}{r} 1110_2 \\ +\ \ 111_2 \\ \hline ? \end{array}
&
\begin{array}{r} 1000_2 \\ 100_2 \\ 10_2 \\ 100_2 \\ 10_2 \\ +\ \ 1 \\ \hline ? \end{array}
&
\begin{array}{r} 1000_2 \\ 1000_2 \\ 100_2 \\ +\ \ 1 \\ \hline ? \end{array}
&
\begin{array}{r} \left.\begin{array}{r} 10000_2 \\ 100_2 \\ +\ \ 1 \end{array}\right\} = 10101_2 \\ \hline ? \end{array}
\end{array}
$$

These computations we could summarize in a form like the one we met in grammar school for base ten,

$$
\begin{array}{r}
(1)\,(1) \\
1\ 1\ 1\ 0_2 \\
+\ \ \ 1\ 1\ 1_2 \\
\hline
1\ 0\ 1\ 0\ 1_2
\end{array}
$$

where the two (1)'s record "carrying," and we add digit by digit from right to left. [Note that at one point we need to reduce $1 + 1 + 1$ to 11_2; to do this requires our knowledge that $1 + 1 = 10_2$, for $1 + 1 + 1 = 1 + (1 + 1) = 1 + 10_2 = 11_2$.]

The reader may feel uncomfortable in this novel arithmetic, even though the addition table he must memorize is so much simpler than that for the decimal system. He should realize, however, that if he had met only the binary system in grammar school, and practiced only *its* arithmetic for years, he would feel ill at ease when confronted with the decimal system. He may feel like those who, after moving to a new land, learn the language perfectly, but, when they compute, continue to use the language of their childhood.

The reader can be comforted by the fact that any computation made in the binary system can be checked in the "good old" decimal system of his childhood. For example, let us compute $1110_2 + 111_2$. Since $1110_2 = 2^3 + 2^2 + 2 = 14_{ten}$ and $111_2 = 2^2 + 2^1 + 1 = 7_{ten}$, we know (from years of practice) that $1110_2 + 111_2$ must be 21_{ten}. Now let us write 21_{ten} as the sum of distinct powers of 2:

$$16 + 4 + 1 = (1 \times 2^4) + (0 \times 2^3) + (1 \times 2^2) + (0 \times 2) + 1 = 10101_2.$$

This agrees with the answer we had obtained before, using only binary arithmetic.

The computation of $A \times B$ in the binary system is much easier than in the decimal system. First of all, the multiplication table is just

$$1 \times 1 = 1,$$

instead of the nine by nine table we had to memorize in grammar school.

To find the product $1010_2 \times 100_2$ is very simple. Let us compute the product when

$$[(1 \times 2^3) + (0 \times 2^2) + (1 \times 2^1) + (0) \times 2^0] \text{ is multiplied by } 2^2.$$

Since

$$2^2 \times 2^3 = 2^5, \qquad 2^2 \times 2^2 = 2^4, \quad \text{and} \quad 2^2 \times 2^1 = 2^3,$$

we have
$$[(1 \times 2^3) + (0 \times 2^2) + (1 \times 2) + (0 \times 2^0)] \times (2^2)$$
$$= (1 \times 2^5) + (0 \times 2^4) + (1 \times 2^3) + (0 \times 2^2).$$

Now
$$(1 \times 2^5) + (0 \times 2^4) + (1 \times 2^3) + (0 \times 2^2)$$
$$= (1 \times 2^5) + (0 \times 2^4) + (1 \times 2^3) + (0 \times 2^2) + (0 \times 2^1) + 0;$$

thus

$$1010_2 \times 100_2 = 101000_2.$$

In short, we just shoved 1010_2 to the left and put two extra zeros to the right of it.

The same reasoning shows that, in the binary system, if all except the first digit of B are zero, then $A \times B$ is computed simply by writing all the zeros of B to the right of A. This is exactly what we do in the decimal system if the left digit of B is one and the rest of its digits are zero.

The computation of $1010_2 \times 111_2$, where neither number is simply a power of 2, is almost as rapid, and will show how easy it is to compute products in the binary system.

We first replace 111_2 by $100_2 + 10_2 + 1_2$ in order to display the powers of 2 which add up to 111_2. Then we replace the product

$$1010_2 \times 111_2$$

by
$$1010_2 \times (100_2 + 10_2 + 1),$$
which is equal to the sum of three easy products:
$$(1010_2 \times 100_2) + (1010_2 \times 10_2) + (1010_2 \times 1).$$

We have already seen that each of these three products can be computed by putting the appropriate zeros to the right of 1010_2. Thus $1010_2 \times 111_2 = 101000_2 + 10100_2 + 1010_2$, and we have replaced our problem, originally concerned with a product, by a problem in addition:

$$
\begin{array}{r}
1010_2 \\
10100_2 \\
+\,101000_2
\end{array}
$$

(2)

which we already know how to solve. The reader will find that the answer (if he is careful in carrying) is 1000110_2. Again, this answer can be checked by translating everything into the decimal system.

We can summarize all the details of our computation in a shorthand scheme (whose resemblance to the decimal technique for multiplication will be evident) as follows:

$$
\begin{array}{r}
1010_2 \\
\times\ \ 111_2 \\
\hline
1010_2 \\
1010_2 \\
1010_2 \\
\hline
1000110_2
\end{array}
$$

(3)

Diagram (3) is a brief summary of (2). Instead of writing out 10100_2, for example, which is the result of shoving 1010 to the left one place and putting a 0 to the right of it, we simply shove the 1010 to the left one place and do not even bother to put a 0 to its right (since the 0 will not affect the addition anyway). Thus *to multiply in the binary system we need only shove and add.*

In the decimal system we have to do more. For example, in computing the product 307×521,

$$
\begin{array}{r}
307 \\
\times\ 521 \\
\hline
307 \\
614 \\
1535 \\
\hline
159947
\end{array}
$$

we must compute the products 307×2 and 307×5 (with a little effort) and then shove the results to the left an appropriate distance.

As a second illustration of the case for multiplication in the binary system, we will compute $11001_2 \times 1011_2$:

$$
\begin{array}{r}
11001_2 \\
\times\ \ 1011_2 \\
\hline
11001_2 \\
11001_2 \\
11001_2 \\
\hline
100010011_2
\end{array}
$$

(Note that we do not bother to write down the result of multiplying 11001_2 by the 0 of 1011_2, since this product is 0—another resemblance to our decimal calculations—but we must remember to shove the next product to the left appropriately.)

For multiplication and addition, the binary system is much easier than the decimal. For comparing the relative size of numbers they are of equal merit. The only superiority of the decimal system is that it provides a shorter notation. The price we pay for this brevity is having to memorize the nine by nine addition and multiplication tables.

Although there is no likelihood that the decimal system will be replaced by the binary system in daily life, it should be pointed out that the binary system is the one best suited to electronic computing machines. First, since only two digits, 0 and 1, are required, each natural number can be recorded by a set of transistors, some conducting (corresponding to 1), some not conducting (corresponding to 0). Second, once the machine is wired to do addition, it can be made to multiply merely by wiring it to shove numbers to the left.

So far we have treated only the representation of the natural numbers. What are the methods for representing (positive) numbers that are not natural numbers? Since any positive number, rational or irrational, can be written as a natural number plus a number less than 1, we can concentrate on the representation of numbers between 0 and 1.

In the decimal system, when we write $\frac{5}{8}$ as 0.625, we are saying that

$$
\frac{5}{8} = \frac{6}{10} + \frac{2}{10^2} + \frac{5}{10^3} = \frac{6}{10} + \frac{2}{100} + \frac{5}{1000}.
$$

In the decimal system we are recording how a number less than 1 can be expressed as a sum of $1/10$'s, $1/10^2$'s, $1/10^3$'s, and so on, if we allow none of these expressions to appear more than 9 times in the sum. The representation of $\frac{5}{8}$, for example, tells us that $\frac{5}{8}$ is the sum of six $1/10$'s, two $1/10^2$'s, and five $1/10^3$'s.

A very simple number, less than 1, can have a terrible representation in the decimal system. For example, recall that

$$
\frac{1}{3} = 0.333333\cdots,
$$

where the ellipsis ($\cdots$) indicates that the 3's go on and on. But what exactly does the equation

$$\frac{1}{3} = 0.333333\cdots$$

mean? We might translate it into

(4) $$\frac{1}{3} = \frac{3}{10} + \frac{3}{10^2} + \frac{3}{10^3} + \frac{3}{10^4} + \frac{3}{10^5} + \cdots,$$

but what does this mean? In particular, what does "$\cdots$" mean? Surely it cannot mean "the sum of all rationals of the form 3 divided by a power of 10," since not even the fastest electronic computer can ever add an endless list of numbers.

The expression "$\frac{1}{3} = 0.333333\cdots$" is a very terse summary of an observation that goes like this: the sequence of numbers

$$\frac{3}{10}, \quad \frac{3}{10} + \frac{3}{(10)^2}, \quad \frac{3}{10} + \frac{3}{(10)^2} + \frac{3}{(10)^3}, \quad \cdots$$

approaches $\frac{1}{3}$. (Note that at no point do we add an endless supply of numbers; we simply make a statement about the way a certain list of numbers behaves. This is discussed in Appendix B.)

The decimal representation of a number less than 1 describes how that number can be written as a sum of rationals of the form $A/10^N$ where A is a natural number at most 9. Once again, there is nothing sacred about the number 10. Let us show that we can just as well use the base 2.

Take, for example, $\frac{5}{8}$. Since $\frac{5}{8}$ is larger than $\frac{1}{2}$, when we subtract $\frac{1}{2}$ from $\frac{5}{8}$ we obtain a positive result. Thus

$$\frac{5}{8} - \frac{1}{2} = \frac{1}{8},$$

$$\frac{5}{8} = \frac{1}{2} + \frac{1}{8}.$$

This gives a representation of $\frac{5}{8}$ as a sum of rationals of the form $1/2^N$. We can say that

$$\frac{5}{8} = \frac{1}{2} + \frac{0}{4} + \frac{1}{8}$$

and record this by

$$\frac{5}{8} = 0.101_2.$$

Let us see how $\frac{1}{3}$ looks when written to the base 2. The rationals of the form $1/2^N$ are $\frac{1}{2}$, $\frac{1}{4}$, $\frac{1}{8}$, $\frac{1}{16}$, $\frac{1}{32}$, $\cdots$. The largest of these that we can subtract from $\frac{1}{3}$ and obtain a nonnegative result is $\frac{1}{4}$. We have $\frac{1}{3} - \frac{1}{4} = \frac{1}{12}$. Thus $\frac{1}{3} = \frac{1}{4} + \frac{1}{12}$. Next let us work on $\frac{1}{12}$. The largest fraction of the form $1/2^N$ that is not larger than $\frac{1}{12}$ is $\frac{1}{16}$. We have $\frac{1}{12} - \frac{1}{16} = \frac{4}{192} = \frac{1}{48}$. Thus $\frac{1}{12} = \frac{1}{16} + \frac{1}{48}$. So far we have

$$\frac{1}{3} = \frac{1}{4} + \frac{1}{16} + \frac{1}{48}.$$

We can continue by subtracting $\frac{1}{64}$ from $\frac{1}{48}$, and so on, at each step obtaining a closer approximation of $\frac{1}{3}$ by a sum of distinct fractions of the type $1/2^N$. Our first approximation of $\frac{1}{3}$ was $\frac{1}{4}$, with an error of $\frac{1}{12}$; our second approximation of $\frac{1}{3}$ was $\frac{1}{4} + \frac{1}{16}$, with a smaller error, $\frac{1}{48}$; the reader may check that the approximation of $\frac{1}{3}$ by $\frac{1}{4} + \frac{1}{16} + \frac{1}{64}$ has an error of only $\frac{1}{192}$.

Just as the decimal representation of $\frac{1}{3}$ does not stop, the binary representation of $\frac{1}{3}$ does not stop. For if it did stop, we would have $\frac{1}{3}$ expressed as a sum of rationals of the type $1/2^N$. This sum could be written as one rational of the form $A/2^M$, where 2^M is the largest power of 2 present in the sum and where A is a natural number. We would thus have

$$\frac{1}{3} = \frac{A}{2^M},$$

and thus

$$2^M = 3A.$$

Hence 3 would divide 2^M, in contradiction with our discovery (in Chapter 4) that if a prime divides the product of several natural numbers, it must divide at least one of them. It turns out that the binary representation of $\frac{1}{3}$ is $0.10101010\cdots$. (See E 26 (a) and suggestion in E 25.)

We could also use bases other than 2 or 10. The Babylonians used the base 60 (but required coefficients as large as 59). With the base 3, every number less than 1 can be expressed as a sum of rationals of the form $1/3^N$, in which sum no such fraction appears more than twice. To see this, divide the line segment from 0 to 1 into 3 equal pieces, and each of these pieces into 3 equal pieces, and so on.

As an example, let us consider $\frac{7}{8}$. It appears in the segment from $\frac{2}{3}$ to 1. Thus $\frac{7}{8}$ is between $\frac{2}{3}$ and 1. The segment from $\frac{2}{3}$ to 1 is divided into three equal pieces:

It can be checked that $\frac{7}{8}$ appears in the little segment from $\frac{7}{9}$ to $\frac{8}{9}$. We have already shown that $\frac{7}{8}$ is between

$$\frac{2}{3} + \frac{1}{9} \quad \text{and} \quad \frac{2}{3} + \frac{2}{9}.$$

This process can be continued as long as we please. It contrasts with our procedure in the decimal system in that we cut each segment into three pieces, not ten.

In the base 3, the rational $\frac{1}{3}$ has the simple representation $\frac{1}{3} = 0.10000\cdots$. But the rational $\frac{1}{2}$, which has a simple representation in the decimal and binary systems, has an endless representation in the base 3 system. It can be shown that this representation is $0.11111\cdots$, an endless string of 1's. Thus, to represent $\frac{1}{3}$ conveniently, we sacrificed our simple representation of $\frac{1}{2}$. Clearly, then, no one base is best when it comes to representing the rationals.

Some 4000 years ago the Egyptians used a system for representing numbers between 0 and 1 that resembles our technique for bases 2, 3, and 10. They represented a rational between 0 and 1 as a sum of rationals of the form $1/n$, the so-called *unit fractions,* such that no unit fraction was repeated. For example, they wrote

$$\frac{2}{31} = \frac{1}{20} + \frac{1}{124} + \frac{1}{155}.$$

The reader may check that the representation is correct.

There are several differences between the Egyptian system and the decimal system. First, their representation for a rational number always stops, whereas the decimal representation need not (consider $\frac{1}{3} = 0.3333\cdots$). Second, there are many ways to represent a number in the Egyptian method, whereas the decimal system provides at most two representations (as an example of two representations, consider $\frac{1}{2} = 0.5000\cdots = 0.49999\cdots$). For example, in the Egyptian system, there are many representations for $\frac{2}{5}$, including these three:

$$\frac{1}{3} + \frac{1}{15} = \frac{1}{4} + \frac{1}{7} + \frac{1}{140} = \frac{1}{5} + \frac{1}{6} + \frac{1}{30}.$$

The Egyptian system has practically nothing to recommend it. It is not easy to determine when one number is larger than another. (Which is larger? $\frac{1}{3} + \frac{1}{11} + \frac{1}{231}$ or $\frac{1}{4} + \frac{1}{7} + \frac{1}{140}$?) By what routine do we represent in the Egyptian style the product or sum of two numbers? (For example, how do we represent $\frac{2}{5} \times \frac{2}{5}$ or $\frac{2}{5} + \frac{2}{5}$?) Perhaps it was their cumbersome technique for representing numbers that prevented the Egyptians from ever developing mathematics beyond the solution of equations of the simplest type.

As a matter of fact, it is not obvious that every rational number between 0 and 1 *has* a representation as a sum of distinct unit fractions. Indeed, it was only in 1880 that anyone bothered to prove that every (positive) rational less than 1 could be represented in the Egyptian style. In that year, Sylvester described a simple technique for constructing such a representation. Before proving that it always works, we will illustrate the technique by applying it to the rational $\frac{4}{13}$.

Step 1. Select the largest unit fraction less than or equal to $\frac{4}{13}$; that is, $\frac{1}{4}$. Subtract $\frac{1}{4}$ from $\frac{4}{13}$:

$$\frac{4}{13} - \frac{1}{4} = \frac{3}{52}.$$

Step 2. Select the largest unit fraction less than or equal to $\frac{3}{52}$; that is, $\frac{1}{18}$. Subtract $\frac{1}{18}$ from $\frac{3}{52}$:

$$\frac{3}{52} - \frac{1}{18} = \frac{2}{936}.$$

Step 3. Select the largest unit fraction less than or equal to $\frac{2}{936}$; that is, $\frac{1}{468}$. Subtract $\frac{1}{468}$ from $\frac{2}{936}$:

$$\frac{2}{936} - \frac{1}{468} = 0.$$

Having reached 0 we stop. Since we have reached 0 by successive subtractions of $\frac{1}{4}$, $\frac{1}{18}$, and $\frac{1}{468}$, we see that

$$\frac{4}{13} = \frac{1}{4} + \frac{1}{18} + \frac{1}{468}.$$

The reader will observe that the same technique of repeated subtractions is also used to find the decimal or binary representation of $\frac{4}{13}$. But, whereas the decimal or binary representation might go on and on and never stop, Sylvester's representation always stops. The reader may apply Sylvester's technique to $\frac{15}{19}$. He will see that it provides the representation $\frac{15}{19} = \frac{1}{2} + \frac{1}{4} + \frac{1}{25} + \frac{1}{1850}$.

We shall prove that Sylvester's technique always stops (though not necessarily in three steps) when applied to a positive rational less than 1.

Observe the successive rationals we met in applying Sylvester's technique to $\frac{4}{13}$. These rationals were $\frac{4}{13}$, $\frac{3}{52}$, $\frac{2}{936}$, and 0. Though the denominators grow swiftly, the numerators 4, 3, 2, and 0 shrink. This suggests a way of proving that the process must always stop when applied to a rational. All we have to do is prove that the numerators shrink at each step. (This would imply, for example, that Sylvester's technique, when applied to $\frac{19}{53}$, would have to stop in fewer than 20 steps, since the numerator is 19.) Thus we need only prove this

LEMMA. *If A and B are natural numbers, and A is less than B, and $1/N$ is the largest unit fraction less than or equal to A/B, then the numerator of the rational $(NA - B)/BN$ (which is $A/B - 1/N$) is less than A.*

PROOF. We wish to prove that $NA - B$ is less than A. Let us first note how we find N in practice. Consider, for example, $\frac{4}{13}$. To find the largest unit fraction less than $\frac{4}{13}$ we can rewrite $\frac{4}{13}$ as follows:

$$\frac{4}{13} = \frac{1}{\frac{13}{4}}.$$

But since $\frac{13}{4} = 3 + \frac{1}{4}$, the largest unit fraction less than $\frac{4}{13}$ has as denominator the first natural number larger than $3 + \frac{1}{4}$; in short, the next natural number after 3.

Similarly, to find the largest unit fraction less than or equal to A/B (if A does not divide B) we write

$$B = Q \times A + R$$

(where R is the remainder when B is divided by A) and then observe that the largest unit fraction less than A/B is

$$\frac{1}{Q+1}.$$

Carrying out the subtraction

$$\frac{A}{B} - \frac{1}{Q+1}$$

we obtain

$$\frac{A(Q+1) - B}{B(Q+1)}.$$

We wish to prove that the new numerator,

$$A(Q+1) - B,$$

is less than A. Recalling that $B = Q \times A + R$, we have

$$A(Q+1) - B = A(Q+1) - (Q \times A + R)$$
$$= A \times Q + A - Q \times A - R$$
$$= A - R.$$

Since R is not 0, $A - R$ is indeed less than A, and the lemma is proved in the case where A does not divide B.

Consider now the case in which A divides B. Then $B = Q \times A$ for some natural number Q, and hence $A/B = 1/Q$. Thus $1/Q$ is the largest unit fraction less than or equal to A/B. Carrying out the subtraction $A/B - 1/Q$, we obtain

$$0 = A/B - 1/Q = (AQ - B)/BQ,$$

and hence $AQ - B = 0$. Thus the new numerator is again less than A, and the proof of the lemma is now complete.

Sylvester's technique suggests a problem, first posed in 1956, that several mathematicians have worked on in vain. Can we use a technique like Sylvester's to represent a rational with an odd denominator as a sum of distinct unit fractions with odd denominators?

For example, let us try to represent $\frac{2}{7}$ as a sum of distinct unit fractions with odd denominators. Were it not for the restriction that the unit fractions must have odd denominators, we would subtract $\frac{1}{4}$. Instead, we must subtract $\frac{1}{5}$, the largest unit fraction with odd denominator that is not larger than $\frac{2}{7}$. We obtain

$$\frac{2}{7} - \frac{1}{5} = \frac{3}{35}$$

as the next rational to work on. Notice that the new numerator, 3, is larger than the old numerator, 2. This means that the lemma that helped Sylvester will not help us.

But let us continue undaunted. The largest unit fraction less than or equal to $\frac{3}{35}$ is $\frac{1}{12}$. But since 12 is even, we must use $\frac{1}{13}$. We obtain

$$\frac{3}{35} - \frac{1}{13} = \frac{4}{455}.$$

Again the numerator has grown, though not so quickly as the denominator.

Let us next consider $\frac{4}{455}$. The largest unit fraction less than or equal to $\frac{4}{455}$ is $\frac{1}{114}$. But since 114 is even, we must use $\frac{1}{115}$. We obtain

$$\frac{4}{455} - \frac{1}{115} = \frac{5}{52325}.$$

Again the numerator has grown. But this time, since the numerator divides the denominator, we can rewrite $\frac{5}{52325}$ as a unit fraction, $\frac{1}{10465}$. Thus our modified version of Sylvester's technique stops and, incidentally, has found for us this representation of $\frac{2}{7}$ as a sum of distinct unit fractions with odd denominators:

$$\frac{2}{7} = \frac{1}{5} + \frac{1}{13} + \frac{1}{115} + \frac{1}{10465}.$$

The reader may check that this same method produces the following representations:

$$\frac{2}{9} = \frac{1}{5} + \frac{1}{45}, \qquad \frac{2}{5} = \frac{1}{3} + \frac{1}{15}, \qquad \frac{5}{13} = \frac{1}{3} + \frac{1}{21} + \frac{1}{273}.$$

The interesting point is that in each of these cases (and in many more that have been done on computing machines) the process stops. Whether the process always stops is not known.

We have seen in this chapter various ways of representing numbers. In our usual system we represent numbers as a sum of powers of 10 and permit each power to occur at most nine times in the sum. In the binary system, we use powers of 2 and permit each power to appear at most once. We should realize that the decimal system is not the only possible method of representing numbers. And, in particular, when we speak of a number such as π or $\sqrt{2}$, we do not need to think of its representation in the decimal system or in any other system.

Too many people feel that a number is not well described until they have its decimal representation. It is more precise to think of π as the ratio between the circumference and diameter of a circle than as $\frac{22}{7}$ or 3.1 or 3.14 or 3.1416, all of which are just rough estimates of π.

And we should all be reminded, by the cumbersome Egyptian representation of rationals, that our usual representation of numbers as the sum of rationals whose denominators are powers of one fixed number is a device of great simplicity.

Exercises

1. Using the formula for the sum of a geometric series (Theorem 2 of Appendix B), prove that
   (a) 999 is one less than 1000.
   (b) 9999 is one less than 10,000.
   (c) 99,999 is one less than 100,000.

2. Using the formula for the sum of a geometric series (Theorem 2 of Appendix B), prove that
   (a) 111_2 is one less than 1000_2.
   (b) 1111_2 is one less than 10000_2.
   (c) 11111_2 is one less than 100000_2.

3. Which is larger?
   (a) 9057 or 8999
   (b) 1000_2 or 1011_2
   (c) 74 or 1010011_2
   (d) 1001_{ten} or 1001_2

4. Write in the binary notation (a) ⩓⩓ ⩓⩓ ⩓⩓ //, (b) 15, (c) 16, and (d) 21.

5. Write in the binary notation (a) 23, (b) 41, (c) 42, (d) 99.

6. Write in the decimal notation (a) 111_2, (b) 110_2, (c) 10101_2.

7. Write in the decimal notation (a) 1011_2, (b) 11111_2, (c) 100001_2.

8. Compute $111_2 + 110_2$ in the following two ways:
   (a) By expressing the two numbers in the decimal notation, computing their sum in the decimal notation, and finally translating the result into the binary notation.
   (b) In the arithmetic of the binary system.

9. Using only the arithmetic of the binary system, compute:
   (a) $1010_2 + 101_2$,   (b) $1110_2 + 1001_2$,   (c) $1011_2 + 11111_2$.
   Check your answers by translating the problem into the decimal system.

10. Compute $11_2 \times 11_2$ in the following two ways:
   (a) By expressing each of the numbers in the decimal system, computing the product in the decimal system, and then translating the result into the binary system.
   (b) Working only in the binary system.

11. Using only the binary system, compute
    (a) $111_2 \times 10_2$,   (c) $1010_2 \times 11_2$,
    (b) $1011_2 \times 101_2$,   (d) $111_2 \times 111_2$.

12. Check your answers to E 11 by translating the problems into the decimal system, computing in the decimal system, and then translating the results into the binary system.

13. Using only the binary system, compute
    (a) $101_2 \times 1011_2$,
    (b) $111_2 \times 1000_2$,
    (c) $1111111_2 \times 1111_2$.

14. Check your answers to E 13 by translating into the decimal system.

15. Using the base 3, instead of 2 or 10, we can represent natural numbers as sums of powers of 3, with coefficients of at most 2. For example $34_{ten} = (1 \times 3^3) + (0 \times 3^2) + (2 \times 3) + 1$ and so, in the base 3 notation, $34_{ten} = 1021_3$. Check that each of the following statements is true:
    (a) $17_{ten} = 122_3$,   (c) $11_{ten} = 102_3$,
    (b) $27_{ten} = 1000_3$,   (d) $54_{ten} = 2000_3$.

16. See E 15. Check each of these statements:
    (a) $104_{ten} = 10212_3$,
    (b) $100_{ten} = 10201_3$,
    (c) $81_{ten} = 10000_3$.

17. To carry out computations in the base 3 we would have to learn the addition and multiplication tables up to $2 + 2$ and 2×2. (Though larger than the tables for the binary system, they are still much smaller than those for the decimal system.) Check that these are the tables we should memorize for the base 3:

	1	2	addition
1	2	10_3	(base 3)
2	10_3	11_3	

	1	2	multiplication
1	1	2	(base 3)
2	2	11_3	

18. The first few powers of 3 are $3^0 = 1$, $3^1 = 3$, $3^2 = 9$, $3^3 = 27$, $3^4 = 81$, and $3^5 = 243$. To represent 200_{ten} in the base 3, proceed as follows. Note first between which two powers of 3 the number 200_{ten} is situated. We see that 200_{ten} is between 3^4 and 3^5; that is, between 1×3^4 and 3×3^4. In fact, 200_{ten} is between 2×3^4 and 3×3^4. Thus, $200_{ten} - (2 \times 3^4)$ must be less than 3^4. Indeed it is 38_{ten}. Next determine between which powers of 3 the number 38_{ten} lies, and proceed as with 200_{ten}. After a sequence of such subtractions we reach 0. Carry out the remaining steps to find that

$$200_{ten} = (2 \times 3^4) + (1 \times 3^3) + (1 \times 3^2) + (0 \times 3) + 2$$

(thus $200_{ten} = 21102_3$).

19. Using the technique of E 18, find representations to the base 3 of (a) 50_{ten}, (b) 82_{ten}, (c) 80_{ten}, (d) 300_{ten}.

20. (a) Represent 1011_2 to the base 3.
    (b) Represent 22010_3 to the base 2.

21. In the base 10 we have the rule for "casting out 9's." Develop the analogous rule for "casting out 2's" for the base 3. In particular, devise a shortcut for determining whether a number written in the base 3 notation is even or odd.

22. (a) Using Theorem 3 of Appendix 2, show that $0.689999999 \cdots = 0.690000000 \cdots$.
    (b) Similarly, show that $0.01111111 \cdots = 0.1000000000 \cdots$ (in the base 2).

23. In E 22 (a) we saw a number less than 1 that could be expressed in more than one way in the decimal notation. Prove that every natural number can be expressed in only one way in the decimal notation for natural numbers (if all digits to the right of the decimal point are 0). (*Hint:* See E 1, and consider size.)

24. (a) What is the remainder when 9053_{ten} is divided by 10?
    (b) What is the remainder when 2001_3 is divided by 3?
    (c) What is the remainder when 10011_2 is divided by 2?

25. Using geometric series (see Appendix B), prove
    (a) that $0.10000 \cdots$ (base 2 notation) is equal to $0.111111 \cdots$ (base 3 notation), where the base 3 representation of numbers less than 1 is analogous to the base 2 and base 10 representations for numbers less than 1;
    (b) that $0.3333333 \cdots$ (base 10 notation) is equal to $0.10000000 \cdots$ (base 3 notation).

26. (a) Prove that $0.10000 \cdots$ (base 3 notation) is equal to $0.010101 \cdots$ (0 and 1 continuing to alternate) (base 2 notation).
    (b) Prove that $0.10101010 \cdots$ (0 and 1 continuing to alternate) (base 3 notation) is equal to 0.011 (base 2 notation).

27. (Base 10 notation.) Since $(1.4)^2 = 1.96$ and $(1.5)^2 = 2.25$, we see that $\sqrt{2}$ is between 1.4 and 1.5. Prove in a similar fashion that $\sqrt{2}$ is between (a) 1.41 and 1.42, (b) 1.414 and 1.415.

28. See E 27. Clearly $\sqrt{3}$ is between 1 and 2. Using the technique suggested by E 27, find the first three digits to the right of the decimal point in the decimal representation of $\sqrt{3}$.

29. See E 28. Same as E 27 for $\sqrt{5}$ instead of $\sqrt{3}$.

30. Some rationals, such as $\frac{3}{8}$, have a decimal representation that stops, whereas others, such as $\frac{1}{3}$, have a decimal representation that never stops.
    (a) Determine, by the usual "long division," the decimal representation of ten rationals of your choice that are less than 1.
    (b) Which stop? Which do not stop?
    (c) Make a conjecture.

31. Let A/B be a rational with $(A, B) = 1$, and assume that its decimal representation stops.
    (a) Prove that B must divide some power of 10.
    (b) Prove that in the expression of B as the product of primes, only the primes 2 and 5 can appear.

32. Let A/B be a rational with $(A, B) = 1$, where no prime other than 2 or 5 divides B. Prove that the decimal representation of A/B stops. (*Hint:* Prove that there exist natural numbers C and n such that $A/B = C/10^n$.)

33. Let A/B be a rational with $(A, B) = 1$. Prove that if there is a prime other than 2 or 5 dividing B, then the decimal representation of A/B does not stop.

34. Check that the following Egyptian representations are correct:
    (a) $\frac{2}{31} = \frac{1}{20} + \frac{1}{124} + \frac{1}{155}$,
    (b) $\frac{2}{17} = \frac{1}{12} + \frac{1}{51} + \frac{1}{68}$.

35. Prove that if A is odd and B is even, then A/B is not the sum of a finite number of unit fractions with odd denominators.

36. Apply Sylvester's technique to (a) $\frac{5}{13}$, (b) $\frac{7}{11}$, (c) $\frac{7}{16}$.

37. Apply Sylvester's technique to (a) $\frac{4}{9}$, (b) $\frac{7}{50}$, (c) $\frac{5}{23}$.

38. If A and B are both odd, what can be said about the number of unit fractions with odd denominator whose sum is A/B?
    (a) Experiment.
    (b) Make a conjecture.
    (c) Prove it.

39. Show that the modified Sylvester technique provides the following representations of rationals with odd denominator as a sum of unit fractions with odd denominators:
    (a) $\frac{3}{7} = \frac{1}{3} + \frac{1}{11} + \frac{1}{231}$,
    (b) $\frac{5}{11} = \frac{1}{3} + \frac{1}{9} + \frac{1}{99}$.

40. Each time the (unmodified) Sylvester technique is applied to a rational, the "new" numerator is less than the "old" numerator. (The lemma asserts this.) Prove that each time the *modified* Sylvester technique is applied to a rational the "new" numerator is less than twice the "old" numerator.

41. Prove that if A is odd and B is even, then the modified Sylvester technique applied to A/B never stops. (*Hint:* See E 35.)

References

1. B. L. van der Waerden, *Science Awakening*, Noordhoff Ltd., Groningen, Holland, 1954. (The first two chapters discuss in detail the art of computing and the representation of numbers in ancient times. In particular, pp. 15–30 are devoted to Egyptian arithmetic; pp. 37–40, to the base 60; pp. 51–61, to the Hindu numerals and the positional system.)

2. O. Ore, *Number Theory and its History*, McGraw-Hill, New York, 1948. (The history of various notational systems is given on pp. 1–24—his "decadic" is the same as our "decimal." Pages 34–37 present a second method for translating from one base to another.)

3. T. Dantzig, *Number, the Language of Science*, Macmillan, New York, 1954. (Chapter 1 and pp. 253–260 discuss the representation of numbers.)

Chapter 15

TYPES OF NUMBERS

The discovery that $\sqrt{2}$ is not rational led us to separate the numbers into two types, rational and irrational, just as we had separated the natural numbers into the odd and the even. In this chapter we will meet a more profound duality, one that, in a very precise sense, generalizes the duality of the rationals and the irrationals.

Moreover, we will be forced to introduce the **complex numbers**—*numbers that do not usually correspond to points on the line. Thus it will be convenient to give a name to the numbers that do correspond to points on the line, which have been adequate for the first fourteen chapters; we will call them the* **real numbers.**

That $\sqrt{2}$ is not the quotient of two natural numbers can be put another way: there is no rational M/N that, when substituted for X in the expression $1X^2 = 2$, gives us a true statement. Looking at X as a place where numbers, not cars, can be parked, we can say that whenever a rational is parked at X we obtain a false statement. But when we place $\sqrt{2}$ (or, for that matter, $-\sqrt{2}$) at X we obtain a true statement.

We will summarize these remarks in the statement, the *equation* $1X^2 = 2$ has the *roots* $\sqrt{2}$ and $-\sqrt{2}$, and neither of these roots is a rational. It is customary to write equations with only a 0 to the right of the equal sign. Thus we could also say that the equation $1X^2 - 2 = 0$ has two roots and that neither of them is rational.

We can consider an even simpler equation, where X, but not X^2, appears; for example, the equation $3X - 4 = 0$. Whenever we place an integer at X we always obtain a false statement, since 3 does not divide 4. But if we substitute $\frac{4}{3}$ for X we get a true statement: $3(\frac{4}{3}) - 4 = 0$. Thus $\frac{4}{3}$ is a *root* of the equation $3X - 4 = 0$. The equation $3X - 4 = 0$ has just one root, and that root is rational.

As long as we deal with equations of the form $AX + B = 0$, where A and B are integers (and A is not 0), we can find a root among the rationals. Indeed, such equations have only one root, namely, $-B/A$. But, as we saw with

217

$X^2 - 2 = 0$, to find a root for an equation of the type $AX^2 + B = 0$ we might have to look outside of the rationals.

But what happens when we meet an equation in which both X^2 and X appear? For example, can we find a root for the equation

(1) $1X^2 + 6X + 9 = 0$?

This particular equation can be rewritten as

(2) $(1X + 3)^2 = 0$,

since $(1X + 3) \times (1X + 3) = 1X^2 + 6X + 9$. (Appendix A discusses such maneuvers.)

The only number whose square is 0 is the number 0. Thus, the only number that can replace X in Equation (2) and yield a true statement is the number -3. Hence Equation (2) has exactly one root, -3. [As a check, we substitute -3 for each X of Equation (1); this gives us the statement $1(-3)^2 + 6(-3) + 9 = 0$, which is true.]

Let us try to find roots for the equation

(3) $1X^2 + 6X + 2 = 0$,

which resembles (1). The reader is invited to substitute various numbers wherever X appears in (3) and see whether he comes upon one that leads to a true statement.

But rather than conduct a random search for a root of (3), let us first add 9 to both sides in order to make it resemble (1), which turned out to be so easy. We then obtain

$$1X^2 + 6X + 9 + 2 = 9,$$

or

$$(1X + 3)^2 + 2 = 9.$$

Subtracting 2 from both sides gives us

$$(1X + 3)^2 = 7.$$

If a number R is to be a root of (3), then $(1R + 3)^2$ must be 7; that is,

$$R + 3 = \sqrt{7},$$

or perhaps

$$R + 3 = -\sqrt{7}.$$

The reader may check that the two numbers thus suggested, $-3 + \sqrt{7}$ and $-3 - \sqrt{7}$, are roots of (3) by showing that each of them leads to a true statement when substituted for each X in (3).

Next, let us consider equations of the type $AX^3 + BX^2 + CX + D = 0$, where X^3 enters the scene. For example, let us see whether the equation

(4) $1X^3 - 2X^2 + 1X - 2 = 0$

has a root.

We are trying to find a number R such that $1R^3 - 2R^2 + R - 2$ is 0. Observe that when C is a very large positive number, C^3 is much larger than C^2 or C; thus, for large C we see that $1C^3 - 2C^2 + 1C - 2$ is positive. On the other hand, when C is large in size, but negative, $1C^3 - 2C^2 + 1C - 2$ will be negative. As C wanders from the large negative numbers to the large positive numbers, there will be at least one point at which $1C^3 - 2C^2 + 1C - 2$ is 0. [Indeed, as the reader may check, 2 is such a point and is therefore a root of (4).] The same reasoning proves, as the reader may check,

THEOREM 1. *Any equation of the type $AX^3 + BX^2 + CX + D = 0$, where A is not 0, has at least one real root.*

It can happen that some equations of the type appearing in Theorem 1 have only one real root. For example, the equation $1X^3 = 0$ has just one real root; namely, 0.

Before we go further it is advisable to define a few terms. *Expressions such as $3X - 4$, $1X^2 + 1X + 1$, $1X^3 - 2X^2 + 1X - 2$, and $1X^5 + 5X - 5$ we shall call* **polynomials.** A polynomial is a sum of terms of the form SX^n, where S is a real number and n is a natural number. *The S is called the* **coefficient** *of X^n.* The largest n such that the corresponding S is not 0 is called the **degree** of the polynomial. A polynomial of degree 0 is thus of the form SX^0, where S is not 0. We will write such a polynomial simply as S; for example, instead of $5X^0$, we will write 5. *The polynomial that has all of its coefficients equal to zero we call the* **zero polynomial** *and write it 0; we do not assign it a degree.*

An equation of the form $P = 0$, where P is a polynomial of degree n, is called an **equation of degree** *n.* We may say, for example, that Theorem 1 concerns equations of degree 3.

The same reasoning that proved Theorem 1 also proves

THEOREM 2. *Any equation of odd degree has at least one real root.*

Having met so often the contrast between odd and even, we would expect

THEOREM 3. *For any even natural number n bigger than 0, there is an equation of degree n that has no real roots.*

PROOF. For any real number a, whether a is negative or positive, a^2, a^4, a^6, and so on are never negative. Thus an equation of the form $1X^n + 1 = 0$, with n even, can have no real root.

Any real number that is a root of an equation of the type $P = 0$, where P is a polynomial whose coefficients are integers (not all 0), we will call **algebraic** (since they are the numbers we meet while doing algebra). The demand that the coefficients be integers is crucial; otherwise any number a would obviously be algebraic since it is a root of the equation $1X + (-a) = 0$.

For example, $\frac{3}{4}$ is algebraic because it is a root of the equation $4X - 3 = 0$. Similarly, $\sqrt{2}$ is algebraic because it is a root of $1X^2 - 2 = 0$, and $-3 + \sqrt{7}$ is algebraic because it is a root of $1X^2 + 6X + 2 = 0$, as we saw earlier. Clearly the rationals are just algebraic numbers of a special type—namely, those algebraic numbers which are roots of equations of degree 1.

Any real number that is not algebraic we will call **transcendental.** The question comes to mind as to whether every real number is algebraic, and hence no number is transcendental. That is, given a number a, is there a polynomial P with integral coefficients such that, when the X's in P are replaced by a, we obtain the value 0? This is not an easy question. Recall how difficult it was to prove that $\sqrt{2}$ is irrational; that is, not the root of any equation of the form $P = 0$, *where P is a polynomial of degree 1, with integral coefficients.* To show that a number is transcendental, we would have to show that it is not the root of *any* equation of the form $P = 0$, no matter how high we allow the degree of P to be, where P is a polynomial whose coefficients are integers (not all 0).

Perhaps we may attack the problem by studying the decimal representation of numbers (discussed in Chapter 14). It might be that the decimal representation of the algebraic numbers looks different from the decimal representation of the transcendentals—if there are transcendentals. Perhaps the algebraic numbers have a more orderly representation.

Let us try. The simplest type of algebraic number is a rational number, a root of an equation of degree 1. Let us examine the decimal representation of a particular rational, say, $\frac{11}{14}$. Carrying out the usual division, we have

```
        0.78571428
14/11.000
        9 8
       ⎛1⎞20
        1 12
         ⑧0
         70
        ⑴00
         98
         ─
         ②0
         14
         ─
         ⑥0
         56
         ─
         ④0
         28
         ─
        ⑫0
        112
         ─
         ⑧0
```
(remainders are circled)

(and so on)

we find that the decimal representation of $\frac{11}{14}$ is quite orderly. It is simply 0.7 followed by the block 857142 repeated endlessly:

$$0.7857142857142857142\cdots,$$

which we will indicate simply as $0.7\underline{857142}$. (Similarly we would write $0.3333\cdots$ as $0.\underline{3}$, and $0.500000\cdots$ as $0.5\underline{0}$.) As soon as we met the remainder 12 for the second time, our computation began to repeat exactly, step for step, remainder for remainder, an earlier part of the division.

Perhaps the decimal representation of every rational, even of every algebraic number, resembles those for $\frac{11}{14}$, $\frac{1}{3}$, and $\frac{1}{2}$ in that they go on and on repeating the same block. *Such a decimal representation we call* **repeating.** In this direction we have

THEOREM 4. *If A and B are natural numbers, then the decimal representation of A/B is repeating.*

PROOF. We will show that when we carry out the division of B into A, a remainder must be repeated. But this is easy to see since there are only B

possible remainders when a number is divided by B; namely, 0, 1, 2, $\cdots$, $B - 1$. By the time we have carried out $B + 1$ divisions, at least one remainder must be duplicated (again, the pigeonhole principle of Chapter 12). Thus the decimal representation of A/B is repeating, and the repeating block has at most B digits.

We might hope that the decimal representation of any algebraic number is repeating. If this were the case, then it would be a simple matter to devise specific examples of transcendental numbers. Such a hope is doomed, however, by

THEOREM 5. *If the decimal representation of a number is repeating, then that number is rational.*

PROOF. We illustrate the reasoning by proving that the number whose decimal representation is 2.61$\underline{45}$ is rational. We rewrite 2.61$\underline{45}$ as

$$(5) \qquad 2 + \tfrac{61}{100} + \tfrac{45}{10000} + \tfrac{45}{1000000} + \tfrac{45}{100000000} + \cdots$$

or, to avoid writing so many 0's, as

$$(6) \qquad 2 + \tfrac{61}{100} + (\tfrac{45}{10000}) + (\tfrac{45}{10000})(\tfrac{1}{100}) + (\tfrac{45}{10000})(\tfrac{1}{100})^2 + \cdots.$$

The part after $2 + \tfrac{61}{100}$ is a geometric series with the first term $\tfrac{45}{10000}$ and the ratio $\tfrac{1}{100}$ between successive terms. (See Appendix B.) By Theorem 3 of Appendix B, the sum of this geometric series is $(\tfrac{45}{10000})/(1 - \tfrac{1}{100})$. Thus (5) and (6) represent the number

$$2 + \tfrac{61}{100} + (\tfrac{45}{10000})/(1 - \tfrac{1}{100}),$$

which, with a little arithmetic, can be reduced to the rational $\tfrac{25884}{9900}$, as the reader may check. Clearly the same technique applies to any repeating decimal, hence Theorem 5 is proved.

Theorems 4 and 5 give us a way of deciding, on the basis of its decimal representation, whether a number is rational, not whether it is algebraic. Even the decimal representation of such a "simple" algebraic number as $\sqrt{2}$ shows no particular order; the first few hundred digits behave quite chaotically. No one has ever found a general technique for deciding whether a number is algebraic or transcendental that depends on some property of its decimal representation.

In Chapter 16 we will prove, using set theory, that there are transcendentals. For that proof we will need

THEOREM 6. *An equation of degree n has at most n real roots.*

This should come as no surprise. Any equation of degree 1, $AX + B = 0$, has one root; namely, $-B/A$. The equation $1X^2 + 6X + 9 = 0$ has one root, and $1X^2 + 6X + 2 = 0$ has two roots, as we have already seen. The equation $1X^2 + 1 = 0$ has no real roots, since no real number has its square equal to -1.

For the proof of Theorem 6 we will need this

LEMMA. *If r is a root of P = 0, then there is a polynomial Q such that* $P = Q \times (1X - r)$.

The proof will be easier to follow if we first try a specific case. As the reader may check, 2 is a root of the equation $3X^2 - 10X + 8 = 0$. We will build a polynomial Q such that $3X^2 - 10X + 8 = Q \times (1X - 2)$. Another way of putting it is this: we will build a polynomial Q such that when we subtract $Q \times (1X - 2)$ from $3X^2 - 10X + 8$ we will obtain just 0.

We will build Q bit by bit in order to get rid of the X^2, and then the X. First, let us get rid of the $3X^2$. To do this we subtract $3X(1X - 2)$ from $3X^2 - 10X + 8$. That is, we form

$$(3X^2 - 10X + 8) - 3X(1X - 2),$$

which reduces to $3X^2 - 10X + 8 - 3X^2 + 6X$, or simply $-4X + 8$.

Next we get rid of $-4X$, in the polynomial $-4X + 8$. To do this we subtract $-4(1X - 2)$ from $-4X + 8$. That is, we form

$$-4X + 8 - (-4)(1X - 2),$$

which reduces to $-4X + 8 + 4X - 8$, or simply 0.

Not only did we get rid of the $-4X$, but, simultaneously, we got rid of the 8. This, as we will see in the proof of the lemma, is no accident.

Collecting our subtractions we see that

$$3X^2 - 10X + 8 - 3X(1X - 2) - (-4)(1X - 2) = 0,$$

or

$$3X^2 - 10X + 8 - (3X - 4)(1X - 2) = 0.$$

Thus

(7) $$3X^2 - 10X + 8 = (3X - 4)(1X - 2).$$

We have found our Q, namely $3X - 4$, and the reader can check it by multiplying out the right side of (7). (The relation (7) yields a true statement no matter what we replace X by. For example, if we replace X by 3, we obtain $5 = 5$; if we replace X by 2, we obtain $0 = 0$; and, if we replace X by $\frac{4}{3}$, we again obtain $0 = 0$.)

The reader is advised to use the same technique to find a polynomial Q such that

$$2X^3 - 3X^2 - 1X - 2 = Q \times (X - 2).$$

(This will involve three subtractions.)

Now we are ready for the

PROOF OF THE LEMMA. Let r be a root of $P = 0$. By repeated subtractions as above we can find a polynomial Q such that, when $Q \times (1X - r)$ is subtracted from the polynomial P, all terms involving X will cancel. We want to show that for this Q, the term in P that has no X will also cancel, as it did in the preceding example.

In any case, we know that there is a real number s such that

(8) $P - Q \times (1X - r) = s.$

We want to prove that $s = 0$. For the first time we will use the fact that r is a root of $P = 0$. Let us place the r at each X in P, Q, and $1X - r$ of (8). Since (8) yields a true statement whenever we replace X by any real number, it will yield a true statement when X is replaced by r. When X is replaced by r, then P takes on the numerical value 0; Q takes on some numerical value q; and $1X - r$ takes on the value $1r - r$, which is 0. Thus from (8) we deduce that

$$0 - (q \times 0) = s.$$

Thus $s = 0$, as we had hoped. This proves the lemma.

We are now ready to give a

PROOF OF THEOREM 6. For equations of degree 1, the theorem is clearly true. Let us consider equations of degree 2. If the equation $P = 0$ has no roots, then Theorem 6 certainly is true for this equation. If $P = 0$ has a root, let r be one of the roots. According to the lemma, there is a polynomial Q such that $P = Q \times (1X - r)$. Since P has degree 2, Q must have degree 1.

Now let r' be another root, different from r, of the equation $P = 0$. That is, when r' replaces each of the X's in P, then P has the numerical value 0. If we replace every X in Q by this same r', then Q will assume a numerical value, which we call q. We will now show that $q = 0$.

When X is replaced by r' at each of its appearances in P, Q, and $1X - r$ in the equation

$$P = Q \times (1X - r),$$

we obtain

$$0 = q \times (r' - r).$$

Since r' is different from r, we see that $r' - r$ is not 0. But $q \times (r' - r)$ is 0. Thus q must be 0. That is, r' is a root of the equation $Q = 0$. Thus every root of the equation $P = 0$, other than r, is also a root of the equation $Q = 0$. But the equation $Q = 0$ has just one root, since Q is of degree 1. Thus the equation $P = 0$ has at most two roots, hence Theorem 6 is proved for equations of degree 2.

If $P = 0$ is an equation of degree 3, the reasoning is similar, and makes use of the fact that an equation of degree 2 has at most 2 roots. In detail, if r is a root of the equation $P = 0$, then according to the lemma there is a polynomial Q (this time of degree 2) such that $P = Q \times (1X - r)$.

Just as in the previous case, we can prove that any root r' of $P = 0$, other than r, must also be a root of $Q = 0$. Since we have already proved that the equation $Q = 0$ has at most two roots, we then conclude that the equation $P = 0$ can have at most three roots. The same argument then applies, step by step, to equations of degree 4, then 5, then 6, and so on, which proves Theorem 6.

Theorem 6 tells us that an equation $P = 0$ has only a limited supply of roots. Theorem 3 tells us that there are equations without any real roots whatsoever; for example, the equation $1X^2 + 1 = 0$ has no roots. This is inconvenient, since such equations are met daily in mathematics and in its applications to the physical world, and it would be useful to have roots for them on which we could operate as we do with the numbers of ordinary arithmetic.

We will now construct a mathematical system in which every equation will have at least one root. In this man-made structure we will define an operation $\oplus$, which will behave like ordinary addition, and an operation $\otimes$, which will behave like ordinary multiplication. These operations will satisfy the rules whose importance is emphasized in Chapter 11 and in Appendix A. We cite the more important ones as a reminder:

$$\left.\begin{array}{c} X \oplus Y = Y \oplus X \\ X \otimes Y = Y \otimes X \end{array}\right\} \text{commutativity;}$$

$$\left.\begin{array}{c} X \oplus (Y \oplus Z) = (X \oplus Y) \oplus Z \\ X \otimes (Y \otimes Z) = (X \otimes Y) \otimes Z \end{array}\right\} \text{associativity;}$$

and the rule that relates $\otimes$ to $\oplus$,

$$X \otimes (Y \oplus Z) = (X \otimes Y) \oplus (X \otimes Z) \qquad \text{(distributivity).}$$

The first hints that man could build such a mathematical system appeared in the sixteenth century, but it was not till the early part of the nineteenth century that it was accepted as a legitimate part of mathematics.

We now define this structure that will enable us to find roots for all equations, including the equation $1X^2 + 1 = 0$. We shall build it on the whole plane, just as the real numbers, with their addition and multiplication, are built on the line. (Recall that the real numbers include the transcendental numbers and the algebraic numbers, and that the algebraic numbers include the rational numbers, which in turn include the integers. The number system we will now construct will include all the reals.) We will not attempt to give the history behind the definitions of $\oplus$ and $\otimes$; we will simply show that these definitions provide a useful mathematical structure.

If X and Y are any two points in the plane, we shall define $X \oplus Y$ as the fourth vertex of the parallelogram, two of whose sides are $0X$ and $0Y$:

Since the parallelogram determined by 0, X, and Y is the same as the parallelogram determined by 0, Y, and X, then $X \oplus Y = Y \oplus X$. It is not so clear, however, that $X \oplus (Y \oplus Z) = (X \oplus Y) \oplus Z$ for any three points X, Y, Z in the plane; thus the reader is urged to draw the (four) necessary parallelograms and check that $\oplus$ is associative for a specific X, Y, and Z. He will be delighted to see the point $X \oplus (Y \oplus Z)$ coincide with the point $(X \oplus Y) \oplus Z$. (E 44 sketches an algebraic proof for the associativity of $\oplus$.)

If 0, X, and Y happen to be on a line, then the parallelogram collapses, and its fourth vertex lies on the same line as 0, X, and Y. For example, as the reader may check, $2 \oplus 1 = 3$, and $4 \oplus (-4) = 0$. The reader may check (with a few diagrams) that whenever X and Y happen to be on the line of real numbers, then $X \oplus Y$ coincides with $X + Y$. Therefore the operation $\oplus$ can be thought of as an expansion to the whole plane of our everyday addition. Or we might prefer to think that our everyday addition is but a small part of the operation $\oplus$ defined throughout the plane.

Next we define the second half of the structure, the operation $\otimes$. Observe first that a point X in the plane (different from 0) determines an angle in this manner, measured counterclockwise from the ray of positive real numbers.

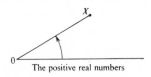
The positive real numbers

In particular, any point on the vertical line through 0, and above 0, determines an angle of 90°. Every negative real number determines the angle 180°. Every positive real number determines the angle 0°. Finally, every point directly below 0 determines the angle 270°.

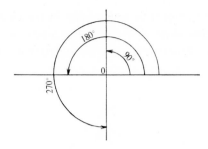

Of course, if we add any multiple of 360° to an angle, we describe the same direction; thus the negative real numbers, for example, also determine the angles 540°, 900°, 1260°, ⋯ .

If X and Y are points in the plane, and if both differ from 0, then we define $X \otimes Y$ in this manner. *The point X lies on a circle whose center is 0. Let us call the radius of this circle r. The point X determines an angle A, as shown in this diagram:*

Similarly, Y will be located at a certain distance, say, s, from 0, and will determine a certain angle, say, B. Here is how we will draw $X \otimes Y$. We must tell how far and in what direction $X \otimes Y$ is to be from 0. The point $X \otimes Y$ will be on the circle with center 0 and radius $r \times s$ (this makes use of ordinary multiplication) and will have the angle $A + B$ (this makes use of ordinary addition). If X or Y happens to be 0, then we define $X \otimes Y$ to be 0.

The reader can check that $X \otimes Y$ is simply the point obtained from Y by rotating Y about 0 by the angle of X, and then magnifying or shrinking the result by a factor equal to the radius of X.

As an example, let us find $X \otimes Y$ for the X and Y in this diagram:

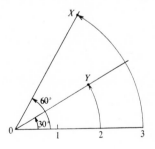

Since r is 3 and s is 2, $X \otimes Y$ is somewhere on the circle with center 0 and radius 6. Where on this circle is $X \otimes Y$? The angle of $X \otimes Y$ is $60° + 30°$; that is, $90°$. Thus $X \otimes Y$ lies on the line through 0 that is perpendicular to the line of real numbers:

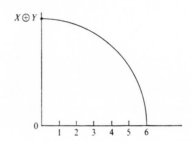

That $X \otimes Y = Y \otimes X$ for any X and Y in the plane follows from the commutativity of ordinary multiplication ($r \times s = s \times r$) and of ordinary addition ($A + B = B + A$). For similar reasons, $X \otimes (Y \otimes Z) = (X \otimes Y) \otimes Z$ for any three points in the plane.

Next we must show that $X \otimes (Y \oplus Z) = (X \otimes Y) \oplus (X \otimes Z)$ for any X, Y, and Z in the plane. We prove this first for the special case in which X is on the circle of radius 1. For any point X' in the plane (since r, the radius of X, is 1), $X \otimes X'$ and X' are at the same distance from 0. In fact $X \otimes X'$ is obtained from X' by rotating X' about 0 through the angle determined by X. This fact we will now use in the three cases where X' is Y, Z, or $Y \oplus Z$.

Consider the parallelogram defining $Y \oplus Z$:

Now rotate this whole parallelogram by the angle of X, whatever it may be:

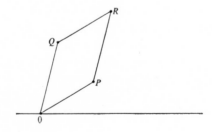

The rotation moves Y to P, Z to Q, and $Y \oplus Z$ to R. Since we are considering only the case in which X lies on the circle of radius 1, we have

(9) $\qquad P = X \otimes Y, \qquad Q = X \otimes Z, \qquad R = X \otimes (Y \oplus Z).$

But inspection of parallelogram $0PQR$ shows that $R = P \oplus Q$. Combining this with (9), we obtain

(10) $\qquad X \otimes (Y \oplus Z) = (X \otimes Y) \oplus (X \otimes Z),$

thus proving distributivity for the special case in which X is on the circle of radius 1.

In case X is not on the circle of radius 1 we must magnify (or shrink) parallelogram $0PQR$ by the distance from 0 to X. (Why?) Since the magnification of a parallelogram is still a parallelogram of the same shape (think of a parallelogram magnified by a slide projector), we see that (10) holds for any X, Y and Z in the plane. Thus distributivity is proved.

Just as we saw that addition on the line is but a small part of the operation $\oplus$, we will now show that multiplication on the line is but a small part of the operation $\otimes$. For example, let us compute $2 \otimes 3$ and see how it compares with 2×3. Clearly $2 \otimes 3$ is somewhere on the circle of radius 6 and center 0. Since the angle of 2 is $0°$ and the angle of 3 is $0°$, the angle of $2 \otimes 3$ is $(0 + 0)°$, which is $0°$. Thus $2 \otimes 3$ is 6, which is the same as 2×3.

As another check, let us see whether $(-1) \otimes (-1)$ is equal to $(-1) \times (-1)$; that is, 1. Since -1 is on the circle of radius 1 and center 0, then $(-1) \otimes (-1)$ is somewhere on the circle of radius 1×1 and center 0; that is, the circle of radius 1 and center 0. Where does $(-1) \otimes (-1)$ lie on this circle? The angle of -1 is $180°$; thus the angle of $(-1) \otimes (-1)$ is $(180 + 180)°$; that is, $360°$. Thus $(-1) \otimes (-1)$ is the point 1, on the line of real numbers. In a similar manner, the reader may check that $2 \otimes (-3)$ is -6, and then go on to show why $X \otimes Y$ is $X \times Y$ whenever both X and Y happen to lie on the real line.

The reader who is suspicious of a multiplication and addition of points on the plane should be reminded that up to the sixteenth century, mathematicians thought that all arithmetic should be done with that part of the real line to the right of 0. If the root of an equation happened to be negative, they call it "fictitious" and threw it away as an absurdity. But today we are as accustomed to working on that part of the real line left of 0 as we are to reading thermometers that record temperatures below 0.

The main object of our construction on the plane is to provide roots for equations that have no real roots. In particular, we hope that the equation $1X^2 + 1 = 0$ now has a root. Let us see whether there is a point B in the plane such that $(B \otimes B) \oplus 1 = 0$; that is, a point B such that $B \otimes B = -1$.

On what size circle would B have to lie, and at what angle? We know that

−1 is on the circle of radius 1 and has the angle 180°, or in general, 180 + multiple of 360)°. Therefore if B is on the circle of radius r, we must have $r \times r = 1$. Thus $r = 1$. Next, what is the angle of B? Since the angle of $B \otimes B$ is twice the angle of B and is to be, say, 180°, we see that B could have the angle 90°. Thus we have found a root for the equation $1X^2 \oplus 1 = 0$ directly above 0 as in this picture:

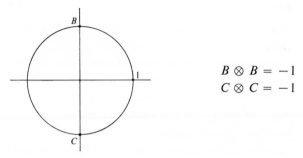

$$B \otimes B = -1$$
$$C \otimes C = -1$$

Moreover, as the reader may check, it is also true that $C \otimes C = -1$. Thus the plane provides at least two roots of $1X^2 \oplus 1 = 0$. The reader may check that the plane provides no more roots of $1X^2 \oplus 1 = 0$.

It is the custom to give B the name i. The symbol i stands for "imaginary," and is a memorial to the uncertainties of the mathematicians who first leaped off the tight rope of the real line into the mysteries of the plane. This might remind us of the "X" in X-ray, which records Roentgen's perplexity when he first noticed them in 1895; little could he know then that they are just part of a whole scale of radiation that includes heat and light as special cases.

In order to feel more at home with the operations $\oplus$ and $\otimes$ let us first of all write $+$ instead of $\oplus$ and $\times$ instead of $\otimes$. After all, $\oplus$ and $+$ do agree on the real line, and so do $\otimes$ and $\times$. For example, instead of the cumbersome $3 \otimes i$ we will write $3 \times i$, or just $3i$. As the reader may check, $3i$ appears on the plane in this position:

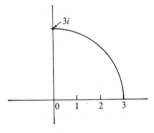

In fact, the reader may easily show that, for any real number b, bi is a point on the vertical line through 0 (above 0 if b is positive, below 0 if b is negative).

Using this observation we will prove that every point P in the plane can be written in the form

$$a + bi,$$

where a and b are real numbers. To do this, we simply draw the parallelogram (in fact, rectangle) determined by P in this manner:

By the definition of $\oplus$, which we have agreed to write $+$, $P = A + B$. But A is a real number, which we can call a, and B is of the form bi (that is, $b \otimes i$) for some real b. Thus

$$P = a + bi.$$

The fact that every point in the plane can be written in the form $a + bi$ gives us a second way of describing these points. In our first method we gave the angle determined by the point and the distance from the point to 0. Now we can give a and b, which relate the point to the line of reals and to the vertical line through 0. For example, the point $-3 + 4i$ is 3 units to the left of the vertical line through 0, and 4 units above the line of reals.

This raises a problem. How can we compute the product of two points given in this new manner? For example, how can we find the real numbers a and b such that

$$(3 + 4i) \times (1 + i) = a + bi?$$

One method is to go back to the definition of multiplication of points in the plane. Using the Pythagorean Theorem, the reader will find that the point $3 + 4i$ lies on the circle of radius 5, and that the point $1 + i$ lies on the circle of radius $\sqrt{2}$, which is approximately 1.41. Thus $(3 + 4i) \times (1 + i)$ lies on the circle whose radius is about 7.05. To determine the angle of $(3 + 4i) \times (1 + i)$ the reader should draw the two points $3 + 4i$ and $1 + i$ and add their angles with the aid of a compass or protractor.

If the reader is careful he will find that $(3 + 4i) \times (1 + i)$ seems to be very close to $-1 + 7i$. That is, the a and the b we were seeking seem to be integers, despite the presence of $\sqrt{2}$ and the numerically inconvenient angle determined by the point $3 + 4i$. But at this moment, because of our approximation of $\sqrt{2}$ and because the accuracy of our drawings is always limited by the thickness of the pencil point, we are not sure that a is -1 and b is 7.

Let us compute $(3 + 4i) \times (1 + i)$ in a different way, without drawing any pictures. Using distributivity, we can reduce our problem to two simpler problems, since

$$(3 + 4i) \times (1 + i) = [(3 + 4i) \times 1] + [(3 + 4i) \times i].$$

As the reader may easily check by going back to our definition of $\otimes$ in the plane,

$$(3 + 4i) \times 1 = 3 + 4i.$$

Using commutativity of multiplication in the plane, we have

$$(3 + 4i) \times i = i \times (3 + 4i).$$

Then, by distributivity,

$$i \times (3 + 4i) = i \times 3 + i \times 4i.$$

By going back to the definition of multiplication in the plane, the reader may check that $i \times 3 = 3i$ and that $i \times 4i = -4$. Thus

$$(3 + 4i) \times (1 + i) = 3 + 4i + 3i - 4,$$

which the reader may simplify to $-1 + 7i$. Our suspicion that a and b are integers in this case is correct. (See E 53 for the generalization of this example.)

As the preceding computation shows, the arithmetic of the operations $\oplus$ and $\otimes$ in the plane closely resembles that of our usual addition and multiplication of real numbers. In fact, since the operations $\oplus$ and $\otimes$ satisfy the basic rules of arithmetic (recorded in Appendix A), computation with these operations differs from computation with ordinary addition and multiplication simply in the appearance of the symbol i and the extra rule, $i^2 = -1$.

When we consider the plane together with the operations $\oplus$ and $\otimes$, we call the points of the plane **complex numbers.** The word "complex" is more awesome than instructive. If history, like a sweater, could be unraveled and knitted again, we might call the points of the plane merely "numbers," and then treat those points that happen to lie on the horizontal line through 0 as a special type of number. Presumably, the word "complex" refers to the fact that a complex number is the sum of a real number and a number on the vertical line through 0 (the line of so-called imaginary numbers).

The real numbers are sufficient to provide every equation of odd degree with at least one root (Theorem 2) and to provide some equations of even degree with roots. The algebraic significance of the complex numbers lies in the fact that every equation with real coefficients has at least one root among the complex numbers. (Of course, all the roots might be real, such as the root of $3X + 1 = 0$, but recall that every real number is also a complex number.) Indeed, far more is true, as we see in the

FUNDAMENTAL THEOREM OF ALGEBRA. *Any equation with complex coeffi-cients has at least one root among the complex numbers.*

The first proof of this theorem was given in 1799 by Gauss. We will not give a proof, but only mention that the result depends both on algebra and topology. (See R 7 for a sketch of the proof.) With the aid of the Fundamental Theorem of Algebra, it can be shown that any equation of degree n, where n is greater than or equal to 1, has n complex roots (if duplications are counted appropriately). Combining this with Theorem 6, we see that the complex num-bers provide all the roots we could expect for equations with real coefficients (and, as is shown in E 39, even for equations with complex coefficients).

The complex numbers were not built in a day. Man began with the counting numbers, 1, 2, 3, 4, 5, $\cdots$. But, to find roots for equations of the type $AX = B$, he had to introduce all the positive rationals (not just those with denominator equal to 1). Zero was introduced to simplify the representation of numbers (for example, consider how important 0 is in distinguishing 37 from 307 and 30070). To find a root for equations of the type $X + A = 0$, he had to invent the negative numbers. To find a root for $1X^2 = 2$, he had to enter the realm of irrationals. But to guarantee that any equation with rational coefficients has a root, he had to build the complex numbers. In searching for roots of equations, man need never go beyond the complex numbers.

Nevertheless, the reader might expect us to construct operations $\oplus$ and $\otimes$ in space, as we did in the plane, which will extend the $\oplus$ and $\otimes$ of the complex numbers in the same sense that the $\oplus$ and $\otimes$ of complex numbers extend the $+$ and $\times$ of the real line.

It is easy to define an addition, $\oplus$, for points in space by using the same parallelogram technique that we used in defining $\oplus$ for the complex numbers; this new $\oplus$ is still commutative and associative. However, it has been known for almost a century (Frobenius, 1878, and C. S. Pierce, 1881) that it is im-possible to construct a $\otimes$ in space such that $\oplus$ and $\otimes$ together satisfy the usual rules of arithmetic, as given in Appendix A.

In four-dimensional space (spaces of all dimensions are defined in Appen-dix C) Hamilton, in 1843, had managed to construct a $\oplus$ and a $\otimes$ that satisfied every rule of ordinary arithmetic except that the multiplication $\otimes$ was not commutative. In 1845, Cayley built a $\oplus$ and a $\otimes$ in eight-dimensional space that satisfied every rule of arithmetic except that $\otimes$ was neither commutative nor associative. The higher the dimension of the space, the more that had to be sacrificed. Note that when we go from the real numbers, built on a space of dimension 1, to the complex numbers, built on a space of dimension 2, we sacrifice the notion of "positive and negative" (that is, right and left of 0).

The reader may have noted that the numbers 1, 2, 4, and 8 of the preceding paragraph are powers of 2, and may ask, "What about other dimensions?" Frobenius and Pierce proved that only for dimensions 1, 2, and 4 can a $\oplus$ and a $\otimes$ be defined that will satisfy the rules of arithmetic, even if we drop the demand that $\otimes$ be commutative. In 1958, R. Bott, M. Kervaire, and J. Milnor, using the machinery of algebraic topology, proved that only for dimensions 1, 2, 4, and 8 can a $\oplus$ and a $\otimes$ be defined that satisfy the rules of arithmetic, even if we drop the demand that $\otimes$ be associative or commutative.

Yet, even in the line or in the plane, there are difficult problems. Among the more challenging problems of the nineteenth century was to decide whether π (the ratio between the circumference and diameter of a circle) is algebraic or transcendental or even whether it is rational or irrational. Hermite, who had already proved certain other numbers transcendental, stated in 1873, "I shall risk nothing on an attempt to prove the transcendence of the number π. If others undertake this enterprise, no one will be happier than I at their success, but believe me, my dear friend, it will not fail to cost them some efforts." Nine years later Lindemann proved that π is transcendental.

But let us consider the number that we will now define. We draw two perpendicular lines as in (11) and the curve traced out by all points P such that the rectangle with diagonal $0P$ has area 1 and horizontal side at least 1. The curve and one such rectangle are shown in (11).

(11)

Then we draw the endless staircase above the curve (11), determined in this manner:

(12)

Though it is known that the total area of the endless shaded region is between 0.577 and 0.578, nobody knows whether this total is rational or irrational, or whether it is algebraic or transcendental. Yet this number, known as Euler's constant, in use for two centuries, is one of the most important numbers in advanced calculus.

Now that we have reached the complex numbers, let us show how the various types of numbers we have met in this book fit together. In this diagram the symbol $\supset$ is short for "contain."

(Every transcendental is irrational; some of the algebraic numbers are irrational.) The reader might well think of this book as a description of the various types of numbers and of some of their many applications.

In the next chapter we will prove that there are transcendental numbers.

Exercises

1. Check that 0, 1, and 2 are roots of $1X^3 - 3X^2 + 2X = 0$.

2. Which of the numbers 0, 1, 2, -2, $\frac{1}{2}$ are roots of $2X^2 - 3X - 2 = 0$?

3. (a) What is the value of $5X^3 - 2X^2 + 6X - 7$ when X is replaced by 0?
   (b) When X is replaced by 1?
   (c) When X is replaced by $\frac{1}{2}$?
   (d) Between what two numbers have we trapped a root of the equation
   $$5X^3 - 2X^2 + 6X - 7 = 0?$$

4. (a) Continuing with the equation of E 3, what is the numerical value of $5X^3 - 2X^2 + 6X - 7$ when X is replaced by 0.8?
   (b) Same as (a) when X is replaced by 0.9.
   (c) Between what two numbers have we trapped a root?
   (d) Which of these two numbers do you think is nearer the root?

5. (a) Compute the numerical value of $8X^3 - 12X^2 - 2X + 3$ when X is replaced by -2, -1, 0, 1, 2.
   (b) Using (a), what can you say about the roots of the equation $8X^3 - 12X^2 - 2X + 3 = 0$?

6. Proceeding as we did with the equation $1X^2 + 6X + 9 = 0$, find all the roots of
   (a) $1X^2 - 6X + 9 = 0$ and (b) $1X^2 + 3X + \frac{9}{4} = 0$.

7. Proceeding as we did with the equation $1X^2 + 6X + 9 = 0$, find all the roots of
   (a) $1X^2 - 8X + 16 = 0$ and (b) $1X^2 + 7X + \frac{49}{4} = 0$.

8. Check that the roots you found in E 7 lead to a true statement when substituted for X in the appropriate equation.

9. Proceeding as we did with the equation $1X^2 + 6X + 2 = 0$, find all the roots of (a) $1X^2 - 6X - 7 = 0$ and (b) $1X^2 - 2X - 4 = 0$.

10. Check that the roots you found in E 9 lead to a true statement when substituted for X in the appropriate equation.

11. There is a very fast way of estimating the square root of a positive real number A; that is to say, of finding the positive root of the equation $1X^2 - A = 0$. We illustrate the method by estimating $\sqrt{19}$. As a first guess we take 4. We then divide 4 into 19, obtaining 4.75. Next, we average 4 and 4.75; that is, we add 4 to 4.75 and divide the sum by 2. This average is 4.375. Now we use 4.375 as the new guess and repeat the process. That is, we divide 4.375 into 19, say, to 3 decimals, getting 4.349; and average 4.375 and 4.349, getting 4.362. If we wish, we can proceed with 4.362 as our guess. In any case, 4.362 is a close estimate for $\sqrt{19}$, as the reader may check by squaring 4.362.
(a) Compute the square of our first guess, 4.
(b) Compute the square of our second guess, 4.375.
(c) Compute the square of our third guess, 4.362.
This technique was used by the Babylonians and, later, by the Greeks (see R 1, p. 45).

12. (a) Using the method of E 11, estimate $\sqrt{5}$, starting with a guess of 2 and applying the process twice.
(b) Compute the square of your final guess, and compare it to 5.

13. The same as E 12, but estimate $\sqrt{7}$, and choose your own first guess.

14. Write out a proof for Theorem 2 in case the degree is 3 and the coefficient of X^3 is positive.

15. Write out a proof for Theorem 2 in case the degree is 3 and the coefficient of X^3 is negative.

16. By dividing 11 into 3, find the decimal representation of $\frac{3}{11}$, and indicate its repeating block.

17. By dividing 13 into 5, find the decimal representation of $\frac{5}{13}$, and indicate its repeating block.

18. What fraction has the decimal representation $0.434343\cdots$; that is, $0.\overline{43}$?

19. Find the number whose decimal representation is $2.1\overline{72}$.

20. (a) Check that 0 is a root of the equation $5X^7 - 2X^3 + 1X^2 - 6X = 0$.
(b) Noting that $X - 0$ is simply X, find a polynomial Q such that
$$5X^7 - 2X^3 + 1X^2 - 6X = Q \times (1X - 0).$$
(c) Does (b) agree with the lemma?

21. If r is 0, then the lemma is very easy to prove. Prove the lemma for the special case, $r = 0$,

22. (a) Check that 2 is a root of $3X^2 - 5X - 2 = 0$.
    (b) Find a polynomial Q such that $3X^2 - 5X - 2 = Q \times (1X - 2)$.

23. (a) Check that -1 is a root of $2X^2 + 5X + 3 = 0$.
    (b) Find a polynomial Q such that $2X^2 + 5X + 3 = Q \times (1X + 1)$.
    (c) Why does (b) illustrate the lemma?

24. Prove the converse of the lemma. That is, prove that if r is a real number and if P and Q are polynomials satisfying $P = Q \times (1X - r)$, then r is a root of the equation $P = 0$.

25. Prove that the product of two repeating decimals is again a repeating decimal.

26. Prove that $1 + \sqrt{2}$ is algebraic by finding an equation with integral coefficients of which it is a root.

27. Find an equation (of degree 4) with integral coefficients of which $\sqrt{2} + \sqrt{3}$ is a root. This will show that $\sqrt{2} + \sqrt{3}$ is algebraic. It can be proved that the sum and the product of any two algebraic numbers are algebraic.

28. (a) Draw three points X, Y, and Z in the plane.
    (b) Drawing the two necessary parallelograms, find the point $X \oplus (Y \oplus Z)$.
    (c) Drawing the two necessary parallelograms, find the point $(X \oplus Y) \oplus Z$.
    (d) Compare the results of (b) and (c) (they should be the same).

29. (a) Prove that if r is a root of the equation $AX^3 + BX^2 + CX + D = 0$, then $1/r$ is a root of the equation $DX^3 + CX^2 + BX + A = 0$.
    (b) Using (a), prove that if r is algebraic, so is $1/r$.

30. (a) Prove that if r is a root of the equation $AX^3 + BX^2 + CX + D = 0$, then $r/2$ is a root of the equation $8AX^3 + 4BX^2 + 2CX + D = 0$.
    (b) Using the idea suggested by (a), prove that if r is algebraic, so is $r/2$.

31. We did not prove that if we magnify a parallelogram we get a parallelogram. What we really needed is this little theorem, which the reader can prove using similar triangles and high school geometry.

THEOREM. *If ABCD is a parallelogram, and if B′, C′, D′ are situated as in this diagram*

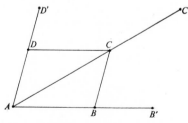

in such a way that

$$\frac{AB'}{AB} = \frac{AC'}{AC} = \frac{AD'}{AD},$$

then AB′C′D′ is a parallelogram.

32. Prove that $(2 \otimes i) \otimes (3 \otimes i) = -6$
    (a) by drawing the points $2 \otimes i$ and $3 \otimes i$ and using only the definition of $\otimes$;
    (b) by using the commutativity and associativity of $\otimes$ and the relation $i^2 = -1$ (draw no pictures).

33. Draw the two points in the plane that are roots of the equation $1X^2 = -4$.

34. Prove that each of the three points shown in this diagram is a root of the equation $1X^3 = 1$.

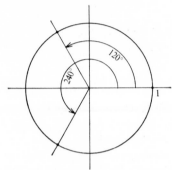

35. Prove that the point C in this diagram is a root of $1X^2 = -1$.

36. Prove that the four points indicated by this diagram are roots of the equation $1X^4 = 16$.

37. Prove that every point on the vertical line through 0 can be written in the form $b \otimes i$ for some real number b.

38. Any point X (other than 0) determines a point S on the circle of radius 1 and a positive real number r, as shown by this diagram.

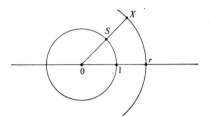

Prove that $S \otimes r = X$.

39. (a) Prove that the lemma remains true if we allow complex coefficients.
    (b) Prove that Theorem 6 remains true if we allow complex coefficients.

40. (a) Using the geometric definition of multiplication for complex numbers, find the point $2i \times (3 + 4i)$.
    (b) Using only the rules of arithmetic, such as distributivity, compute $2i \times (3 + 4i)$, and draw the result. (Whenever you see i^2, replace it by -1.)
    (c) Compare the results of (a) and (b).

41. (a) Using the geometric definition of multiplication for complex numbers, compute and draw $(2 + i) \times (1 + 2i)$.
    (b) Compute $(2 + i) \times (1 + 2i)$ arithmetically, and draw the result.
    (c) Compare the two points drawn in (a) and (b).

42. (a) Using the geometric definition of multiplication of complex numbers, compute and draw $(1 + i) \times (-1 + i)$.
    (b) Compute $(1 + i) \times (-1 + i)$ arithmetically, and draw the result.
    (c) Compare the two points drawn in (a) and (b).

43. (a) Using the geometric definition of multiplication of complex numbers, compute and draw $(3 + 4i) \times (4 + 3i)$.
    (b) Compute $(3 + 4i) \times (4 + 3i)$ arithmetically, and draw the result.
    (c) Compare the points drawn in (a) and (b).

44. We did not prove that $\oplus$ for complex numbers is associative, but merely suggested that the reader check that this is so with an example. We now outline a proof.
    (a) Prove by an inspection of the necessary parallelograms that if $P = a \oplus bi$ and $Q = c \oplus di$, where a, b, c, and d are real numbers, then $P \oplus Q = (a + c) + (b + d)i$. (First take the simplest case, where a, b, c, and d are all positive.)
    (b) Part (a) expresses the sum of two complex numbers in terms of the sum of real numbers. Using the fact that the $+$ for real numbers is associative, prove that the $\oplus$ for complex numbers is also associative.

45. Prove that the total area of the endless supply of shaded rectangles formed from the curve (*11*) in the manner shown in the following diagram is 1.

(*13*)

(*Hint:* Without changing its distance from the horizontal line, slide each rectangle to the left until it is directly above the line segment whose ends are 1 and 2.)

46. Prove that the shaded area of (*12*) is
    (a) less than the shaded area of (*13*);
    (b) more than half the shaded area of (*13*).

47. From E 45 and 46, prove that Euler's constant is between 1 and $\frac{1}{2}$.

48. By the size or "absolute value" of a real number r, we shall mean r if r is positive, and $-r$ if r is not positive. Thus the size of 3 is 3, the size of -3 is also 3, and the size of 0 is 0. Clearly, the size of a real number is its distance from 0. Let $|r|$ denote the size of r.
    (a) Let s be any real number. Prove that there is an integer M such that $|s - (M/13)|$ is less than $\frac{1}{26}$. (*Hint:* Draw the rationals with denominator 13.)
    (b) Let s be any real number and N any natural number bigger than 0. Prove that there is an integer M such that $|s - (M/N)|$ is less than $1/2N$.

49. In E 48 we saw that any real number can be approximated closely by a rational if we allow the denominator of the rational to be large. In 1955, K. F. Roth obtained a profound result on the approximation of algebraic numbers by rationals, of which the following is a consequence: If s is an irrational algebraic number, then there are only a finite number of rationals M/N with the property that $|s - (M/N)|$ is less than $2/N^3$. This suggests that if a number s can be approximated "too" closely by rationals, then s must be transcendental. This will be exploited in E 50.

50. Using E 49, prove that

$$s = \left(\frac{1}{10}\right)^3 + \left(\frac{1}{10}\right)^9 + \left(\frac{1}{10}\right)^{27} + \cdots + \left(\frac{1}{10}\right)^{3^n} + \cdots$$

is transcendental. The following steps outline the proof.
    (a) Prove that s is irrational (by Theorem 4).
    (b) Prove that $|s - [(\frac{1}{10})^3 + \cdots + (\frac{1}{10})^{3^n}]|$ is less than $2/(10^{3^n})^3$.
    (*Hint:* Observe that $|s - [(\frac{1}{10})^3 + \cdots + (\frac{1}{10})^{3^n}]|$ is equal to $(\frac{1}{10})^{3^{n+1}} + (\frac{1}{10})^{3^{n+2}} + \cdots$, which is less than the geometric series with first term $(\frac{1}{10})^{3^{n+1}}$ and ratio $\frac{1}{2}$.)
    (c) Now use Roth's theorem to prove that s must be transcendental.

51. Prove that $(a + bi) \otimes (c + di) = (ac - bd) \oplus (ad + bc)i$. (*Hint:* Begin by using distributivity.)

52. E 44 and E 51 suggest a very direct and short way of defining the complex numbers, $\oplus$ and $\otimes$—a way that avoids geometry but exploits the real numbers, with their $+$ and $\times$.
    (a) Define a complex number to be a pair of real numbers, (a, b).
    (b) Define $(a, b) \oplus (c, d)$ to be $(a + c, b + d)$.
    (c) Define $(a, b) \otimes (c, d)$ to be $(ac - bd, ad + bc)$.
    (d) Show that E 51 and E 44 motivate (c) and (b), respectively.
    (e) Which is the (a, b) that we should name -1?
    (f) Which is the (a, b) that we should name i?

53. If a and b are integers, then $a + bi$ is called a "Gaussian integer." Prove that the sum and the product of two Gaussian integers are Gaussian integers. (*Hint:* Use E 44 and E 51.) The theory of Gaussian integers has been used to obtain results concerning the primes (see R 14).

References

1. B. L. van der Waerden, *Science Awakening*, Noordhoff Ltd., Groningen, Holland, 1954. (The Babylonian treatment of equations of degree 2 is described on pp. 69–70.)

2. L. Weisner, *Introduction to the Theory of Equations*, Macmillan, 1949. (The complex numbers are developed on pp. 1–19.)

3. E. T. Bell, *The Development of Mathematics*, McGraw-Hill, New York, 1945. (Pages 155–164, 215–218 discuss the complex numbers. How the attitude toward the negative and complex numbers has changed through the centuries is shown on pp. 172–180. For a discussion of the work of Pierce and Frobenius and for further references see pp. 249–251. The Fundamental Theorem of Algebra is discussed on p. 178.)

4. E. T. Bell, *Men of Mathematics*, Simon and Schuster, New York, 1937. (See p. 464, on which the remark of Hermite appears, for a discussion of the geometric significance of the transcendence of π. Remarks on Gauss's proof of the Fundamental Theorem of Algebra are made on pp. 332–334.)

5. *I. Niven, *Irrational Numbers*, Carus Mathematical Monograph 11, Mathematical Association of America, distributed by Wiley, New York. (On p. 20 the irrationality of π and π^2 is proved with the aid of the elementary integral calculus. Chapter 7 presents Liouville's proof, of 1844, for the existence of transcendentals.)

6. D. J. Struik, *A Concise History of Mathematics*, Dover, New York, 1948. (A concise history of the work of Tartaglia and Ferrari on roots of equations of degree at most 4 is given on pp. 109–116.)

7. R. Courant and H. Robbins, *What is Mathematics?*, Oxford University Press, New York, 1941. [A sketch of a proof of the Fundamental Theorem of Algebra (for the reader familiar with trigonometry) is presented on pp. 269–271. Liouville's proof of the existence of transcendentals is to be found in pp. 104–107.]

8. O. Veblen and J. W. Young, *Projective Geometry*, vol. 1, Ginn, Boston, 1938. (Addition for points on the line is defined geometrically on pp. 141–142; see, in particular, the footnote on p. 142. On pp. 144–145 the same is done for multiplication; see, in particular, the footnote on p. 145. The resulting addition and multiplication form a field, as defined in Appendix A.)

9. A. Seidenberg, *Lectures in Projective Geometry*, Van Nostrand, New York, 1962. (Geometry is built out of algebra on pp. 34–35.)

10. J. B. Roberts, *The Real Number System in an Algebraic Setting*, Freeman, San Francisco, 1961. (Beginning with the natural numbers, this book constructs the integers, then the rationals, and, finally, all the real numbers.)

11. *L. E. Dickson, *Linear Algebra*, Hafner, New York. (On p. 14 the 8-dimensional algebra of Cayley is defined.)

12. *K. F. Roth, Rational approximations to algebraic numbers, *Mathematika*, vol. 2, 1955, pp. 1–20. (For a history of this problem see the review by E. R. Kolchin in *Mathematical Reviews*, vol. 17, 1956, p. 242.)

13. *B. L. van der Waerden, *Modern Algebra*, vol. 1, Ungar, New York, 1949. (A proof of the Fundamental Theorem of Algebra is given on pp. 225–228.)

14. *C. C. MacDuffee, *An Introduction to Abstract Algebra*, Wiley, New York, 1956. (On pp. 117–121 the Fundamental Theorem of Arithmetic is extended to the complex numbers of the form $a + bi$, where a and b are integers. As exercise 2 on p. 121 shows, Theorem 51.4 of p. 120 can be used to prove that every prime natural number of the form $4k + 1$ can be expressed uniquely as the sum of the squares of two natural numbers.)

15. T. Dantzig, *Number, the Language of Science*, Macmillan, New York, 1954. (Chapters 8 and 9 discuss the real numbers; Chapter 10, the complex numbers; Chapter C, roots and their relation to geometry.)

Chapter **16**

INFINITE SETS

Infinity has fascinated man at least since the time of the Greeks. Who has not looked into the sky and wondered whether the stars are without end? Galileo even interrupts his *Dialogue on Two New Sciences* to record, in the year 1638, a conversation among three Renaissance gentlemen on some perplexing questions concerning infinity. We shall listen in on this conversation, examine it in detail, and, in the process of deciding which remarks are correct and which fallacious, present the fundamental discoveries of Georg Cantor, who, near the end of the nineteenth century, founded the mathematical theory of the infinite.

Now let us hear what the three gentlemen, Salviati, Simplicio, and Sagredo, have to say on this intriguing subject.

>*Simplicio:* Here a difficulty presents itself which appears to me insoluble. Since it is clear that we may have one line segment longer than another, each containing an infinite number of points, we are forced to admit that, within one and the same class, we may have something greater than infinity, because the infinity of points in the long line segment is greater than the infinity of points in the short line segment. This assigning to an infinite quantity a value greater than infinity is quite beyond my comprehension.

>*Salviati:* This is one of the difficulties which arise when we attempt, with our finite minds, to discuss the infinite, assigning to it those properties which we give to the finite and limited; but this I think is wrong, for we cannot speak of infinite quantities as being the one greater or less than or equal to another. To prove this I have in mind an argument, which, for the sake of clearness, I shall put in the form of questions to Simplicio who raised this difficulty.

>I take it for granted that you know which of the numbers are squares and which are not.*

>*Simplicio:* I am quite aware that a squared number is one which results from the multiplication of another number by itself: thus 4, 9, etc., are squared numbers which come from multiplying 2, 3, etc. by themselves.

>*Salviati:* Very well; and you also know that just as the products are called

---

* In this context, the word "number" is short for natural number, 1, 2, 3, 4, 5···. (Zero is not included.)

squares the factors are called roots; while on the other hand those numbers which do not consist of two equal factors are not squares. Therefore if I assert that all numbers, including both squares and non-squares, are more than the squares alone, I shall speak the truth, shall I not?

Simplicio: Most certainly.

Salviati: If I should ask further how many squares there are, one might reply truly that there are as many as the corresponding number of roots, since every square has its own root and every root its own square, while no square has more than one root and no root more than one square.

Simplicio: Precisely so.

Salviati: But if I inquire how many roots there are, it cannot be denied that there are as many as there are numbers because every number is a root of some square. This being granted we must say that there are as many squares as there are numbers because they are just as numerous as their roots, and all the numbers are roots. Yet at the outset we said there are many more numbers than squares, since the larger portion of them are not squares. Not only so, but the proportionate number of squares diminishes as we pass to larger numbers. Thus up to 100 we have 10 squares, that is, the squares constitute 1/10 part of all the numbers; up to 10,000 we find only 1/100th part to be squares; and up to a million only 1/1000th part; on the other hand in an infinite number, if one could conceive of such a thing, he would be forced to admit that there are as many squares as there are numbers all taken together.

Sagredo: What then must one conclude under these circumstances?

Salviati: So far as I see we can only infer that the totality of all numbers is infinite, that the number of squares is infinite, and that the number of their roots is infinite; neither is the number of squares less than the totality of all numbers, nor the latter greater than the former; and finally the attributes "equal," "greater," and "less" are not applicable to infinite, but only to finite, quantities. When, therefore, Simplicio introduces several lines of different lengths and asks me how it is possible that the longer ones do not contain more points than the shorter, I answer him that one line does not contain more or less or just as many points as another, but that each line contains an infinite number. Or if I had replied to him that the points in one line segment were equal in number to the squares; in another, greater than the totality of numbers; and in the little one, as many as the number of cubes, might I not, indeed, have satisfied him by thus placing more points in one line than in another and yet maintaining an infinite number in each? So much for the first difficulty.

Sagredo: Pray stop a moment and let me add to what has already been said an idea which just occurs to me. If the preceding be true, it seems to me impossible to say that one infinite number is greater than another····.

Before we analyze this conversation to see what is true and what false, let us make sure we agree on some fundamental terms to serve as tools in building a theory of infinity. *First of all, we shall use the word* **set** *to refer to any collection of objects or numbers.* We will say "a set of girls" rather than "a bevy of girls"; "a set of sheep" rather than "a flock of sheep"; "a set of fish" rather than "a school of fish." For example, in the foregoing conversation, Salviati mentioned the set of squares 1, 4, 9, 16, $\cdots$ and also the set of numbers 1, 2, 3, 4, $\cdots$. (He and Cantor do not include 0 among the natural numbers, and we will go along with them throughout this chapter. The reader will see that Cantor's investigation of infinity could have been carried out with only slight changes if he had included 0 among the natural numbers.)

The **elements** *or* **members** *of a set are the individuals of which the set is composed.* For example, 9 is an element of the set of squares.

Let us give a precise meaning to such phrases as "equal in number," "just as numerous," and "there are as many." *We will call two sets S and S'* **conumerous** *if there is a way of marrying off each element in S to an element in S' in such a way that no element is committing bigamy and every element is married to some element. Such a pairing of the elements of S with the elements of S' we will call a* **one-to-one correspondence** *between S and S'.* Salviati was saying that the set of squares 1, 4, 9, $\cdots$ and the set of natural numbers are conumerous. This was his way of arranging one-to-one correspondence between the two sets; each square is married to its square root:

$$1, \quad 4, \quad 9, \quad 16, \quad \cdots, \quad N^2, \quad \cdots$$
$$\updownarrow \quad \updownarrow \quad \updownarrow \quad \updownarrow \qquad\quad \updownarrow$$
$$1, \quad 2, \quad 3, \quad 4, \quad \cdots, \quad N, \quad \cdots$$

(We will use the symbol $\leftrightarrow$ to indicate "is married to" or "is paired with.") If two sets are conumerous, we might also say that "they are equal in number" or that "they are just as numerous," and so on.

If S' and S are two sets such that each element of S is also an element of S', we will say that S is a **subset** *of S'.* (For instance, every set is a subset of itself.) Thus the set of squares is a subset of the set of all natural numbers. What surprises the three gentlemen and ourselves is that a subset of a set S can be conumerous with S and yet fail to be all of S.

We will use braces, { }, as an abbreviation for "the set whose elements are." Thus {4, 7} is the set with two elements, namely, 4 and 7; and {1, 2, 3, $\cdots$} is the set of natural numbers (0 being excepted in this chapter).

By a **proper subset** *of a set S we mean any subset of S other than S itself.* For example, {1, 2, 3} has seven proper subsets: {1}, {2}, {3}, {1, 2}, {1, 3}, {2, 3}, and the empty set. As the reader may check, {1, 2, 3, 4} has fifteen proper subsets.

The set of natural numbers {1, 2, 3, $\cdots$} (which, from now on, we will call N) is conumerous with many of its proper subsets, not just with the set of squares. As Salviati hinted, N is conumerous with the set of cubes. (The reader may arrange the marriage.) Similarly, N is conumerous with the set of all primes. The rule for marrying the set N of natural numbers to the set of all primes is very simple: marry 1 to the smallest prime; marry 2 to the next larger prime; marry 3 to the next prime, and so on. Thus, since 2 is the first prime, 3 the second, 5 the third, and so on, we have:

$$
\begin{array}{ccccccccc}
1, & 2, & 3, & 4, & 5, & 6, & \cdots, & N, & \cdots \\
\updownarrow & \updownarrow & \updownarrow & \updownarrow & \updownarrow & \updownarrow & & \updownarrow & \\
2, & 3, & 5, & 7, & 11, & 13, & \cdots, & P_N, & \cdots
\end{array}
$$

where P_N denotes the Nth prime.

Similarly, the set A of all points on the line segment from 0 to 2 is conumerous with the set B of all points on the shorter line segment from 0 to 1. To justify this statement we must marry off the elements of A to the elements of B. A simply way of doing this is to marry off the typical element a in A to $a/2$, which is an element of B. (Observe that every element b in B is married, by this rule, to some element in A, namely $2b$.)

Thus Simplicio's claim, "The infinity of points in the long line segment is greater than the infinity of points in the short line segment" is not justified, since the two sets are conumerous, even though one set is a proper subset of the other.

This phenomenon may seem strange to us, since it does not occur in daily life. After all, as the reader may check, the set $\{1, 2, 3, 4\}$ is not conumerous with any of its fifteen proper subsets. This phenomenon shows a fundamental distinction between the finite sets and the infinite sets. *We will call a set* **finite** *if it is conumerous with a set of natural numbers* $\{1, 2, 3, 4, \cdots, n\}$ *for some natural number n.* Thus, for example, the set of planets is finite, since it is conumerous with $\{1, 2, 3, 4, 5, 6, 7, 8, 9\}$. *Any set that is not finite we will call* **infinite.** For example, the set of primes is infinite (Theorem 2, Chapter 3). Whether the set of pairs of twin primes is finite or infinite is not known. (See Chapter 3.) The reader may easily convince himself that *no finite set is conumerous with a proper subset of itself.* But for infinite sets, as Salviati points out, this no longer holds. In fact, in 1887, Dedekind, rather than fight this seeming paradox, based his definition of infinite sets on it.

Although the number of elements in a finite set is greater than the number of elements in any proper subset, Simplicio should have been more careful than to jump to the conclusion that "The infinity of the points in the longer line segment is greater than the infinity of points in the shorter line segment." When we talk of infinite sets we must not use a word like "greater" until we have given it a precise meaning. Whether Salviati was right in saying, "We cannot speak of infinite quantities as being the one greater or less than or equal to another," or "The attributes 'equal,' 'greater,' and 'less' are not applicable to infinite, but only to finite, [sets]" was not settled until the year 1873.

Salviati and Sagredo seem to be of the opinion that any two infinite sets are conumerous. The evidence is quite persuasive: N, the set of squares, the set of cubes, and the set of primes are all conumerous. Indeed, we can prove

THEOREM 1. *Any infinite subset of N is conumerous with N.*

PROOF. Let N' be an infinite subset of N. Then N' has a smallest element which we call n_1 and marry to 1. We let n_2 be the smallest element (other than n_1) in N', and marry n_2 to 2. Next we let n_3 be the smallest element (other than n_1 and n_2) in N', and marry n_3 to 3. In this way we may continue, gradually marrying off all the elements of N to elements of N':

$$
\begin{array}{cccc}
1, & 2, & 3, & 4, \\
\updownarrow & \updownarrow & \updownarrow & \updownarrow \quad \cdots \\
n_1, & n_2, & n_3, & n_4,
\end{array}
$$

Since N' is infinite, all the elements of N can be married by this rule. Moreover, each element of N' will be married eventually to some element of N. In fact, if n' is an element of N', then there are at most $n' - 1$ elements in N' less than n'. Thus n' will be married by our rule; indeed, n' will be married to some element of N no larger than n'.

Further evidence in favor of Salviati and Sagredo's opinion is our observation that the set of real numbers between 0 and 1 is conumerous with the set of real numbers between 0 and 2. Moreover, the borders of any two concentric circles are conumerous, as this diagram shows:

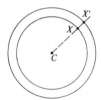

Here we marry X to X' if they are on the same ray from the center, C, of the two circles. (A similar argument applies to circles that are not concentric.)

We might also provide a geometric proof that any two line segments are conumerous by this rule:

Place the two line segments AB and $A'B'$ parallel to each other; denote by C

the point where the line through A and A' intersects the line through B and B', and marry X to X' if C, X, and X' are on a line.

Salviati goes on to say, "The points in one line segment were equal in number to the squares," but doesn't bother to justify his statement. Perhaps he had in the back of his mind something like this:

Salviati: It is clear to me that the squares 1, 4, 9, $\cdots$ are conumerous with the set of all reals between 0 and 1. I picture two bags: one containing all the squares; the other, all the reals from 0 to 1. I put my left hand into the bag of squares and my right hand into the bag of reals, and I marry the two numbers I happen to select. These two numbers I remove from the bags. Now I repeat the process as often as necessary until both bags are empty.

We: But, Salviati, might you not empty one bag while the other is still far from empty? Your rule is so vague that it is impossible to predict what square will be married to what real. Can you guarantee that you will not use up the squares before the reals, or the reals before the squares? What if it turns out that you pluck out the square 1 and the real 1? Next, you might pluck out the square 4 and the real $\frac{1}{2}$. After that, you might pluck out the square 9 and the real $\frac{1}{3}$, and so on. In this way, you might accidentally be marrying each square to a real of a very special form. Or what if you should have the misfortune of marrying each square to itself? We fear that many reals might go unmarried.

Salviati: It is quite unlikely that I would be so unfortunate as to pluck out such an orderly set of reals.

We: But you must grant that it might happen. Besides, even if you live to be a hundred, you will never empty either bag. I would much prefer to see a more precise procedure for marrying off the squares to the reals from 0 to 1.

Salviati: At the moment I cannot think of one.

Thus, when the chips were down, Salviati did not convince us that the set of squares and the set of reals from 0 to 1 are conumerous. We still face the question: Are any two infinite sets conumerous? If the answer is "yes," then we ought to be able to find, in particular, a rule that marries off the natural numbers to the reals from 0 to 1. If the answer is "no," then we can introduce into infinite sets the notions of "greater" and "less," which we have for finite sets.

Before trying to devise a one-to-one correspondence between the natural numbers and the reals from 0 to 1 we might consider this simpler question: Can the set of natural numbers 1, 2, 3, $\cdots$ be married to the set of positive rationals?*

It would seem highly unlikely that there could be such a one-to-one correspondence, since the set of positive rationals is formed by varying both the

---

* For simplicity we restrict our attention to positive rationals. As Corollary 2 shows, the set of positive rationals is conumerous with the set of all rationals.

numerator p and the denominator q. For example, the set of positive rationals with numerator 1 is conumerous with the set of natural numbers, since we can arrange this one-to-one correspondence:

$$1, \quad 2, \quad 3, \quad 4, \quad \cdots, \quad n, \quad \cdots$$
$$\updownarrow \quad \updownarrow \quad \updownarrow \quad \updownarrow \qquad\quad \updownarrow$$
$$\frac{1}{1}, \quad \frac{1}{2}, \quad \frac{1}{3}, \quad \frac{1}{4} \quad \cdots, \quad \frac{1}{n}, \quad \cdots$$

Yet, in 1873, Cantor discovered that the set of natural numbers and the set of positive rationals are conumerous. This is how he devised a one-to-one correspondence between the two sets. The reader will notice how he avoids pairing all the natural numbers with positive rationals of a fixed numerator.

First he placed the positive rationals on the plane, as indicated here:

(1)

$$
\begin{array}{ccccccc}
\cdot & \cdot & \cdot & \cdot & & & \\
\cdot & \cdot & \cdot & \cdot & & & \\
\cdot & \cdot & \cdot & \cdot & & & \\
\frac{5}{1} & \frac{5}{2} & \frac{5}{3} & \frac{5}{4} & \cdot & \cdot & \cdot \\
\frac{4}{1} & \frac{4}{2} & \frac{4}{3} & \frac{4}{4} & \cdot & \cdot & \cdot \\
\frac{3}{1} & \frac{3}{2} & \frac{3}{3} & \frac{3}{4} & \cdot & \cdot & \cdot \\
\frac{2}{1} & \frac{2}{2} & \frac{2}{3} & \frac{2}{4} & \cdot & \cdot & \cdot \\
\frac{1}{1} & \frac{1}{2} & \frac{1}{3} & \frac{1}{4} & \cdot & \cdot & \cdot \\
\end{array}
$$

and then married them to the natural numbers as indicated by this rule:

(2)

$$
\begin{array}{ccccc}
\cdot & & & & \\
15 & \cdot & \cdot & \cdot & \\
10 & 14 & \cdot & \cdot & \\
6 & 9 & 13 & \cdot & \\
3 & 5 & 8 & 12 & \\
1 & 2 & 4 & 7 & 11 \quad \cdot \\
\end{array}
$$

Of course, expressions such as $\frac{6}{3}$, $\frac{4}{2}$, and $\frac{2}{1}$, which have equal value, all appear in (1). If we erase any rational not in its lowest terms (such as $\frac{4}{2}$ and $\frac{6}{3}$) from (1), then we can still arrange the one-to-one correspondence by placing no natural number at a dot from which the rational has been erased:

$$
\begin{array}{ccccccccc}
\cdot & \cdot & \cdot & \cdot & & & & \cdot & \\
\cdot & \cdot & \cdot & \cdot & & & & \cdot & \cdot \\
\cdot & \cdot & \cdot & \cdot & & & & \cdot & \cdot \\
\frac{5}{1} & \frac{5}{2} & \frac{5}{3} & \frac{5}{4} & \cdot & \cdot & \cdot & 11 & \cdot & \cdot \\
\frac{4}{1} & \cdot & \frac{4}{3} & \cdot & \frac{4}{5} & \cdot & \cdot & 9 & \cdot & \\
\frac{3}{1} & \frac{3}{2} & \cdot & \frac{3}{4} & \frac{3}{5} & \cdot & \cdot & 5 & 8 & \\
\frac{2}{1} & \cdot & \frac{2}{3} & \cdot & \frac{2}{5} & \cdot & \cdot & 3 & 7 & \\
\frac{1}{1} & \frac{1}{2} & \frac{1}{3} & \frac{1}{4} & \frac{1}{5} & \cdot & \cdot & 1 & 2 & 4 & 6 & 10 \\
\end{array}
$$

$$(3) \qquad\qquad\qquad\qquad (4)$$

Calling a set **denumerable** *if it is conumerous with N, we can state*

THEOREM 2. *The set of positive rationals is denumerable.*

The reader might look over Cantor's technique and try to devise another one-to-one correspondence between N and the positive rationals; the key thing is to be sure not to restrict yourself to rationals of a special type.

We can use the same idea to prove a more general result. *Let us begin by defining the* **union** *of sets S_1, S_2, $\cdots$ as the set of all elements that appear in at least one of S_1, S_2, $\cdots$.* For example, the union of $\{1, 2\}$ and $\{1, 3\}$ is $\{1, 2, 3\}$. As another example, if S_1 is the set of positive rationals with numerator 1, if S_2 is the set of positive rationals with numerator 2, and, in general, if S_n is the set of positive rationals with numerator n, then the union of S_1, S_2, S_3, $\cdots$, S_n, $\cdots$ is simply the set of all positive rationals.

THEOREM 3. *If we have a denumerable collection of denumerable sets S_1, S_2, S_3, $\cdots$ (for convenience, no two of which share an element), then the union of all the S_1, S_2, S_3, $\cdots$, S_n, $\cdots$ is also denumerable.*

PROOF. Let S be the union of S_1, S_2, S_3, $\cdots$; that is, the set of elements belonging to at least one of S_1, S_2, S_3, $\cdots$ (in fact, exactly one, since no two share an element).

Since S_1 is denumerable we may place each of its elements on one of the dots of an endless line of equally spaced dots:

(S_1)

Since S_2 is denumerable, we may place its elements on the line of dots to the right of S_1:

(S_1) (S_2)

Similarly, S_3 can be sprinkled to the right of S_2, and so on. Thus the set S, the union of S_1, S_2, S_3, $\cdots$, is married off, element by element, with the following endless arrangement of dots:

(5)

By the technique shown in (2), S is denumerable. Theorem 3 is proved.

In a similar mood, we have

THEOREM 4. *The union, S, of a denumerable collection of finite sets S_1, S_2, S_3, $\cdots$ is either finite or denumerable.*

PROOF. This time we are allowing the individual sets S_1, S_2, S_3, $\cdots$ to share elements.

To prove that S is either finite or denumerable we must present a one-to-one correspondence between S and the set $\{1, 2, 3, \cdots , n\}$ for some n, or else between S and the set N of natural numbers. To arrange such a correspondence, we begin with S_1. Since S_1 is finite, it has, say, n_1 elements, and these elements can be named $a_1, a_2, a_3, \cdots , a_{n_1}$.

If S_2 is a subset of S_1 we go on to S_3. If S_2 is not a subset of S_1, then there will be among the elements of S_2 a finite set $b_1, b_2, \cdots , b_{n_2}$ of elements not already in S_1. We then marry these elements to the next n_2 integers, $n_1 + 1, n_1 + 2, \cdots , n_1 + n_2$.

So far we have

$$\underbrace{1, 2, \cdots , n_1,}_{\substack{\text{paired to} \\ S_1}} \qquad \underbrace{n_1 + 1, \cdots , n_1 + n_2}_{\substack{\text{paired to the part} \\ \text{of } S_2 \text{ not in } S_1}}{}^*$$

If S_3 is a subset of the union of S_1 and S_2 we go on to S_4. Otherwise, if S_3 has n_3 elements not already accounted for, we can marry them to the next n_3 integers, $n_1 + n_2 + 1, n_1 + n_2 + 2, \cdots , n_1 + n_2 + n_3$.

So far we have

$$\underbrace{1, 2, \cdots , n_1}_{\substack{\text{paired to} \\ S_1}} \qquad \underbrace{n_1 + 1, \cdots , n_1 + n_2}_{\substack{\text{paired to the part} \\ \text{of } S_2 \text{ not in } S_1}} \qquad \underbrace{n_1 + n_2 + 1, \cdots , n_1 + n_2 + n_3}_{\substack{\text{paired to the part of } S_3 \text{ not} \\ \text{in the union of } S_1 \text{ and } S_2}}$$

---

* This part, from $n_1 + 1$ to $n_1 + n_2$, of course, does not appear if S_2 is a subset of S_1.

If we continue in this manner, one of two things happens. We might meet an m such that all the sets S_{m+1}, S_{m+2}, $\cdots$ are subsets of the union of S_1, S_2, $\cdots$, S_m; in this case, S is finite. On the other hand, we might meet no such m; in this case, S is denumerable, for every element of S is eventually married to some element of N.

The following two corollaries illustrate the use of Theorems 3 and 4.

COROLLARY 1. *The set of all integers is denumerable; and so is the set of integers exclusive of zero.*

PROOF. Let S_1 be $\{1, -1, 0\}$; let S_2 be $\{2, -2\}$; let S_3 be $\{3, -3\}$; generally, let S_n be $\{n, -n\}$ for any natural number n larger than 1. Theorem 4 then asserts that the union of S_1, S_2, S_3, $\cdots$ is denumerable (since this union is obviously not finite). But this union is precisely the set of all integers. This proves the first part of the corollary. Changing S_1 to $\{1, -1\}$ is all that is necessary to obtain a proof of the second part.

COROLLARY 2. *The set of rationals is denumerable.*

PROOF. Let S_1 be
$$\{0, 1/1, -1/1, 1/-1, -1/-1, 1/2, -1/2,$$
$$1/-2, -1/-2, 1/3, -1/3, 1/-3, -1/-3, \cdots\}.$$
Let S_2 be the set of all rationals with numerator 2 or -2. Let S_3 be the set of all rationals with numerator 3 or -3. Let S_n be, in general, the set of all rationals with numerator n or $-n$ for any natural number n larger than 1. By Corollary 1, each S_n is denumerable. Thus, by Theorem 3, the union of S_1, S_2, S_3, $\cdots$ is denumerable. But this union is precisely the set of rationals. This proves the corollary.

Theorems 2, 3, and 4 and their corollaries seem to suggest that any infinite set is denumerable. But we still have not been able to make any headway in this chapter in proving that the reals between 0 and 1 are denumerable. Perhaps Salviati has misled us. As regards this problem, Cantor wrote in a letter to Dedekind, dated November 29, 1873:

> May I ask you a question, which has a certain theoretical interest for me but which I cannot answer; maybe you can answer it and would be so kind as to write to me about it. It goes as follows: take the set of all natural numbers n and denote it N. Further, consider, say, the set of all positive real numbers x and denote it R. Then the question is simply this: can N be paired with R in such a way that to every individual of one set corresponds one and only one individual of the other? At first glance, one says to oneself, "No, this is impossible, for N consists of discrete parts and R is a continuum." But nothing is proved by this objection. And much as I too feel that N and R do not permit such a pairing, I still cannot find the reason. And it is this reason that bothers me; maybe it is very simple.

Would not one at first glance be led to the conjecture that N cannot be paired off with the set of all positive rational numbers p/q? And yet it is not hard to show $\cdots$ that such an ordering can be found.

The rationals are distributed on the line quite generously (see E 39 of Chapter 5)—between any two points, no matter how close they are to each other, there is an infinite set of rationals—and yet the set of rationals, as we saw, is denumerable. Intuition is an inadequate guide through the world of infinite sets. Cantor was asking Dedekind to prove rigorously that intuition is right when it says "the real numbers are not denumerable" and that Salviati, reaching into the two bags, is wrong.

Dedekind did not solve Cantor's problem. On December 2, 1873, Cantor wrote again to Dedekind:

I was extremely pleased to receive today your answer to my latest letter. I proposed my question to you for the following reason. I had asked it several years ago and had always remained in doubt whether the difficulty which it presents is a subjective one or whether it is inherent in the substance. As you write to me that you too are unable to answer it I may assume the latter. Besides, I would like to add that I have never seriously thought about it because it has no particular practical interest for me and I fully agree with you if you say that for this reason it doesn't deserve too much labor. Only it would be a beautiful result $\cdots$.

Soon after, Cantor discovered a proof that the set of real numbers is not denumerable. On December 7, 1873, he wrote to Dedekind:

Recently I had time to follow up a little more fully the conjecture which I mentioned to you; only today I believe I have finished the matter. Should I have been deceived, I would not find a more lenient judge than you. I thus take the liberty of submitting to your judgment what I have written, in all the incompleteness of a first draft.

Thus, sometime between December 2 and December 7, 1873, Cantor had laid the cornerstone of the theory of infinity. In 1890 he discovered a second proof, much simpler than his proof of 1873. It is this second proof that we now give for

THEOREM 5 (Cantor's Theorem). *The set of real numbers is not denumerable.*

PROOF. We will argue very much as we did in proving that no finite list of primes can be complete. Instead of the Prime-manufacturing Machine of Chapter 3, we will require a "Real-manufacturing Machine," that will manufacture from any denumerable list of reals a real number not on that list.

Let us take any denumerable list of real numbers. In order to be able to treat all such lists, let us assume that each real number in a list is written in decimal form. We will denote the jth digit to the right of the decimal point in the nth number by $d_{n,j}$, or simply d_{nj}; L_n will denote the part to the left of the decimal point. Thus our list will look like this:

$$1 \longleftrightarrow L_1.d_{11} \quad d_{12} \quad d_{13} \quad d_{14} \quad \cdots$$
$$2 \longleftrightarrow L_2.d_{21} \quad d_{22} \quad d_{23} \quad d_{24} \quad \cdots$$
$$3 \longleftrightarrow L_3.d_{31} \quad d_{32} \quad d_{33} \quad d_{34} \quad \cdots$$

(6)

$$n \longleftrightarrow L_n.d_{n1} \quad d_{n2} \quad d_{n3} \quad d_{n4} \quad \cdots$$

The rule by which the particular numbers in the list are computed will not concern us. All that matters to us is that it is a denumerable list of real numbers; every natural number, no matter how large, is married by the list to some real number. One example of such a list might be computed in a very orderly manner by using square roots:

$$1 \longleftrightarrow 1.00000 \cdots \qquad (= \sqrt{1})$$
$$2 \longleftrightarrow 1.414 \cdots \qquad (= \sqrt{2})$$
$$3 \longleftrightarrow 1.732 \cdots \qquad (= \sqrt{3})$$

(7)

$$n \longleftrightarrow L_n.d_{n1} \quad d_{n2} \quad d_{n3} \quad \cdots \quad (= \sqrt{n})$$

In this list we have, for example, $d_{11} = 0$, $d_{12} = 0$, $d_{21} = 4$, $d_{22} = 1$.

Another quite orderly list consists of those rationals whose form is $1/n$:

$$1 \longleftrightarrow 1.0000 \cdots \qquad \left(= \frac{1}{1}\right)$$

$$2 \longleftrightarrow 0.5000 \cdots \qquad \left(= \frac{1}{2}\right)$$

$$3 \longleftrightarrow 0.3333 \cdots \qquad \left(= \frac{1}{3}\right)$$

(8)

$$n \longleftrightarrow .d_{n1} \quad d_{n2} \quad d_{n3} \quad \cdots \qquad \left(= \frac{1}{n}\right)$$

The reader can clearly see that neither list contains all the positive reals; for example, $\frac{1}{2}$ is not in list (7), and $\frac{2}{3}$ is not in list (8). What we will prove is that any list of the type (6), no matter how complicated the rule by which it was made, is not complete. For we will manufacture from any such list a real number that could not possibly be on the list.

In the construction of this unlikely number, the part to the left of the decimal point in (6) will not concern us. In fact, the only digits that will concern us are those that lie on the diagonal to the right of the decimal point in (6). These are:

$$.d_{11}$$
$$d_{22}$$
$$d_{33}$$
(9) $$d_{44}$$

The number that we will build will turn out to be less than 1. Its decimal representation will look like this:

$$.b_1b_2b_3\cdots b_n\cdots ,$$

where b_1, b_2, b_3, $\cdots$ are each, of course, one of the ten integers from 0 to 9.

We will now give a rule for constructing the decimal representation of this number, which we will call B. The nth digit, b_n, will be 2 if d_{nn} in our original list is not 2, and will be 1 if d_{nn} happens to be 2. Thus, to begin, if we find that d_{11} is 2, we take b_1 to be 1; and if d_{11} is not 2, we take b_1 to be 2. Continuing in this way, we obtain b_2, b_3, $\cdots$ and thus define B.

For example, if we apply this procedure to (7), we find that $b_1 = 2, b_2 = 2, b_3 = 1$; and if we apply it to (8), we find that $b_1 = 2, b_2 = 2, b_3 = 2$.

Now we must show why $B = .b_1b_2b_3\cdots$ cannot appear in the list (6). First, it is not married to 1, since b_1 is not d_{11}. Second, it is not married to 2, since b_2 is not d_{22}. Third, it is not married to 3, since b_3 is not d_{33}. As the reader may gather, B appears nowhere on the list (6), since it differs from the nth real number in the list in at least the nth digit to the right of the decimal point.

Since no denumerable list of positive real numbers is complete, it follows that the positive reals are not denumerable. This proves Cantor's Theorem.

By combining Theorems 2 and 5, the reader may give a new proof for

THEOREM 6. *There exist irrational real numbers.*

This is our third way of showing that not all numbers are rational. The first way (in Chapter 5), which depends on the Fundamental Theorem of Arithmetic, showed that $\sqrt{2}$, $\sqrt{3}$, $\sqrt{5}$, and $\sqrt{6}$, for example, are irrational. The second way (in Chapter 15) showed that any decimal, such as $0.101001000100001\cdots$, that is not repeating, represents an irrational number.

But from Cantor's Theorem we can deduce much more than Theorem 6. In his letter of December 2, five days before he had proved Theorem 5, Cantor said concerning the question of whether the reals and the natural numbers are conumerous, "Provided that the answer is 'no,' we would this way have obtained a new proof of Liouville's theorem that there exist transcendental numbers." (Liouville in 1844 had already shown that there exist transcendentals, by exhibiting specific examples.) But Theorem 5 shows that Cantor's question, "Is the set of positive reals denumerable," must be answered "no." We will now use Theorem 5 to prove that there are transcendental numbers. To do this we will prove

THEOREM 7. *The set of algebraic numbers is denumerable.*

PROOF. Every polynomial P whose coefficients are integers contributes only a finite number of algebraic numbers; namely, the roots of the equation $P = 0$. (See Theorem 6 of Chapter 15.)

If we could prove that the set of polynomials with integral coefficients is denumerable, we would then, by Theorem 4, be assured that the set of algebraic numbers is denumerable.

If we let S_n be the set of polynomials of degree n with integral coefficients, we see that the set of all polynomials with integral coefficients is the union of the sets S_1, S_2, S_3, $\cdots$. Recalling Theorem 3, we see that it is enough to prove that each S_n is denumerable.

Let us prove, for example, that S_2 is denumerable. (The reader will see that the same reasoning works for all S_n.) Each polynomial in S_2 is determined by its three coefficients; for example, $3X^2 + 0X^1 + 1$ is determined by $(3, 0, 1)$, and $-1X^2 + 5X + 1$ is determined by $(-1, 5, 1)$. To prove that S_2 is denumerable, we will prove that the set T of triplets of integers (A, B, C), where A is not 0, is denumerable.

To prove that T is denumerable, we will break it up into a denumerable collection of finite sets and apply Theorem 4. For this purpose it will be convenient to let $|x|$ denote the size of the integer x; that is, $|x| = x$ if x is positive, and $|x| = -x$ if x is negative. For example, $|-5| = 5$, and $|5| = 5$. Clearly $|x|$ is simply the distance between x and 0. (This notion was used in E 48 of Chapter 15.)

Let T_1 be the set of all triplets (A, B, C) such that A is not 0 and

$$|A| + |B| + |C| = 1.$$

Clearly there are only two such triplets: $(1, 0, 0)$ and $(-1, 0, 0)$. Let T_2 be the set of all triplets (A, B, C) such that A is not 0 and

$$|A| + |B| + |C| = 2.$$

The triplets in T_2 are: $(1, 0, 1)$, $(1, 0, -1)$, $(1, 1, 0)$, $(1, -1, 0)$, $(-1, 0, 1)$, $(-1, 0, -1)$, $(-1, 1, 0)$, $(-1, -1, 0)$, $(2, 0, 0)$, and $(-2, 0, 0)$.

For each natural number n (larger than 0), let T_n be the set of triplets (A, B, C) such that A is not 0 and

$$|A| + |B| + |C| = n.$$

It is clear that for each such triplet, $|A|$, $|B|$, and $|C|$ are each at most n, and so A, B, and C must each be between n and $-n$. Thus there are at most $2n + 1$ choices for each of A, B, and C; namely,

$$-n, \quad \cdots, \quad -2, \quad -1, \quad 0, \quad 1, \quad 2, \quad \cdots, \quad n.$$

(Of course, since A itself cannot be 0, there are only $2n$ choices for A.) We have $2n$ choices for A and, for each choice of A, we have at most $2n + 1$ choices for B; and then, for each choice of A and B, we have at most $2n + 1$ choices for C. Thus we see that T_n is a finite set.

Observe next that the set T is precisely the union of the sets

$$T_1, T_2, T_3, T_4, \cdots .$$

Since each of the latter sets is finite, it follows from Theorem 4 that T is denumerable. Thus S_2, the set of polynomials of degree 2, is denumerable.

Similarly, as the reader is invited to check, S_3, the set of polynomials of degree 3, is denumerable. Furthermore, in the same fashion, we can prove that each of the sets $S_4, S_5, S_6, \cdots$ is denumerable.

Finally, since the union of a denumerable collection of denumerable sets is denumerable (Theorem 3), we find that the set of all polynomials with integer coefficients is denumerable. Thus the set of algebraic numbers is denumerable, and Theorem 7 is proved.

Combining Theorems 5 and 7 we obtain this strengthening of Theorem 6:

THEOREM 8. *There exist transcendental real numbers.*

Cantor's Theorem, which asserts that the set of real numbers is not conumerous with the set of natural numbers, shows that Salviati was not correct when he said, "The attributes of 'equal,' 'greater,' and 'less' are not applicable to infinite quantities." On the contrary, we can, following Cantor, give a very precise meaning to the statement "Set A is less numerous than set B" even when A and B are infinite.

We will say that set A is **less numerous** *than set B if A is conumerous with* *some subset of B, but not with B itself.* As an example, we know from Theorem 5 that the set of natural numbers is less numerous than the set of real numbers.

We will say that two sets are **equally numerous** *if they are conumerous.* For example, the set of positive rationals, the set of squares, and the set of natural numbers are all equally numerous.

Finally, we will say that B is **more numerous** *than A if A is less numerous than B.*

This notion of "less numerous," agreeing with our experience with finite sets, introduces a scale even among the infinite sets and raises questions that could not be considered before. For example, is there a set more numerous than the set of real numbers? Cantor showed that the answer is "yes." He even went on to prove that if A is any set, then the set B whose elements are the subsets of A is more numerous than A. (If A is finite, this is easy to see.) In particular, the set of all subsets of the real numbers is more numerous than the set of real numbers.

But Cantor raised a second question, which to this day is not settled: Is every infinite subset of the reals either conumerous with the reals or else conumerous with the set of natural numbers? The Continuum Hypothesis states Cantor's belief that the answer is "yes," but for almost a century it has remained unproved. ("Continuum" is another name for the set of real numbers.)

Following his discovery that not all infinite sets are conumerous, Cantor created an arithmetic that extends into the realm of infinite sets the familiar arithmetic of finite sets. First of all, he introduced symbols to denote the various sizes of infinite sets, just as the natural numbers 1, 2, 3, $\cdots$ denote the various sizes of finite sets. We will glance briefly at just two of these "infinite numbers."

Any denumerable set, Cantor would say, "has $\aleph_0$ elements." [The symbol $\aleph$ (alef) is the first letter of the Hebrew alphabet; the subscript, 0, distinguishes $\aleph_0$ (read alef null) from other "infinite numbers," $\aleph_1$, $\aleph_2$, $\cdots$ that Cantor defined.] The letter $\aleph_0$ we will use to represent the smallest of the infinite numbers. Theorem 2 can now be read, "There are $\aleph_0$ positive rationals"; Theorem 3, "$\aleph_0$ times $\aleph_0$ is $\aleph_0$"; and Theorem 7, "There are $\aleph_0$ algebraic numbers."

Any set conumerous with the set of reals, Cantor said, "has c elements" (the "c" stands for "continuum"). The Continuum Hypothesis now can be read, "Every infinite subset of the reals has either $\aleph_0$ elements or c elements."

Furthermore, Cantor defined a multiplication and addition for these new numbers, using ideas suggested by finite sets. The reader can find a detailed presentation of Cantor's arithmetic in R 4, R 8, or R 14.

Cantor's work on infinite sets, carried out at the end of the nineteenth century, not only resolves the riddles that troubled Simplicio, Salviati, and Sagredo in the seventeenth century, but also provides an important tool for twentieth century mathematicians, who, in many branches of their art, must work with infinity.

Exercises

1. (a) Prove that there are exactly 1000 squares among the first million natural numbers larger than 0.
   (b) Prove that a thousandth part of the first million natural numbers larger than 0 are squares.

2. How many cubes are there among the first million natural numbers larger than 0?

3. Prove that the set of all squares is conumerous with the set of all cubes. ("Squares" and "cubes" here refer to numbers, not geometric figures.)

4. List the 15 proper subsets of $\{1, 2, 3, 4\}$ (remember the empty set).

5. List the 32 subsets of $\{1, 2, 3, 4, 5\}$ (remember the empty set).

6. Prove that for any natural number n, the set $\{1, 2, 3, \cdots, n\}$ has 2^n subsets.

7. Prove geometrically that the border of a square and the border of a circle are conumerous.

8. Prove that the set $\{2, 3, 4, \cdots\}$ and the set $\{1, 2, 3, 4, \cdots\}$ are conumerous.

9. A very introspective man requires a year to record in his diary the events of a single day of his life. Each day that he is alive he gets further behind. At the end of 100 years he would have written up just the first 100 days of his eventful life. Prove that if he lives forever, he does eventually write up each day of his life.

10. Use this diagram to prove that the set of positive reals is conumerous with the set of reals between 0 and 1 (but excluding 1).

11. Cantor's method (2) gives one way of marrying the natural numbers to regularly spaced dots in the plane. The following steps outline another way.
    (a) Prove that every natural number 1, 2, 3, 4, $\cdots$ can be written in the form $2^{a-1}(2b - 1)$ for some pair (a, b) of natural numbers larger than 0.
    (b) Prove that for any natural number n, larger than 0, there is precisely one pair (a, b) of natural numbers larger than 0 such that $n = 2^{a-1}(2b - 1)$; that is, prove that the representation of part (a) is unique.
    (c) Now marry n to the pair (a, b) given in part (b). We may think of the pair (a, b) as describing a dot in this manner:

12. The Fundamental Theorem of Arithmetic can be used to prove that the set of pairs (a, b) is denumerable, where a and b are elements of $\{1, 2, 3, 4, \cdots\}$. The following is an outline of the proof:
   (a) Using Theorem 1, prove that the set of natural numbers of the form $2^a \times 3^b$ is denumerable, where a and b are elements of $\{1, 2, 3, 4, \cdots\}$.
   (b) Using the Fundamental Theorem of Arithmetic, prove that the set of natural numbers of the form $2^a \times 3^b$ is conumerous with the set of all pairs (a, b), where a and b are elements of $\{1, 2, 3, 4, \cdots\}$.

13. Using the technique of E 12, prove that the set of all triplets (a, b, c), where a, b, and c are elements of $\{1, 2, 3, 4, \cdots\}$, is denumerable.

14. Using the technique of E 12, prove that the set of quadruplets (a, b, c, d) that can be formed from the numbers $\{1, 2, 3, 4, \cdots\}$ is denumerable.

15. In (3) and (4), what natural number is married to $\frac{2}{3}$? To $\frac{3}{4}$?

16. In (3) and (4), what rational is married to 8? To 10? To 20?

17. Prove that the set of integers $\{\cdots, -3, -2, -1, 0, 1, 2, 3, \cdots\}$ is denumerable by marrying the integer n to the rational 2^n and applying Theorems 1 and 2.

18. Prove in the following three ways that the set of regularly spaced dots

extending throughout the plane is denumerable:
   (a) by a direct geometric argument like that for Theorem 2;
   (b) by the use of Corollary 1 and Theorem 3;
   (c) by the technique used in E 12.

19. Prove that the union of two denumerable sets is denumerable by assuming (a) that they share no element; (b) that they overlap.

20. Combining E 19, Theorem 5, and Theorem 2, prove that the irrationals are not denumerable.

21. Cantor's proof of the nondenumerability of the reals involves looking at the digits on the diagonal $d_{11}, d_{22}, \cdots$. Show that his argument would hold just as well if he had made b_n different from d_{n2n} instead of d_{nn}.

22. Why is it that the same argument used in the proof of Theorem 5 does not also prove that the rationals are not denumerable? Point out exactly where the argument breaks down.

23. Prove that the set of polynomials of degree 3 with integral coefficients is denumerable.

24. If A and B are finite sets such that A is conumerous with a subset of B, and B is conumerous with a subset of A, prove that A and B are conumerous. (The same result holds for infinite sets, but it is more difficult to prove. It is called the Schröder-Bernstein Theorem. See R 4 or R 14.)

25. Prove that a line segment of length 1 is conumerous with some subset of the square of side 1.

26. Prove that the square of side 1 is conumerous with a subset of the line segment of length 1. [*Hint:* Marry the point $(.a_1a_2a_3\cdots, .b_1b_2b_3\cdots)$ of the square to the point $.a_1b_1a_2b_2a_3b_3\cdots$ of the line segment.]

27. Combining E 25, E 26, and the Schröder-Bernstein Theorem of E 24, prove that the line segment and the square are conumerous.

28. Prove that if A and B are finite sets and have the same number of subsets, then A and B must be conumerous. (See E 6.) Whether this is true for infinite sets A and B is not known.

29. Show why the fact that a finite set is not conumerous with a proper subset of itself is the basis of the pigeonhole principle of Chapter 12.

30. Prove that the set of positive reals other than 0 is conumerous with the set of all reals
    (a) geometrically (draw a curve as indicated below and marry the positive real, P, to the real, Q; A is fixed, B varies and is directly above P).

    (b) algebraically (marry the real, x, to the positive real, 2^x).

31. Prove Corollary 1 by marrying the integer n to the rational 2^n and applying Theorem 1.

32. Prove Corollary 2 by using Theorems 1 and 7.

33. If A and B are sets, denote their union, $A \cup B$.
    (a) Prove that $\cup$ is idempotent, commutative, and associative. (These terms are defined in Chapter 11.)
    (b) Give an example of sets A, B, and C such that B is different from C, yet $A \cup B = A \cup C$.

    The reader may have the impression that all the unsolved problems of set theory concern infinite sets. The following exercises present a problem concerning finite sets which is over a century old, and is far from being completely solved.

34. Check that each of the 21 subsets of $\{1, 2, 3, 4, 5, 6, 7\}$ having exactly 2 elements is a subset of exactly one of these 7 sets:

$$\{1, 2, 3\}, \quad \{1, 4, 5\}, \quad \{1, 6, 7\}, \quad \{2, 4, 6\}, \quad \{2, 5, 7\}, \quad \{3, 4, 7\}, \quad \{3, 5, 6\}.$$

For example, the set $\{1, 7\}$ is a subset of $\{1, 6, 7\}$, but of none of the others.

35. Check that each of the 36 subsets of $\{1, 2, 3, 4, 5, 6, 7, 8, 9\}$ having exactly two elements is a subset of exactly one of these 12 sets:

$\{1, 2, 3\}$, $\{7, 8, 9\}$, $\{1, 5, 9\}$, $\{2, 4, 9\}$, $\{2, 6, 7\}$, $\{3, 5, 7\}$,
$\{4, 5, 6\}$, $\{1, 4, 7\}$, $\{1, 6, 8\}$, $\{2, 5, 8\}$, $\{3, 4, 8\}$, $\{3, 6, 9\}$.

36. Each of the 78 subsets of $\{a, b, c, d, e, f, g, h, i, j, k, l, m\}$ having 2 elements is a subset of precisely one of these 13 sets:

$\{a, b, c, j\}$, $\{a, d, g, k\}$, $\{a, f, h, l\}$, $\{a, e, i, m\}$, $\{d, e, f, g\}$,
$\{b, e, h, k\}$, $\{b, d, i, l\}$, $\{b, f, g, m\}$, $\{j, k, l, m\}$, $\{g, h, i, j\}$,
$\{c, f, i, k\}$, $\{c, e, g, l\}$, $\{c, d, h, m\}$.

Check the above statement only for the sets $\{a, b\}$, $\{b, f\}$, $\{h, j\}$, and $\{c, m\}$. (We use the letters a through m instead of the integers 1 through 13 for visual simplicity.)

37. Each of the 210 subsets of $\{a, b, c, d, e, f, g, h, i, j, k, l, m, n, o, p, q, r, s, t, u\}$ having two elements is a subset of exactly one of these 21 sets:

$\{a, b, c, d, q\}$, $\{a, e, i, m, r\}$, $\{a, f, k, p, s\}$, $\{a, g, l, n, t\}$, $\{a, h, j, o, u\}$,
$\{e, f, g, h, q\}$, $\{b, f, j, n, r\}$, $\{b, e, l, o, s\}$, $\{b, h, k, m, t\}$, $\{b, g, i, p, u\}$,
$\{i, j, k, l, q\}$, $\{c, g, k, o, r\}$, $\{c, h, i, n, s\}$, $\{c, e, j, p, t\}$, $\{c, f, l, m, u\}$,
$\{m, n, o, p, q\}$, $\{d, h, l, p, r\}$, $\{d, g, i, m, s\}$, $\{d, f, i, o, t\}$, $\{d, e, k, n, u\}$,
$\{q, r, s, t, u\}$.

Check the above statement for only 5 of the 210 sets in question.

38. If k and n are natural numbers (both at least 1), then by a (k, n)-collection we mean a collection of subsets of $A = \{1, 2, 3, \cdots, n\}$ such that
    (i) each member of the collection has exactly k elements, and
    (ii) each subset of A that consists of two elements is a subset of exactly one member of the collection.

    For example, E 34 presents a $(3, 7)$-collection; E 35 presents a $(3, 9)$-collection; E 36 presents a $(4, 13)$-collection; and E 37 presents a $(5, 21)$-collection.
    (a) Construct a $(2, 4)$-collection.
    (b) Show that for each n larger than 1 there is precisely one $(2, n)$-collection.
    (c) Construct a $(4, 4)$-collection.
    (d) Why is there no $(5, 4)$-collection?

39. (a) Prove that a set with n elements has $n \times (n - 1)/2$ subsets having two elements each.
    (b) Prove that if a $(3, n)$-collection has p sets, then $3 \times p = n \times (n - 1)/2$. [*Hint:* Use (a).]
    (c) Using (b), prove that if there is a $(3, 8)$-collection, then 3 must divide 28.

40. Using the ideas of E 39, prove that if there is a $(3, n)$-collection, then 3 divides $n \times (n - 1)/2$.

41. Let m be the number of triplets that belong to a $(3, n)$-collection and that have 1 as one of their elements.
    (a) Check that for the $(3, 7)$-collection of E 34, m is 3.
    (b) Prove that $n - 1 = 2m$ for any $(3, n)$-collection.
    (c) Prove that if n is even, then there is no $(3, n)$-collection. [*Hint:* See (b).]

42. Combining E 40 and E 41 (c), we see that if n is a natural number for which there exists a $(3, n)$-collection, then n is odd and 3 divides $n \times (n - 1)/2$.
    (a) Prove that if 3 divides $n \times (n - 1)/2$, then 6 divides $n \times (n - 1)$.
    (b) Prove that if n is odd and 6 divides $n \times (n - 1)$, then n must have the remainder 1 or 3 when divided by 6 [in the language of congruence, $n \equiv 1$ or 3 (mod 6)].
    (c) Prove that there is no $(3, 17)$-collection.
    (d) For which n, less than 20, are there definitely no $(3, n)$-collections?
    In 1859 M. Reiss proved that whenever n has the remainder 1 or 3 when divided by 6, there exists a $(3, n)$-collection.

43. Using the same kind of reasoning as in E 40 and E 41, prove that if n is a natural number such that a $(4, n)$-collection exists, then
    (a) 6 divides $n \times (n - 1)/2$,
    (b) 3 divides $(n - 1)$.

44. (a) Using E 43, prove that there is no $(4, 10)$-collection.
    (b) For which n, less than 20, are there definitely no $(4, n)$-collections?
    In 1960 H. Hanani proved that if n is any natural number (other than 0) satisfying E 43 (a) and (b), then there exists a $(4, n)$-collection. He also determined for which n there exists a $(5, n)$-collection. In recent years, (k, n)-collections have assumed an important role in the design of experiments. For this reason, and to satisfy their curiosity, mathematicians would like to know for which k and n there exists a (k, n)-collection. It is not known, for example, whether there is a $(6, 46)$-collection. Clearly, not all the challenging questions of set theory concern infinite sets.

References

1. Galileo Galilei, *Dialogues Concerning the Two New Sciences*, Dover, New York. (A highly readable account of the beginnings of the sciences: strength of materials and motion.)

2. T. Katigawa and M. Mitome, *Tables for the design of factorial experiments*, Dover, New York, 1955. (Table VII contains many other examples of (k, n) collections.)

3. *Briefwechsel Cantor-Dedekind*, edited by E. Noether and J. Cavaillès, Hermann and Co., Paris, 1937. (The correspondence between Cantor and Dedekind, in German.)

4. Joseph Breuer, *Introduction to the Theory of Sets*, Prentice-Hall, Englewood Cliffs, 1958. (This includes the sum and product of infinite numbers and the proof of the theorem referred to in E 24.)

5. T. Dantzig, *Number, the Language of Science*, Macmillan, New York, 1954. (Chapter 6 discusses the algebraic and transcendental numbers.)

6. J. R. Newman, *The World of Mathematics*, Simon and Schuster, New York, 1956, vol. 3, pp. 1576–1611. (Essays by Bertrand Russell and Hans Hahn on infinity.)

7. G. Gamow, *One, Two, Three, ∙∙∙ Infinity*, Viking, New York, 1948, pp. 14–23. (Infinite sets.)

8. A. Fraenkel, *Abstract Set Theory*, North-Holland Publishing Company, Amsterdam, 1953. (A good deal of set theory is presented in a leisurely and concrete style on pp. 1–84.)

9. *G. Birkhoff and S. MacLane, *A Survey of Modern Algebra*, Macmillan, New York, 1953. (Pages 356–369, set theory.)

10. M. Kline, *Mathematics in Western Culture*, Oxford University Press, New York, 1953. (Chapter 25 is devoted to infinity.)

11. L. Zippin, *Uses of Infinity*, Random House (New Mathematics Library), 1962. (The use of the pigeonhole principle in infinite sets is discussed on pp. 112–120.)

12. E. T. Bell, *Men of Mathematics*, Simon and Schuster, New York, 1937. (Chapter 29 is devoted to Cantor.)

13. B. Russell, *Introduction to Mathematical Philosophy*, George Allen and Unwin, Ltd., London, 1950. (Chapters 2 and 8 define "number," both finite and infinite.)

14. E. Kamke, *Theory of Sets*, Dover, New York, 1950. (A proof of the theorem mentioned in E 24 is given on pp. 23–25; a proof of the theorem that the collection of subsets of a set is more numerous than the set is given on p. 21. A clear presentation of the arithmetic of infinity is given on pp. 1–51.)

15. J. B. Roberts, *The Real Number System in an Algebraic Setting*, Freeman, San Francisco, 1962. (Infinite sets are discussed on pp. 55–61, 113–125.)

Chapter **17**

A GENERAL VIEW

The universe of mathematics grows out of the world about us like dreams out of the events of the day. The world serves as a cue, a point of departure, suggesting questions that lure the mathematician. Out of these questions, or their answers, grow more questions. As long as there are questions that demand an answer, mathematics expands.

The universe of mathematics is now so vast that in order to have some idea of its nature and extent, it is necessary to divide it into smaller constellations, even though these constellations are not separated by clearcut barriers. We will describe some of the major mathematical structures, and see where the various topics treated in this book fit into the overall pattern. We will conclude with a brief description of the mathematics that examines the foundations of all mathematical structures; namely, symbolic logic.

We first describe various kinds of geometry. Consider a rigid iron wire bent into a circle. As we move it rigidly through space it remains a circle of the same radius. Notions such as circle, radius, distance, straight line, angle, which are preserved by such rigid motions, are the subject of *congruence geometry*. In particular, the Pythagorean Theorem (Chapter 5) belongs to congruence geometry, since it involves distance, angle, and straight line.

Next, consider a rubber band in the form of a circle. As we move it through space and stretch parts of it, it could become a triangle, a square, an ellipse, or some quite irregular figure. Distance, angle, and straightness are not preserved. But some properties survive all these distortions of the rubber band. For example, the rubber band remains a loop; it never changes into

Moreover, if we have two rubber bands, interlocked like two links of a chain, then, as we move them both about, bending, stretching, or shrinking them, they still remain linked. *The study of properties preserved under such operations is called* **topology** (from the Greek *topo*, space; and *logia*, study). Topology studies such concepts as "loop," "being linked," "able to hold air," "having a hole." Chapters 2, 8, and 13 belong to topology.

265

Now we come to what might be called the most general possible geometry. Starting again with a rubber band in the form of a circle, this time we permit ourselves to rip the rubber into its individual points and scatter them however we choose. Though we lose distance, angle, straightness, and now, even the property of being a loop; still, something is preserved. The number of points remains the same; that is, the set of points occupied by the rubber is always conumerous (in the sense of Chapter 16) with the set of points originally occupied. *The study of properties preserved under all one-to-one correspondences is called* **set theory.** Such properties as "having two elements" or "being finite" or "being infinite" are in the domain of set theory.

So far we have presented three mathematical disciplines: (1) congruence geometry, (2) topology, and (3) set theory, each more general than its predecessors. Set theory, the most fundamental, has the smallest collection of properties to work with, but in return its results have the widest range of application. Both topology and set theory can be considered as examples of geometries.

We will now go in a different direction from the iron wire that gave us congruence geometry. This time, let us mount the wire on a glass slide. If we place a screen parallel to the slide, and shine parallel rays of light through the slide onto the screen, then the shadow of the circle on the screen will be a circle of the same size:

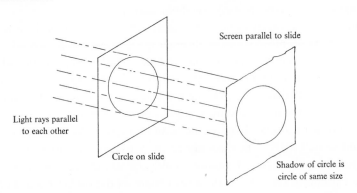

Properties preserved under this kind of projection are simply those preserved under rigid motions. Thus we could describe "congruence geometry" as the geometry that studies properties preserved under projection by parallel rays of light on a screen that is parallel to the slide.

But now we follow a different path from the one that led us to topology and set theory. Keep the screen parallel to the slide, but this time use a small bulb as the source of light, in order that the rays of light, instead of being parallel, will all come from one point. The shadow of the circle is still a circle, but perhaps much larger.

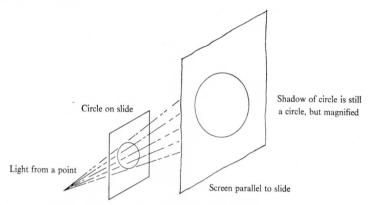

Circle on slide

Shadow of circle is still a circle, but magnified

Light from a point

Screen parallel to slide

This type of projection, which is just magnification, preserves angle and straightness, but not distance. The shadow of a geometric object under this kind of projection is said to be "similar" to the original figure. *The study of properties preserved under magnifications or under congruences is called* **Euclidean geometry,** part of which we meet in high school.

Before we go on to two more general types of geometry, we will have to define the conic sections: ellipse, parabola, and hyperbola. To do this, take a double, endless (ice cream) cone and place it in a vertical position, as in this diagram:

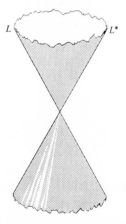

L L^*

A horizontal or slightly tilted plane cuts the cone in an oval curve, called an *ellipse*. (Note that a circle is a special case of an ellipse.) As an illustration of this figure we have

When the plane is tilted further, until it is parallel to one of the lines L or L^*, it meets the cone in a *parabola* (shaped like the profile of an unbounded head-light), as is shown by this diagram.

When tilted still more steeply, the plane meets *both* halves of the hourglass in a *hyperbola:*

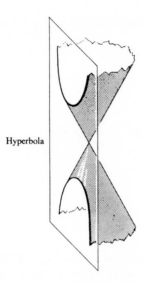

Hyperbola

These three types of curves are called *"conic sections."*

Now that we have defined conic sections, let us consider shadows cast by parallel rays of light, but with the screen no longer parallel to the slide:

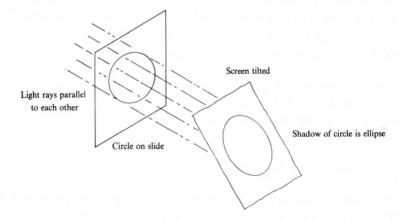

Screen tilted

Light rays parallel
to each other

Shadow of circle is ellipse

Circle on slide

The shadow of a circle will now be an ellipse, and the shadow of a square will be a parallelogram. In fact, the shadow of any parallelogram will be a parallelogram; and the shadow of any ellipse, an ellipse. *The study of properties or concepts preserved under the first three types of projections (pp. 266–269) is called* **affine geometry.** Not all of these three types preserve distance and angle, but the notions of "straight line" and of "two lines being parallel" are preserved. For example, in affine geometry the ellipse (but not the circle) and the parallelogram (but not the square or rectangle) are studied.

Finally, let us have the light come from a point and let the screen be tilted:

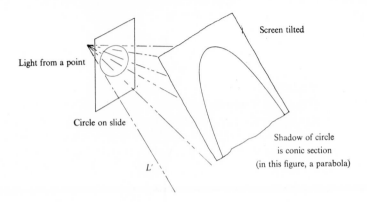

The shadow of a circle need no longer be a circle or an ellipse. However, the shadow will still be a conic section; in the above figure, for example, where line L' and the screen are parallel, the shadow of the circle is a parabola. Moreover, the shadow of any conic section is, again, a conic section. *The study of properties preserved under all four of these types of projections (pp. 266–270) is called* **projective geometry.** Straight lines and their intersections, and conic sections and their tangents are studied in projective geometry, but concepts involving distance, angle, or even parallel lines are not. As an example of an important result in projective geometry, we have

PASCAL'S THEOREM. *If six points labeled 1, 2, 3, 4, 5, and 6 are on a conic section, and if the straight lines 1-2, 2-3, 3-4, 4-5, 5-6, and 6-1 are drawn, then the three points defined by the intersections of*

1-2 and 4-5,   2-3 and 5-6,   3-4 and 6-1

are all on one straight line.

(The reader may check Pascal's theorem by selecting six points, located, for convenience, on a circle.)

In this book we have met several of the six branches of mathematics so far described. The Pythagorean Theorem and the tiling of rectangles by squares belong to Euclidean geometry. Complete triangles (Chapter 2), highway systems (Chapter 8), and map coloring (Chapter 13) belong, for the most part, to topology, since the various results never really depend on the lines being straight or the sphere perfectly round. If the sphere were made of rubber and then stretched, countries would remain countries, adjacent countries would remain adjacent, and the degree of each vertex would not change. Cantor's theorem, showing that there are two infinite sets that are not conumerous, belongs to set theory. In fact, Chapter 16 is an introduction to set theory.

Within set theory we find **combinatorics,** *which is devoted primarily to finding out how many elements there are in sets that are known to be finite.* As examples of problems belonging to combinatorics, we have these: How long a list of orthogonal tables of order N can be found (Chapter 12); How many memory wheels of N-tuplets of 0 and 1 are there (Chapter 9)?

Algebra, *a large branch of mathematics, is concerned with operations that assign to each pair of elements of a set an element of that set subject to specified rules.* For example, the operation $+$ assigns to each pair of natural numbers (integers, rationals, reals, and complex numbers) their sum, which is in turn a natural number (integer, rational, real, or complex number, respectively). Moreover, these five examples satisfy such rules as commutativity and associativity. Chapter 11 exhibits operations $\circ$ on finite sets that satisfy not only the usual rules of arithmetic but, in one case, this unusual rule: $X \circ (X \circ Y) = Y \circ X$. Appendix A belongs to algebra.

Within algebra lies **number theory,** *the study of $+$ and $\times$, usually on the integers.* The notions of divisor, prime and composite, even and odd, and congruence modulo M belong to number theory. Thus Chapters 3, 4, and 10 are primarily number theory.

Statements such as "P_N is approximately $N \times (1/1 + 1/2 + \cdots + 1/N)$" (Chapter 3) or "The sequence of numbers $\frac{3}{10}$, $\frac{3}{10} + \frac{3}{100}$, $\frac{3}{10} + \frac{3}{100} + \frac{3}{1000}$, $\cdots$ approaches $\frac{1}{3}$" (Chapter 14) or "$1/1 + 1/2 + \cdots + 1/N$ grows as large as we please" (Appendix B) belong to **analysis.** Analysis, which begins with calculus, studies such topics as the behavior of endless sequences of numbers, the steepness of a tangent to a curve, and the total area under a curve. It is the branch of mathematics most frequently applied to physics and engineering. Indeed, Newton developed the calculus as a tool for studying the motion of the heavenly bodies.

Within analysis is to be found the theory of **probability,** *which examines the long-run behavior of events determined in part by chance.* (An example of this theory is to be found in "The average winner's score," treated in Appendix B.)

It would be wrong to take these divisions too seriously, as though they were watertight compartments. Recall how the proof of the topological Five-color Theorem (Chapter 13) depends in part on the addition, subtraction, and multiplication of integers; that is, on number theory. The proof of the two-color theorem exploits properties of the even and odd numbers; hence, number theory. The proof of the geometric theorem that some rectangles cannot be cut into squares (Chapter 7) uses a good deal of algebra, as well as the number theoretic result that there are irrationals.

As Hilbert warned the twentieth century in an address he delivered in 1900:

> $\cdots$The question is urged upon us whether mathematics is doomed to the fate of those other sciences that have split up into separate branches, whose representatives scarcely understand one another and whose connection becomes ever more loose. I do not believe this nor wish it. Mathematical science is in my opinion an organism whose vitality is conditioned upon the connection of its parts.

We may take as an expression of Hilbert's scope the fact that he himself helped to develop the mathematics with the broadest vista, the logic of the foundations of all mathematical systems. This part of mathematics, called **mathematical logic,** or **symbolic logic,** *is concerned with such questions as the following: "What do we mean by a mathematical system?" "What is a proof?" "What is a theorem?" "Are the assumptions free of contradiction?" "Is each true statement also a theorem?"*

Let us be a little more specific. Each mathematical structure has its axioms, which describe what we propose to study. For instance, rules I and II of Chapter 7 are axioms for a certain kind of structure (and as examples of such structures we have electrical networks and tilings of rectangles by rectangles). Chapter 11 treats operations satisfying such axioms as $X \circ X = X$, $X \circ Y = Y \circ X$, $X \circ (X \circ Y) = Y \circ X$, or $X \circ (Y \circ Z) = (X \circ Y) \circ Z$. The axioms for a structure record our assumptions and thus help us keep our thinking straight. As mathematicians, we try to discover what conclusions follow from the axioms. As one simple example, we discovered that any table satisfying the axiom $X \circ (X \circ Y) = Y \circ X$ is idempotent.

The reasoning by which we justify our conclusions drawn from the axioms is called a **proof.** There are various kinds of proofs. For example, we have met on several occasions *proof by contradiction.* In this style of proof we show that a certain statement is true by showing that its denial leads to a contradiction—an inconsistency. For example, in Chapter 1 we proved certain Fifteen puzzles unsolvable by showing that if they were solvable, then a certain natural number would be both odd and even. In Chapter 3 we proved that there is no end to the primes by showing that if there were an end, then there would be a finite complete list of primes, thus contradicting the existence of the Prime-manufacturing Machine. In Chapter 5 we proved various square roots irrational by showing that if they were rational, then a certain natural number would be both odd and even. In Chapter 6 we proved that a box could not be filled with a finite number of cubes of unequal size, for if it could be, then there would be within the finite set of boxes an infinite set of boxes. In Chapter 6 we also proved that a 1 by $\sqrt{2}$ rectangle could not be tiled with squares, for if it could, then $\sqrt{2}$, which we already knew to be irrational, would be rational. In Chapter 11 we proved that there are no idempotent commutative tables of even order, for if there were, then the order would also have to be odd. In Chapter 12 we proved that there is no list of N orthogonal tables of order N, for if there were, then two of the tables would not be orthogonal.

We have also met **proof by induction.** *A proof by induction can be described in terms of a fairy princess who lives in a castle with an infinite set of rooms numbered 1, 2, 3, 4, $\cdots$.* She has in her hand the key to room 1. Moreover, each room contains a key that unlocks the door to the next room. Thus, if the princess can get into room 1, she can also enter room 2. In room 2 she finds the key to room 3; and soon we conclude that she, being immortal, can enter *any* room in the castle.

In a proof by induction we first prove a statement for 1, and then show that if the statement is true for a natural number N, it is also true for the next natural number $N + 1$. Recall, for example, our proof in Chapter 15 that every polynomial of degree N has at most N roots. We first proved it for degree 1 (this corresponds to the princess having the key to room 1). Then we used the truth of the statement for degree 1 to prove that it is also true for degree 2 (this corresponds to the princess finding in room 1 the key to room 2). Then we proved, essentially, that room 2 has the key to room 3, and stated that "the same argument then applies, step by step, to equations of degree 4, then 5, then 6, and so on." We were actually outlining a proof by *induction on the degree*, asserting that for each N, room N contains the key to room $N + 1$. Just as we concluded that the princess can enter *any* room, we can now conclude that the number of roots of *any* polynomial is less than or equal to its degree.

In Chapter 13, by using a slight variation in proof by induction, we proved LEMMA 6: *Any regular map on a sphere can be colored in five (or fewer) colors.* We first observed that the lemma is true for any map with at most five countries. This corresponds to the princess having the keys to rooms 1, 2, 3, 4, and 5. Then we said, "Let C be a natural number, at least 5, and let us assume that any map with at most C countries can be colored with five colors. Now we will show that any map with $C + 1$ countries can be colored with five colors." Notice the phrase "at most" appearing in the assumption. If the reader looks over the proof he will see that Case 2 uses the fact that any map with $C - 1$ countries can be colored with five colors. Case 1 and Case 2 together tell the princess that she will find the key to room $N + 1$ either in room N or in room $N - 1$. Even so, she would still be able to enter all the rooms of the castle. Our proof of the lemma was an *induction on the number of countries.*

Another technique for proving certain theorems is *exhaustion*, a device of little appeal to a mathematician. In Chapter 12 we mentioned that the proof that there are no orthogonal tables of order 6 was done by listing all possible tables of order 6 and then checking that no two of them were orthogonal. In Chapter 3 we mentioned that every odd natural number through 5775 can be written as the sum of a prime and twice a square. This can be proved by testing, one by one, each odd natural number up through 5775. But this is proof without revelation. Why the theorem should suddenly be false at 5777 is not explained. Nor, for tables of order 6, has any peculiarity of the number 6 been exploited (Euler had thought that the fact that 6 is twice an odd number would be important).

Another defect of proof by exhaustion is that even the fastest electronic computer can check only a finite number of cases. A computer has shown that Goldbach's conjecture is true up to 2,000,000, but no machine will ever prove that Goldbach's conjecture is true by testing *all* even numbers larger than 2.

In a somewhat different vein, we have *disproof by counterexample*. For instance, the conjecture that every odd natural number is the sum of a prime and twice a square is shown to be false by the counterexample, 5777. Euler's conjecture that there are no orthogonal tables of order twice an odd number was disproved by Bose, Parker, and Shrikhande, who constructed counterexamples of all the orders 10, 14, 18, $\cdots$.

Consider the fate of a conjecture that Polya made in 1919. In order to state it we must define two terms. From the Fundamental Theorem of Arithmetic we know that each natural number larger than 1 is either a prime or is uniquely expressible as a product of primes. Call a natural number *of odd type* if, when expressed in terms of primes, an odd number of primes appears. Thus any prime is of odd type, and so are, for example, $8 = 2 \times 2 \times 2$ and $12 = 2 \times 2 \times 3$. Similarly, we shall say that a natural number is *of even type* if it is the product of an even number of primes. Thus $4 = 2 \times 2$, $6 = 2 \times 3$, $9 = 3 \times 3$, and $10 = 2 \times 5$ are of even type. Up through 12 there are seven numbers of odd type, 2, 3, 5, 7, 8, 11, and 12, and four numbers of even type, 4, 6, 9, and 10. Note that up through 12 there are more numbers of odd type than of even. We might say that the numbers of odd type are in the lead. Polya checked that up through 1500 the numbers of even type never catch up with the numbers of odd type, and then made this conjecture: the numbers of even type never catch up with the numbers of odd type. Computers later showed that the conjecture is true through 600,000. But, in 1958, Haselgrove, combining computers with theory, proved the conjecture false, but he did not find a specific case where it fails. Finally, in 1960, Lehman, also combining computers with theory, proved that up through 906,180,359 there are exactly as many numbers of even type as of odd type. But whether Polya's conjecture is false for some smaller number was not settled, though there is some numerical evidence for the belief that numbers of odd type hold their lead up to at least 900,000,000.

The fate of Polya's conjecture raises new worries. If we make a conjecture about the natural numbers, we should fear two possibilities. First it might be false, but false only for such large numbers that not even the fastest computer could reach them in a million years. Or it might turn out that the conjecture is true, but true only "by accident," just as the statement "every odd natural number up through 5775 is the sum of a prime and twice a square" is true seemingly without rhyme or reason. Could it perhaps be that a conjecture about the natural numbers is true for each natural number "by accident" in the sense that it "happens" to be true, but for which a proof is logically impossible and hence no one will ever know for sure that it is true?

Consider the three centuries of work put in on a problem posed by Fermat in 1637. He conjectured that there do not exist two cubes whose sum is a cube, or generally, two *Nth* powers whose sum is again an *Nth* power if *N* is larger than 2. That is, he conjectured that the equation

$$X^N + Y^N = Z^N$$

has no solution in natural numbers *X*, *Y*, *Z*, and *N* if *N* is at least 3 and if *X*, *Y*, and *Z* are at least 1.

Fermat himself proved that his conjecture is true for $N = 4$. Euler, before 1770, proved it for $N = 3$. Dirichlet and Legendre, in 1825, proved it independently for $N = 5$. The case $N = 6$ is implied by the case $N = 3$, since $X^6 + Y^6 = Z^6$ can be rewritten as $(X^2)^3 + (Y^2)^3 = (Z^2)^3$. The case $N = 7$ was settled in 1839 by Lamé. Kummer, in 1857, disposed of all *N* less than 100. And now, more than 320 years after Fermat made his conjecture, it has been settled for all *N* up through 4000. Could his conjecture be true for all *N* and yet no proof possibly exist for this fact?

Or consider the question of whether there is an end to the twin primes. There is little hope of devising a "twin-prime-manufacturing machine" that would play the role that the Prime-manufacturing Machine did in Chapter 3 in proving that there is no end to the primes. If there is a proof that the set of twin primes is infinite, as most mathematicians believe it is, that proof will probably not resemble the proof we gave for the infinity of primes. Could the set of pairs of twin primes be infinite and yet a proof of this fact be a logical impossibility—forever inaccessible, not because of the limits of man's insight, but because of the limits of the mathematical structure itself that man has created?

What will be the fate of the Four-color problem? Could it, like Polya's conjecture, be true only up to a certain number; say, for all maps on the sphere with at most a billion countries? If so, even the fastest electronic computer might fail to reach a map that cannot be colored with four colors. On the other hand, perhaps the Four-color conjecture is true for all maps on the sphere. But would this imply that a proof could be found that would show *why* the conjecture is true?

In that same address of 1900, Hilbert expressed his views about such problems:

> $\cdots$ [Our experience] gives rise to the conviction (which every mathematician shares but which no one has yet supported by a proof) that every definite mathematical problem must necessarily be susceptible of an exact settlement, either in the form of an actual answer to the question asked, or by the proof of the impossibility of its solution and therewith the necessary failure of all attempts. Take any definite unsolved problem, such as the question of $\cdots$ the existence of an infinite number of prime numbers of the form $2^n + 1$. However unapproachable these problems may seem to us and however helpless we stand before them, we have, nevertheless, the firm conviction that their solution must follow by a finite number of purely logical processes.
>
> Is this axiom of the solvability of every problem a peculiarity characteristic of mathematical thought alone, or is it possibly a general law inherent in the nature of the mind, that all questions which it asks must be answerable? For in other sciences also one meets old problems which have been settled in a manner most satisfactory and most useful to science by the proof of their impossibility. I instance the problem of perpetual motion. After a vain search for the construction of a perpetual motion machine, the relations were investigated which must subsist between the forces of nature if such a machine is to be impossible; and this inverted question led to the discovery of the law of the conservation of energy, which, again, explained the impossibility of perpetual motion in the sense originally intended.
>
> This conviction of the solvability of every mathematical problem is a powerful incentive to the worker. We hear within us the perpetual call: There is the problem. Seek its solution. You can find it by pure reason, for in mathematics there is no "we will not know."

But this mystical belief was shattered in 1931 in a remarkable work by Gödel, who proved that, in any mathematical system rich enough to include number theory, there is an assertion expressible within the system that is true, yet is not provable within the system. Gödel's reasoning itself was not expressible in terms of the axioms and methods of proof of the system.

The implications of this "Incompleteness Theorem" are vast. First, no set of axioms and rules of proof will be sufficient to make each true statement in a mathematical system a theorem in that system. Second, it suggests that there may be questions whose answers we will never know, no matter what new techniques of proof we may someday discover, or how far we go outside of the structure in which the question was originally phrased. That Fermat's conjecture or the Four-color problem might be essentially unsolvable now looms as a possibility. Though every provable statement is true, it may not be that every true statement is provable. The true and the provable may not coincide. Even mathematics may have its limits as a means for determining what is true and what is false.

In spite of this uncertainty looming in the background, the mathematician, driven by his curiosity and love of order and beauty, will continue to extend his universe.

Exercises

1. The reader can easily demonstrate the four types of conic sections with a flashlight (or by using a lamp with a dark shade). The light from the flashlight fills out a cone. A wall can serve as the plane cutting the cone; note that it is easier to tilt the flashlight than the wall. With a flashlight in a darkened room, show:
   (a) That when the flashlight is aimed directly at the wall, the bright spot is a circle.
   (b) That when the flashlight is tilted a little, the bright spot becomes an ellipse.
   (c) That when the flashlight is tilted such that it is in this position,

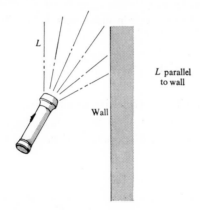

L parallel to wall

Wall

   the bright spot is a parabola.
   (d) That when the flashlight is tilted a little more, we obtain (part of) a hyperbola.

2. Using a flashlight in a darkened room, show that the shadow of a parallelogram is not always a parallelogram. For the parallelogram, the reader could use either a thin book, an index card, or a parallelogram cut out of stiff cardboard. (It is necessary to tilt the book such that it is not parallel to the wall; the book corresponds to the slide, and the wall corresponds to the screen.)

3. (a) Draw a circle, select six points on it, and label them 1, 2, 3, 4, 5, and 6 in some order.
   (b) Check Pascal's Theorem for the six points chosen in (a).

4. Draw an ellipse with the aid of two tacks and a piece of string. Stick the two tacks into a piece of paper in such a way that they are closer together than the length of the string. Tie the two ends of the string to the two tacks. Keeping the string taut with a pencil, as in this diagram,

trace out a curve (to make a complete loop, lift the string over one of the tacks when necessary). It can be proved that this curve is an ellipse. Draw three such curves. If the two tacks coincide, what curve results? Kepler and Newton showed that the orbit of the earth is an ellipse with the sun at one tack.

5. (a) By the method of E 4, use a piece of string about six inches long to draw an ellipse on a piece of paper.
   (b) Shine a flashlight on the paper in such a way that the illuminated region coincides with the ellipse drawn in (a).

6. (a) Using the method of E 4, draw an ellipse.
   (b) Select six points on this ellipse, and check Pascal's Theorem for these points.

7. Another important result from projective geometry is

   DESARGUES' THEOREM. *Let ABC and A'B'C' be two triangles situated in the plane in such a way that the lines AA', BB', and CC' all meet at a point:*

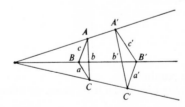

Then the three points aa', bb', and cc' are all on one line. (The symbol *aa'* denotes the point where line *a* meets line *a'*.) Check Desargues' Theorem in two examples.

8. Show that the proof of Lemma 2 of Chapter 13 can be phrased as an induction on the number of countries.

9. Using induction, prove that every natural number larger than 1 is either a prime or a product of primes. (*Hint:* The idea behind the proof of Theorem 3 of Chapter 3 can be incorporated into an inductive proof.)

10. (a) Show that the first catless proof of Theorem 1 of Chapter 2 was by induction on the number of dots.
    (b) Did we succeed in finding for Theorem 2 of Chapter 2 a proof by induction on the number of dots?
    (c) Show that the proof of Theorem 2 of Chapter 2 and the proof of E 11 of Chapter 2 suggest the beginning of an induction on the dimension of the figure on which the dots are drawn.

11. *A natural number that is equal to the sum of its divisors other than itself is called* **perfect.**
    (a) Show that the four numbers 6, 28, 496, and 8128 are perfect.
    (b) Show that each of the numbers in (a) is of the form $2^m \times$ prime, where the prime is of the form $2^{m+1} - 1$. [For example, $28 = 2^2 \times (2^3 - 1)$.]
    There are no odd perfect numbers less than $1,000,000,000,000,000,000$ $(= 10^{18})$. Whether there are any odd perfect numbers is not known. It has been proved that any even perfect number must be of the form described in (b). (Whether there is an infinite set of primes that are one less than a power of 2 is not known.) (See R 1 and R 5. The problem goes back to Euclid.)

12. Prove that Fermat's conjecture is true for $X = 1$. That is, if N is a natural number larger than 2, prove that there are no natural numbers Y and Z, both different from 0, such that
    $$1^N + Y^N = Z^N.$$

13. In E 34 of Chapter 16 we had the $(3, 7)$-collection
    $$\{1, 2, 3\}, \quad \{1, 4, 5\}, \quad \{1, 6, 7\}, \quad \{2, 4, 6\}, \quad \{2, 5, 7\}, \quad \{3, 4, 7\}, \quad \{3, 5, 6\}.$$
    From this collection, which arose from set theory, or combinatorics, obtain a table of order 7 in the following manner:
    (a) Label the guide row and guide column with the numbers 1, 2, 3, 4, 5, 6, and 7.
    (b) For each N from 1 through 7, define $N \circ N$ to be N, thus filling in the boxes on the main diagonal.
    (c) If M and N are unequal, define $M \circ N$ as the third number in the member of the collection that contains M and N. (For example, $3 \circ 5 = 6$, since 3 and 5 appear in $\{3, 5, 6\}$.)
    (d) Fill in the 49 boxes of the table.

14. Prove that the table built in E 13 satisfies the rules
    (a) $X \circ X = X$,   (b) $X \circ Y = Y \circ X$,   (c) $X \circ (X \circ Y) = Y$.
    The moral of E 13 and E 14 is: there is no barrier between one branch of mathematics and another.

15. We now show that a miniature geometry can be obtained from the $(3, 7)$-collection of E 13. *A* **point** *will be any one of the natural numbers 1, 2, 3, 4, 5, 6, and 7.* Thus our geometry has a total of seven points. *By a* **line** *we shall mean one of the sets listed in E 13.* Thus there are seven lines. A line *passes through* a point if that point is an element of the line.
    (a) Show that any two distinct points determine a unique line passing through them.

(b) Show that any two distinct lines meet in a unique point. The moral of this exercise is the same as that for E 13 and E 14. (See pp. 94–103 of R 10 for more material in this direction.)

16. Show that the proof of Theorem 5 of Chapter 10 is by induction.

17. Show that the proof sketched for E 6 of Chapter 8 can be the basis of a proof by induction on the number of edges.

18. (a) Let N be a natural number. Prove that if no prime less than or equal to $\sqrt{N}$ divides N, then N is prime. (*Hint:* Assume that N is composite, and obtain a contradiction.)
    (b) Use (a) to show that 211 is prime. (Note that since $15^2 = 225$, we know that $\sqrt{211}$ is less than 15. Thus 211 will be prime if no prime less than 15 divides it.)
    (c) Use (a) to show that 307 is prime.

19. Tie the two ends of a piece of string or rubber together such that it forms a self-knotted loop like this:

    (a) Show (experimentally) that when you move it through space it remains knotted.
    (b) Why does the theory of knots belong to topology but not to set theory?

20. Solve E 22 (b) of Chapter 8 by an induction on the number of towns.

21. Using induction, give a complete proof of Theorem 2 of Chapter 4.

References

1. E. Nagel and J. R. Newman, *Gödel's Proof*, New York University Press, 1958. (An introduction to the ideas involved in Gödel's proof.)

2. F. DeSua, Consistency and completeness—a resumé, *American Mathematical Monthly*, vol. 63, 1956, pp. 295–305. (Discussion of Gödel's theorem and its implications.)

3. David Hilbert, Mathematical Problems, lecture delivered in 1900, *Bulletin of the American Mathematical Society*, vol. 8, 1902, pp. 437–479. (This is a discussion of the past and future of mathematics; it contains 23 problems, several of which have since been solved.)

4. L. J. Mordell, *Reflections of a Mathematician*, École Polytechnique, Montreal, Canada, 1959. (The use of electronic computers in solving problems is discussed on p. 23.)

5. C. B. Haselgrove, Applications of digital computers in mathematics, *Mathematical Gazette*, vol. 42, 1958, pp. 259–260.

6. E. T. Bell, *Men of Mathematics*, Simon and Schuster, New York, 1937. (Brief biographies of many mathematicians, including Fermat, Pascal, Newton, and Hermite.)

7. M. Kline, *Mathematics, a Cultural Approach*, Addison Wesley, Reading, Mass., 1962. (The chapter "Mathematics and Painting in the Renaissance" discusses the origins of projective geometry.)

8. T. Dantzig, *Number, the Language of Science*, Macmillan, New York, 1954. (Chapter 4 discusses induction.)

9. J. R. Newman, *The World of Mathematics*, vol. 1, Simon and Schuster, New York, 1956. (On pp. 622–641 is reprinted from the Scientific American, 1955, "Projective Geometry," by M. Kline.)

10. D. Hilbert and S. Cohn-Vossen, *Geometry and the Imagination*, Chelsea, New York, 1952. (The conic sections are discussed on pp. 1–11.)

11. W. M. Ivins, Jr., *Art and Geometry*, Harvard University Press, Cambridge, Mass., 1946.

12. M. Kline, *Mathematics in Western Culture*, Oxford University Press, New York, 1953. (Chapters 4, 10, and 11 discuss geometry.)

13. N. Bourbaki, The architecture of mathematics, *American Mathematical Monthly*, vol. 57, 1950, pp. 221–232.

14. A. Weil, The future of mathematics, *American Mathematical Monthly*, vol. 57 1950, pp. 295–306.

Appendix **A**

THE RUDIMENTS
OF ALGEBRA

Most of this text uses only the arithmetic met in grammar school. However, Chapters 4, 7, 10, 13, and 15 (mainly 7, 10, and 15) use algebra in the manipulations of expressions and equations involving the two fundamental operations, addition and multiplication, and their respective offspring, subtraction and division. This appendix describes and justifies the more common algebraic gymnastics. It is a reference to be read if and when needed. Proofs are included for the convenience of the reader who wants to know the "why."

Just as we can do all of arithmetic by memorizing a few facts (such as the addition and multiplication tables up to nine by nine), so can we reduce all the manipulations of algebra to a few key assertions. Instead of the 162 entries in the addition and multiplication tables, it turns out that for algebra we will have just eleven rules to memorize. With these eleven rules we can do all of elementary algebra: for example, removing parentheses, inserting parentheses, factoring, finding roots, and collecting terms.

We will now state those eleven rules (or axioms) and derive their consequences in the logical style of Euclidean geometry—statement and reason. We choose this formal manner of writing proofs for three reasons: to show that algebra is just as logical as geometry, to emphasize how much can lie hidden in a few axioms, and to divide the arguments into small enough steps to be justified by a citation of the appropriate axiom.

By a **field** *we will mean any mathematical structure possessing an addition, denoted* $+$, *and a multiplication, denoted* $\times$, *both defined on some set S and satisfying these eleven rules:**

---

* A stands for "addition," M stands for "multiplication," and D stands for "distributivity." A 1 through A 5 refer only to addition; M 1 through M 5 refer only to multiplication (except for M 5, which does mention 0 and hence involves A 4); D links multiplication and addition.

A 1. *If a and b are in S, so is a + b.*

A 2. *For all a and b in S we have*

$$a + b = b + a.$$

A 3. *For all a, b, and c in S we have*
a + (b + c) = (a + b) + c.

A 4. *There is an element in A, called*
0, such that 0 + a = a for all a
in S.

A 5. *For each pair a and b in S there*
is exactly one x in S such that
a + x = b.

M 1. *If a and b are in S, so is a × b.*

M 2. *For all a and b in S we have*

$$a \times b = b \times a.$$

M 3. *For all a, b, and c in S we have*
a × (b × c) = (a × b) × c.

M 4. *There is an element in S, called*
1, such that 1 × a = a for all a
in S.

M 5. *For each pair a and b in S (where*
a is not 0) there is exactly one x
in S such that a × x = b.

D. *For all a, b, and c in S, a × (b + c) = (a × b) + (a × c).*

We meet several *fields* in this book; specifically:

Example 1. (Chapter 5)
S is the set of real numbers (usual + and ×);
Example 2. (Chapter 5)
S is the set of rationals (usual + and ×);
Example 3. (Chapter 15)
S is the set of complex numbers and the $\oplus$ and $\otimes$ defined in Chapter 15 play the role of + and × respectively;
Example 4. (Chapter 10)
S has just five elements {0, 1, 2, 3, 4}, and the $\oplus$ and $\otimes$ defined on p. 132 play the role of + and ×, respectively.

Before checking that Example 4 is truly a field, the reader should first meet some structures that *fail* to qualify as fields. The following four exercises present some structures that satisfy some, but not all, of the eleven rules.

E 1. Let S be the set of natural numbers {0, 1, 2, 3, $\cdots$}, and let + and × be the usual addition and multiplication. Show that this structure satisfies all of the eleven rules for a field except A 5 and M 5.

E 2. Let S be the set of integers {$\cdots$, −3, −2, −1, 0, 1, 2, 3, $\cdots$}, and let + and × be the usual addition and multiplication. Show that this structure satisfies all of the eleven rules for a field except M 5.

E 3. Let S be the set of positive rationals (including 0) and let + and × be the usual addition and multiplication. Show that this structure satisfies all of the eleven rules for a field except A 5.

E 4. Let S be the set of irrationals (defined in Chapter 5), and let + and × be the usual addition and multiplication. Show that this structure satisfies only rules A 2, M 2, A 3, M 3, and D of a field. (*Hint:* Show that the sum and product of irrationals need not be irrational.)

In Example 4 we met a field with only five elements. We now examine a field with two elements. Let S be the set $\{0, 1\}$. Define $+$ and $\times$ by these two arrays

(*1*)

$+$	0	1
0	0	1
1	1	0

$\times$	0	1
0	0	0
1	0	1

Clearly $+$ satisfies A 1 and $\times$ satisfies M 1. Since $0 + 1 = 1$ and $1 + 0 = 1$ we see that $+$ satisfies A 2. As the following six exercises show, (*1*) satisfies all eleven rules for a field.

E 5. Show that $\times$ of (*1*) satisfies M 2.

E 6. (a) Make the (eight) checks necessary to show that (*1*) satisfies A 3.
    (b) Make the (eight) checks necessary to show that (*1*) satisfies M 3.

E 7. (a) Make the (two) checks necessary to show that (*1*) satisfies A 4.
    (b) Make the (two) checks necessary to show that (*1*) satisfies M 4.

E 8. (a) Make the (four) checks necessary to show that (*1*) satisfies A 5.
    (b) Make the (two) checks necessary to show that (*1*) satisfies M 5.

E 9. Make the (eight) checks necessary to show that (*1*) satisfies D.

E 10. Make a few sample checks for the fact that Example 4 is a field.

The structures of Example 4 and (*1*) are called Galois fields. Any field for which S is a finite set is called a Galois field. It is known that the number of elements in a Galois field must be either a prime or a power of a prime. For one application of Galois fields see Chapter 12 (p. 164), where they are used in the proof of Theorem 5.

The eleven rules are the *axioms* for *fields*. Any theorems we deduce from them apply to any field, in particular to the fields of Examples 1, 2, 3, and 4.

Axiom A 2 asserts that addition is commutative; axiom M 2 asserts that multiplication is commutative. Several examples of commutative operations are to be found in Chapter 11, where the virtue of commutativity is discussed. Axioms A 3 and M 3 say that both the operations $+$ and $\times$ are associative. Axiom A 4 says that there is an element "with no effect when added to an element." Axiom M 4 says that there is an element "with no effect when multiplying an element."

But when we come to axioms A 5 and M 5 we meet a crucial distinction between $+$ and $\times$. Though we can solve the equation $0 + x = 1$, for example, we cannot solve the equation $0 \times x = 1$. In fact, we have

THEOREM 1. *For any element a in a field, $0 \times a = 0$, and $a \times 0 = 0$.*

PROOF. We will prove only the first assertion, $0 \times a = 0$.

STATEMENT	REASON
(1) $a \times 0 = a \times (0 + 0)$	A 4
(2) $a \times (0 + 0) = a \times 0 + a \times 0$	D
(3) $a \times 0 = a \times 0 + a \times 0$	(1) and (2)
(4) $a \times 0 = 0 + a \times 0$	A 4
(5) $0 + a \times 0 = a \times 0 + 0$	A 2
(6) $a \times 0 = a \times 0 + 0$	(4) and (5)
(7) $a \times 0 = 0$	A 5 (If $a \times 0$ were not equal to 0, then (3) and (6) would tell us that the equation $a \times 0 = a \times 0 + x$ has at least two solutions.)

The reader may easily deduce that $0 \times a = 0$. Theorem 1 is proved.

Note the key role that *D* plays in the proof of Theorem 1. Rule D, the main link between $+$ and $\times$, asserts that "multiplication *distributes* over addition." (The reverse, however, does not hold.) The proof of Theorem 1 shows "why" $0 \times a = 0$, a fact that might not surprise the reader. But, with no more difficulty, we will be able, in Theorem 11, to show why $(-a) \times (-b) = a \times b$, a fact which many find mysterious.

THEOREM 2. *For all a, b, and c in a field we have $b + (c + a) = a + (b + c)$.*

PROOF.

STATEMENT	REASON
(1) $b + (c + a) = (b + c) + a$	A 3
(2) $(b + c) + a = a + (b + c)$	A 2
(3) $b + (c + a) = a + (b + c)$	(1) and (2)

This proves Theorem 2.

E 11. Using axioms A 2 and A 3 prove that $a + (b + (c + d)) = c + (b + (a + d))$. (*Hint:* A similar problem is worked out in Chapter 11, p. 150.)

Theorem 2 suggests

THEOREM 3. *The sum of several elements in the field does not depend on the order in which we write them or on the way we insert parentheses.*

The proof of Theorem 3 depends only on A 2 and A 3 but is quite tedious and will be omitted. We also omit the proof of the similar

THEOREM 4. *The product of several elements in a field does not depend on the order in which we write them or on the way we insert parentheses.*

E 12. Using rules M 2 and M 3 prove that

$$(a \times b) \times (c \times d) = (a \times c) \times (b \times d).$$

This is a special case of Theorem 4; do not use Theorem 4 in your proof.

THEOREM 5. *For all a, b, and c in S we have*

$$(b + c) \times a = (b \times a) + (c \times a).$$

PROOF.

STATEMENT	REASON
(1) $(b + c) \times a = a \times (b + c)$	M 2
(2) $a \times (b + c) = (a \times b) + (a \times c)$	D
(3) $a \times b = b \times a; a \times c = c \times a$	M 2
(4) $a \times (b + c) = (b \times a) + (c \times a)$	(2) and (3)
(5) $(b + c) \times a = (b \times a) + (c \times a)$	(1) and (4)

This proves Theorem 5.

Theorem 3 says that as long as we work only with addition we can omit parentheses. Theorem 4 says that as long as we work only with multiplication we can omit parentheses. But Theorem 5 says that we cannot omit parentheses in $(b + c) \times a$, since the two possible interpretations of $b + c \times a$, namely $(b + c) \times a$ and $b + (c \times a)$, will usually give different results.

Agreement. *It is the custom to omit the multiplication sign $\times$ when such an omission cannot lead to confusion. Thus we frequently write ab instead of $a \times b$. Frequently $a \times a$ is written a^2 instead of aa.*

Example 5.

Instead of $(M \times A) + (N \times B)$ we might write $(MA) + (NB)$, or simply $MA + NB$ (the gain in brevity more than balances the slight risk that we might try to form the sum of A and N first).

Though in general (as in Example 5) we cannot change the sum of two products very much, we can do a good deal to the product of two sums, as is shown by

THEOREM 6. $(a + b) \times (c + d) = ac + ad + bc + bd$.

PROOF.

STATEMENT	REASON
(1) $(a + b) \times (c + d) = (a + b)c + (a + b)d$	D
(2) $(a + b)c = ac + bc, (a + b)d = ad + bd$	Theorem 5
(3) $(a + b) \times (c + d) = (ac + bc) + (ad + bd)$	(1) and (2)
(4) $(ac + bc) + (ad + bd) = ac + ad + bc + bd$	Theorem 3
(5) $(a + b) \times (c + d) = ac + ad + bc + bd$	(3) and (4)

This proves Theorem 6.

Example 6.

By Theorem 6, $(2a + 1) \times (2b + 1) = (2a)(2b) + (2a)(1) + 1(2b) + 1(1)$. By Theorem 4, $(2a)(2b) = 4ab$. By axioms M 4 and M 2 we see that $(2a)(1) = 2a$. By rule M 4 we have $1(2b) = 2b$ and $1(1) = 1$. Thus $(2a + 1)(2b + 1) = 4ab + 2a + 2b + 1$. This is used in Chapter 4 to prove that the product of two odd numbers is odd.

Example 7.

In a similar manner we could show that $(a + 3) \times (a + 3) = a^2 + 6a + 9$. This is used in Chapter 15.

E 13. Prove that $(5a + 1) \times (5a + 3) = 25a^2 + 20a + 3$. (Number each step as in our proofs, and give the reason for it.)

E 14. A, P, Q, and M, are four elements in a field that happen to satisfy the relation $1 = PA + QM$. Prove that for any element B in the field it is then true that $B = (B \times P)A + (B \times Q)M$. (Number the steps, and give reasons.) This result is used in the proof of Theorem 7 of Chapter 10.

E 15. In Chapter 4 we used the fact that if a natural number D is a divisor of a natural number A, then it is also the divisor of AB for any natural number B. Prove this fact. (*Hint:* Use the definition of divisor given in Chapter 3, together with the appropriate rules on multiplication.)

E 16. See E 15. Prove that, if D is a divisor of A and also of B, then it is a divisor of $A + B$. (*Hint:* This will involve the distributive axiom, D.) This is used in Chapter 4.

On a few occasions in this book we manipulated expressions involving "$-$" (the minus sign). *The trouble with this symbol is that it has two meanings*, just as some words have two meanings. (For example, "bat" means one thing on the baseball diamond and another in a dark cave.) Unhappily, the two meanings for "minus" both occur in the same context, arithmetic and algebra.

First Meaning of "Minus." If a is any element of a field, then according to rule A 5, *there is exactly one element x in the field such that $a + x = 0$. That unique x we give the name* $-a$ *and call it* **the additive inverse of a.** Thus, by this definition, $a + (-a) = 0$.

Example 8.

Since $0 + 0 = 0$ we have $-0 = 0$.

Example 9.

In the Galois field of (*1*), p. 284, we have $1 + 1 = 0$. Thus in that field $-1 = 1$.

Example 10.

In the Galois field of Example 4 we have $2 + 3 = 0$. Thus in that particular field we have $-2 = 3$.

E 17. See Chapter 15 for the definition of complex numbers and their sum.

     (a) Show that if X and Y are complex numbers located such that the midpoint of the line segment with ends X and Y is 0, then $X + Y = 0$.

     (b) Using (a), show that if X is any complex number, then $-X$ is located in such a way that the line segment from X to $-X$ has 0 as its midpoint.

THEOREM 7. $-(-a) = a$.

PROOF. All that we know about $-a$ is that $a + (-a) = 0$. We wish to prove that a is the additive inverse of $-a$. To do so we must prove $(-a) + a = 0$. But this follows by axiom A 2 from the fact that $a + (-a) = 0$.

E 18. (a) Check that $-(-4)$ is 4 in the field of rationals.

     (b) Check that $-(-4)$ is 4 in the field of Example 4.

The next few theorems tell how the additive inverse behaves with respect to multiplication.

THEOREM 8. $(-a)b = -(ab)$ *and* $a(-b) = -(ab)$.

PROOF. We prove only the first assertion.

STATEMENT	REASON
(1) $a + (-a) = 0$	definition of additive inverse
(2) $0b = 0$	Theorem 1
(3) $[a + (-a)]b = 0$	(1) and (2)
(4) $[a + (-a)]b = ab + (-a)b$	Theorem 5
(5) $ab + (-a)b = 0$	(3) and (4)
(6) $(-a)b = -(ab)$	(5) and definition of additive inverse

Theorem 8 is proved.

E 19. Using Theorem 8 compute $(-5)9$, $(-2)1$, and $(-7)8$.
E 20. Using Theorem 8 and rule M 4 prove that $(-1) \times (-3) = 3$.

THEOREM 9. $(-1)a = -a$.

PROOF. By Theorem 8, $(-1)a = -(1 \times a)$. By rule M 4, $(1 \times a) = a$.

Theorem 9 shows that the additive inverse of 1 determines the additive inverse of any element of the field.

THEOREM 10. $(-1)(-1) = 1$.

PROOF. By Theorem 9, $(-1)(-1) = -(-1)$. But, by Theorem 7,

$$-(-1) = 1.$$

Theorem 10 generalizes to

THEOREM 11. $(-a)(-b) = ab$.

PROOF.

STATEMENT	REASON
(1) $-a = (-1)a; \; -b = (-1)b$	Theorem 9
(2) $(-a)(-b) = [(-1)a][(-1)b]$	(1)
(3) $[(-1)a][(-1)b] = (-1)(-1)ab$	Theorem 4
(4) $(-1)(-1) = 1$	Theorem 10
(5) $(-a)(-b) = 1ab$	(2), (3), and (4)
(6) $1ab = ab$	M 4
(7) $(-a)(-b) = ab$	(5) and (6)

End of proof.

Theorem 11 shows, for instance, that $(-2)(-3) = 6$.

Theorems 8 and 11 tell us how the additive inverse behaves with respect to $\times$. We will now learn how it behaves with respect to $+$. Our result will involve the **Second Meaning of "Minus."** *If a and b are elements of a field, then there is, by rule A 5, exactly one element x in the field such that $a + x = b$. That unique x we give the name $b - a$ and call it* **the result of subtracting a from b.** Thus, by this definition, $a + (b - a) = b$.

Note how different are the two meanings of the one symbol $-$ ("minus"). The additive inverse, $-a$, is defined for each element a in the field; subtraction, $b - a$, is defined for each *pair* of elements in the field. Though the two roles of "minus" are quite different, they are intimately related by

THEOREM 12. $b - a = b + (-a)$.

PROOF. In order to prove that $b + (-a)$ is $b - a$, we must show that $a + [b + (-a)]$ is b. This we now do.

STATEMENT	REASON
(1) $a + [b + (-a)] = [a + (-a)] + b$	Theorem 3
(2) $a + (-a) = 0$	Definition of additive inverse
(3) $a + [b + (-a)] = 0 + b$	(1) and (2)
(4) $0 + b = b$	A 4
(5) $a + [b + (-a)] = b$	(3) and (4)

Example 11.
By Theorem 12, $5 - 3 = 5 + (-3)$.

Example 12.
By Theorem 12, $6 - (-5) = 6 + [-(-5)]$. But $-(-5) = 5$ by Theorem 7. Thus $6 - (-5) = 6 + 5 = 11$.

E 21. The symbol $-$ appears eight times in Example 12. Determine which of its two meanings it has at each of these appearances.

THEOREM 13. $-(a + b) = -a - b$ [*where $-a - b$ is short for $(-a) - b$*].

PROOF. We wish to prove that $(a + b) + (-a - b) = 0$. This we now do.

STATEMENT	REASON
(1) $-a - b = -a + (-b)$	Theorem 12
(2) $(a + b) + (-a - b) = (a + b) + [-a + (-b)]$	(1)
(3) $(a + b) + [-a + (-b)] = [a + (-a)] + [b + (-b)]$	Theorem 3
(4) $a + (-a) = 0; b + (-b) = 0$	Definition of additive inverse
(5) $(a + b) + (-a - b) = 0 + 0$	(2), (3), and (4)
(6) $0 + 0 = 0$	A 4
(7) $(a + b) + (-a - b) = 0$	(5) and (6)

This ends the proof of Theorem 13.

(Note the contrast between Theorems 8 and 13.)

E 22. Decide which meaning the symbol $-$ has at each of its appearances in the statement $-(a + b) = -a - b$.

E 23. Use Theorem 9 and rule D to provide a different proof of Theorem 13.

(This alternate proof is shorter than the one we have given, but it goes outside of addition to prove something about addition.)

E 24. Prove that $-(a - b) = -a + b$. (Number each step in your proof, and cite the reason.)

E 25. Showing and justifying all steps, prove that $4 - (-9) = 13$.

In E 31 and E 32 of Chapter 3, we used the fact that $(a - 1)(a + 1) = a^2 - 1$. This is a special case of

THEOREM 14. $(a - b)(a + b) = a^2 - b^2$.

PROOF.

STATEMENT	REASON
(1) $(a - b)(a + b) = [a + (-b)](a + b)$	Theorem 12
(2) $[a + (-b)](a + b) = a^2 + ab + (-b)a + (-b)b$	Theorem 6
(3) $ab + (-b)a = ab + a(-b)$	M 2
(4) $ab + a(-b) = a[b + (-b)]$	D
(5) $b + (-b) = 0$	Definition
(6) $ab + (-b)a = a0$	(3), (4), and (5)
(7) $a0 = 0$	Theorem 1
(8) $ab + (-b)a = 0$	(6) and (7)
(9) $(a - b)(a + b) = a^2 + 0 + (-b)b$	(1), (2), and (8)
(10) $a^2 + 0 + (-b)b = a^2 + (-b)b$	A 4 and Theorem 3
(11) $(-b)b = -(b^2)$	Theorem 8
(12) $(a - b)(a + b) = a^2 + [-(b^2)]$	(9), (10), and (11)
(13) $a^2 + [-(b^2)] = a^2 - b^2$	Theorem 12
(14) $(a - b)(a + b) = a^2 - b^2$	(12) and (13)

End of proof.

Example 13.

$(5 - 1)(5 + 1) = 5^2 - 1^2$. Thus $5^2 - 1^2 = 4 \times 6$.

E 26. Show how the equation $(a - 1)(a + 1) = a^2 - 1$ plays a key role in E 2 of Chapter 3.

E 27. Use Theorem 14 as a shortcut in computing 98×102. (*Hint:* $98 = 100 - 2$, and $102 = 100 + 2$.)

E 28. See E 27. Compute, by the shortcut, (a) 49×51; (b) 37×43.

THEOREM 15. $a(b - c) = ab - ac$.

PROOF.

STATEMENT	REASON
(1) $a(b - c) = a[b + (-c)]$	Theorem 12
(2) $a(b + (-c)) = ab + a(-c)$	D
(3) $a(-c) = -ac$	Theorem 8
(4) $a(b - c) = ab + (-ac)$	(1), (2), and (3)
(5) $ab + (-ac) = ab - ac$	Theorem 12
(6) $a(b - c) = ab - ac$	(4) and (5)

End of proof.

E 29. Prove that if a natural number divides two integers, then it divides the difference of these two integers. (For a definition of "divides," see Chapter 3, p. 24; Theorem 15 is a key tool.)

E 30. (a) Prove that if a natural number divides two integers, then it divides their product.

(b) Prove that a divisor of a divisor of the natural number, B, is a divisor of B.

E 31. While solving electrical networks in Chapter 7, we met such equations as

$$3(V_1 - V_3) + 4(V_2 - V_3) = 3V_1 + 4V_2 - 7V_3.$$

Justify this equation. Number each step, and cite a pertinent rule or theorem.

E 32. (a) Prove that $(a - b) + b = a$.

(b) Using (a), show that if $x - 5 = 9$, then $x = 9 + 5$. (*Hint:* Add 5 to both sides of $x - 5 = 9$.)

E 33. Prove that $(V - 1) - (E - 1) = V - E$. (This appears in Chapter 13.)

E 34. Prove that if $-E + 3C = 6$, then $3C = 6 + E$. (This appears in Chapter 13.)

E 35. In the proof of Theorem 1 of Chapter 10 we used

(a) $(-1)(A - B) = -A + B$;

(b) $(A - B) + (B - C) = A - C$.

Prove that (a) and (b) are true in any field.

E 36. In the proof of Theorem 2 of Chapter 10 we used

$$(A - B) + (a - b) = (A + a) - (B + b).$$

Justify in detail this equation; that is, prove it.

E 37. In Chapter 4 we asserted that

$$2 = 32 - 5 \times 230 + 35 \times 32 = -5 \times 230 + 36 \times 32.$$

Justify this "collecting of the 32's" by proving this little theorem: $a - 5b + 35a = (-5)b + 36a$. Number each step of your proof, and give the reason.

Having obtained the basic properties of $+$, $\times$, and $-$, we next consider division, which we meet occasionally in this book.

Definition of Quotient. *If a and b are elements of a field, where a is not 0, then there is, by rule M 5, exactly one element x in the field such that $ax = b$. This unique x we give the name b/a and call it the* **quotient** *of b divided by a.* Thus, by this definition, $a(b/a) = b$.

Sometimes b/a is written as $\dfrac{b}{a}$ or $b \div a$.

Example 14.
Since $(3)(2) = 6$, we have $6/2 = 3$.
Definition. *If a is not 0, then $1/a$ is called the* **"reciprocal of a,"** *or the "multiplicative inverse of a."*

E 38. The multiplicative inverse is defined in terms of division. Show how we could have defined the additive inverse in terms of subtraction. (*Hint:* Prove that $-a = 0 - a$.)

E 39. (a) Prove that the reciprocal of the reciprocal of a is a.
(b) What theorem about the additive inverse does (a) resemble?

THEOREM 16. *If $ab = 0$, then at least one of a and b is 0.*

PROOF. We will prove that if a is not 0, then b must be 0.

STATEMENT	REASON
(1) $ab = 0$	Given
(2) a has a reciprocal, denoted $1/a$	M 5
(3) $(1/a)ab = (1/a)0$	(1)
(4) $(1/a)ab = [a(1/a)]b$	Theorem 4
(5) $a(1/a) = 1$	Definition of $1/a$
(6) $1b = b$	M 4
(7) $b = (1/a)0$	(3), (4), (5), and (6)
(8) $(1/a)0 = 0$	Theorem 1
(9) $b = 0$	(7) and (8)

End of proof.

Theorem 16 is used in Chapter 15, p. 224.
We will now show how division behaves with respect to multiplication.

THEOREM 17. $(a/b)(c/d) = ac/bd$ (where b and d are not 0).

PROOF. Call a/b simply p. Call c/d simply q. We know that $bp = a$ and that $dq = c$. We wish to prove that $(bd)(pq) = ac$. This we now do.

STATEMENT	REASON
(1) $(bd)(pq) = (bp)(dq)$	Theorem 4
(2) $bp = 1$ and $dq = 1$	Definition of p and q
(3) $bd(pq) = 1 \times 1$	(1) and (2)
(4) $1 \times 1 = 1$	M 4
(5) $(bd)(pq) = 1$	(3) and (4)

End of proof.

Example 15.
$(\frac{3}{5})(\frac{7}{9}) = \frac{21}{45}$.

THEOREM 18. $(ab)/c = a(b/c)$ (where c is not 0).

PROOF. Let $p = b/c$. By definition of / we know that $cp = b$. We will deduce that $c(ap) = ab$, that is, $ap = (ab)/c$. This would prove the theorem.

STATEMENT	REASON
(1) $c(ap) = a(cp)$	Theorem 4
(2) $cp = b$	Definition of p
(3) $c(ap) = ab$	(1) and (2)

End of proof.

E 40. Prove that $(b + c)/a = (b/a) + (c/a)$ (for a not 0).
E 41. Prove that $-(a/b) = (-a)/b$ (for b not 0).
E 42. Prove that $ac/bc = a/b$ (for b and c not 0).

The following theorem says that "to divide by a quotient, first turn it upside down, and then multiply."

THEOREM 19. $a/(b/c) = a(c/b)$ (for b and c not 0).

PROOF. Let p be c/b and q be b/c. We wish to prove that $a/q = ap$. In other words, from $bp = c$ and $cq = b$ we want to deduce that $q(ap) = a$. To do so we will prove that $pq = 1$.

STATEMENT	REASON
(1) $bp = c$; $cq = b$	Given
(2) $(bp)q = b$	(1)
(3) $b(pq) = b$	M 3
(4) $(1/b)b(pq) = (1/b)b$	(3)
(5) $(1/b)b = 1$	Definition of quotient; M 2
(6) $1(pq) = 1$	(4) and (5)
(7) $pq = 1$	(6) and M 4

End of proof.

Example 16.
$(\frac{3}{4})/(\frac{9}{7}) = (\frac{3}{4})(\frac{7}{9})$, which, by Theorem 17, is equal to $\frac{21}{36}$.

E 43. Using E 42, show that $(-5)/(-7) = 5/7$.

We conclude with a detailed justification of a typical manipulation made in Chapter 7. We will list twelve steps; in practice, one does several at a time.

Example 17. From p. 85 of Chapter 7.

We will show that the equation $V_1 - V_2 = 4V_2 - 4V_3 + V_2$ implies the equation $0 = -V_1 + 6V_2 - 4V_3$. In slow motion, we have:

STATEMENT	REASON
(1) $V_1 - V_2 = 4V_2 - 4V_3 + V_2$	Given
(2) $V_1 - V_2 = 4V_2 + (-4V_3) + V_2$	Theorem 12
(3) $V_1 - V_2 = 4V_2 + V_2 + (-4V_3)$	Theorem 3
(4) $V_1 - V_2 = 5V_2 + (-4V_3)$	Theorem 5
(5) $(V_1 - V_2) + V_2 = 5V_2 + (-4V_3) + V_2$	(4)
(6) $V_1 = 5V_2 + (-4V_3) + V_2$	E 32
(7) $V_1 + (-V_1) = 5V_2 + (-4V_3) + V_2 + (-V_1)$	(6)
(8) $0 = 5V_2 + (-4V_3) + V_2 + (--V_1)$	First meaning of "minus"
(9) $0 = (-V_1) + (5V_2 + V_2) + (-4V_3)$	Theorem 3
(10) $0 = (-V_1) + 6V_2 + (-4V_3)$	Theorem 5
(11) $0 = (-V_1) + 6V_2 - 4V_3$	Theorem 12
(12) $0 = -V_1 + 6V_2 - 4V_3$	Parentheses dropped in (11)

End of justification.

E 44. (a) Prove that $(a + b) - c = a + (b - c)$.

    (b) Use (a) to show why we can be careless and omit parentheses in going from (10) to (11) in the preceding justification.

E 45. (a) Prove that $-5(a - 7b) = -5a + 35b$.

(b) Where on p. 45 of Chapter 4 is this used?

References

1. W. W. Sawyer, *A Concrete Approach to Abstract Algebra*, Freeman, San Francisco, 1959. (Pages 26–31 discuss fields and give a different proof of Theorem 1; pp. 71–77 discuss finite fields.)
2. G. Birkhoff and S. MacLane, *A Survey of Modern Algebra*, Macmillan, New York, 1953. (A structure weaker than a field is discussed on pp. 1–6; the demand that the equation $ax = b$ have a solution is omitted.)

THE GEOMETRIC AND HARMONIC SERIES

Appendix **B**

In Chapter 14 we used the fact that $3/10 + 3/10^2 + \cdots + 3/10^N$ gets closer and closer to $\frac{1}{3}$ as N grows. This we prove in Theorem 3 (p. 300). In Chapter 3 we used the expression $1/1 + 1/2 + 1/3 + \cdots + 1/N$ as an estimate of the average gap between the first N primes. We shall examine the behavior of this sum in Theorem 1, which is quite a contrast to Theorem 3. Theorem 2 is the basis for the fact that 99,999 is one less than 100,000, which illustrates an important property of the decimal system.

Consider first the endless sequence of numbers $1, \frac{1}{2}, \frac{1}{4}, \cdots$, each obtained from its predecessor through multiplying by $\frac{1}{2}$. Let S_N be the sum of the first N numbers of that sequence. Thus

$$
\begin{aligned}
S_1 &= 1 & &= 1.000, \\
S_2 &= 1 + \tfrac{1}{2} & &= 1.500, \\
S_3 &= 1 + \tfrac{1}{2} + \tfrac{1}{4} & &= 1.750, \\
S_4 &= 1 + \tfrac{1}{2} + \tfrac{1}{4} + \tfrac{1}{8} &&= 1.875.
\end{aligned}
$$

As N grows, so does S_N. Do the S_N's grow without bound, passing 10, even 100, eventually 1000, and so on? Or is their growth restricted by some real number that they are approaching? If so, what is that number?

Two forces influence the growth of S_N. First, since we add more and more numbers together, we might suspect that there is no limit to the growth of S_N. Second, since the amounts we add are getting smaller and smaller, we might suspect that the S_N's cannot grow very large, and hence must be approaching some number.

Before we jump to any conclusion concerning which force is the more powerful for the sequence $1, \frac{1}{2}, \frac{1}{4}, \frac{1}{8}, \cdots$, it would be wise to examine another sequence, the so-called *harmonic series:*

$$\frac{1}{1}, \quad \frac{1}{2}, \quad \frac{1}{3}, \quad \frac{1}{4}, \quad \frac{1}{5}, \quad \cdots .$$

Let s_N stand for the sum of the first N terms of the harmonic series. Thus

$$
\begin{aligned}
s_1 &= 1 & &= 1.000, \\
s_2 &= 1 + \tfrac{1}{2} & &= 1.500, \\
s_3 &= 1 + \tfrac{1}{2} + \tfrac{1}{3} & &= 1.833\cdots, \\
s_4 &= 1 + \tfrac{1}{2} + \tfrac{1}{3} + \tfrac{1}{4} &&= 2.083\cdots
\end{aligned}
$$

(and the reader may compute a few more such sums).

What happens to s_N as N gets larger and larger? The same two forces are acting as in the first example. Which will be the more powerful? We answer this question with

THEOREM 1. *If s_N is $1/1 + 1/2 + 1/3 + \cdots + 1/N$, then s_N grows without bound as N gets larger and larger.*

PROOF. We shall examine closely s_2, s_4, s_8, s_{16}, and so on; that is, s_N when N is a power of 2.

First of all,

$$s_2 = 1 + \tfrac{1}{2} = \tfrac{3}{2}.$$

Next, $s_4 = 1 + \tfrac{1}{2} + \tfrac{1}{3} + \tfrac{1}{4} = s_2 + \tfrac{1}{3} + \tfrac{1}{4}$, which is larger than $s_2 + \tfrac{1}{4} + \tfrac{1}{4}$. Thus,

$$s_4 \text{ is larger than } s_2 + \tfrac{1}{2},$$

and so

$$s_4 \text{ is larger than } \tfrac{4}{2}.$$

Next, $s_8 = s_4 + \tfrac{1}{5} + \tfrac{1}{6} + \tfrac{1}{7} + \tfrac{1}{8}$ is larger than $s_4 + \tfrac{1}{8} + \tfrac{1}{8} + \tfrac{1}{8} + \tfrac{1}{8}$. Thus s_8 is larger than $s_4 + \tfrac{1}{2}$, and we conclude that

$$s_8 \text{ is larger than } \tfrac{5}{2}.$$

Similarly, as the reader may show, s_{16} is larger than $s_8 + \tfrac{1}{2}$. Thus,

$$s_{16} \text{ is larger than } \tfrac{6}{2}.$$

Using the same idea, the reader may show that s_{32} is larger than $\tfrac{7}{2}$ and that s_{64} is larger than $\tfrac{8}{2}$.

Since the s_N's for large N can be made larger than the sum of any given number of $(\tfrac{1}{2})$'s, there is no bound to the growth of s_N. This proves Theorem 1.

In the harmonic series the first force conquers. Now let us see which of the two forces conquers in the case of our first sequence, $1, \frac{1}{2}, \frac{1}{4}, \frac{1}{8}, \cdots$. Let S_N be the sum of the first N terms of this sequence. Theorem 2 will tell us that

(1)
$$S_N = \frac{1 - (\frac{1}{2})^N}{(\frac{1}{2})},$$

a formula which is much shorter than the one we began with,

(2)
$$S_N = 1 + \tfrac{1}{2} + \tfrac{1}{4} + \tfrac{1}{8} + \cdots + (\tfrac{1}{2})^{N-1}.$$

(The reader should note that the Nth term is $(\frac{1}{2})^{N-1}$; for example, check this for $N = 4$.)

Though (2) gets more and more unwieldy as N grows, (1) remains concise. Using (1) instead of (2), we can easily predict the behavior of S_N as N gets larger and larger. Since $(\frac{1}{2})^N$ approaches 0 as N increases, we see that S_N approaches

$$\frac{1 - 0}{(\frac{1}{2})},$$

which is 2. For this sequence the force that dominates is the second, "the swift decrease in the size of the terms."

We will obtain a result of which formula (1) is just a special case.

If a and r are two real numbers, then the N numbers

$$a, \quad ar, \quad ar^2, \quad ar^3, \quad \cdots, \quad a(r)^{N-1}$$

are called a *geometric series* or *geometric progression*. For example, if a is 1 and r is $\frac{1}{2}$, we obtain the geometric progression $1, \frac{1}{2}, \frac{1}{4}, \cdots$. If a is $\frac{3}{10}$ and r is $\frac{1}{10}$, we obtain the geometric series $3/10, 3/10^2, 3/10^3, \cdots$. For any geometric series we have

THEOREM 2. *SUM OF A FINITE GEOMETRIC SERIES. Let a and r be real numbers with r not equal to 1. Let $S_N = a + ar + ar^2 + \cdots + ar^{N-1}$. Then S_N is given by this short formula:*

$$S_N = \frac{a(1 - r^N)}{1 - r}.$$

PROOF. We have

(3)
$$S_N = a + ar + ar^2 + \cdots + ar^{N-1},$$

and

(4)
$$rS_N = ar + ar^2 + \cdots + ar^{N-1} + ar^N.$$

Subtracting (4) from (3) and performing many cancellations, we obtain

$$S_N - rS_N = a - ar^N,$$

which we can simplify to

(5)
$$(1 - r)S_N = a(1 - r^N).$$

Dividing both sides of (5) by $1 - r$ (which fortunately is not 0), we obtain

$$S_N = \frac{a(1 - r^N)}{1 - r},$$

and Theorem 2 is proved.

With the aid of Theorem 2 we will easily obtain

THEOREM 3. *SUM OF AN INFINITE GEOMETRIC SERIES. Let S_N be the sum of the first N terms of the geometric series*

$$a, \quad ar, \quad ar^2, \quad ar^3, \quad \cdots ,$$

where r is less than 1 and larger than -1. Then as N gets larger and larger, S_N approaches

$$\frac{a}{1 - r}.$$

PROOF. By Theorem 2 we know that S_N is equal to

$$\frac{a(1 - r^N)}{1 - r}.$$

As N grows, r^N approaches 0, since r is a number between 1 and -1. Thus S_N approaches

$$\frac{a(1 - 0)}{1 - r},$$

and Theorem 3 is proved.

Theorem 3 is usually stated in this terse but misleading shorthand:

(6) $$a + ar + ar^2 + ar^3 + \cdots = \frac{a}{1 - r}.$$

The reader should be careful in using this shorthand. It does not describe the addition of an infinite set of numbers; rather, it describes the behavior of sums of finite sets of numbers.

Example 1. With $a = 1$ and $r = \frac{1}{2}$, formula (6) gives

$$1 + \frac{1}{2} + \frac{1}{4} + \frac{1}{8} + \cdots = \frac{1}{1 - (\frac{1}{2})} = 2.$$

Example 2. With $a = \frac{3}{10}$ and $r = \frac{1}{10}$, formula (6) gives

$$\frac{3}{10} + \frac{3}{100} + \frac{3}{1000} + \cdots = \frac{\frac{3}{10}}{[1 - (\frac{1}{10})]} = \frac{1}{3}.$$

(In decimal notation, Example 2 reads: $0.3333\cdots = \frac{1}{3}$.)

We now give an *application of geometric series to probability.* Two equally matched volleyball teams representing Hawaii and Texas play each other until one of them has a lead of two points. For example, if Hawaii wins the first two points, then the game is over quickly; the winner's score being 2, and the loser's score being 0. Or it might happen that Hawaii scores the first point and Texas scores the next three points to get a lead of 2. Then the game would be over; the winner's score would be 3, and the loser's 1.

Using an *H* to record a point for Hawaii, and *T* a point for Texas, we could tell the story of each game in a string of *H*'s and *T*'s. For example, *H T T H H H* tells us that Hawaii scored the first point, Texas scored the second and third, and Hawaii scored the next three points to win the game. The winner's score was 4; and the loser's, 2.

Some games will be short and some will be quite long. This is the

Problem. *If Hawaii and Texas play millions of games what will the average winning score tend to be?*

Even though we have no volleyball or equally matched teams we can still attack the problem experimentally. Select a penny. Flip it. If it turns up heads, give Hawaii a point; if it turns up tails, give Texas a point. With a penny the reader may easily play out ten games and compute their average winning score.

In the ten experimental games I performed with a penny, the winner's score was successively

$$2, 5, 3, 2, 3, 6, 2, 7, 3, \text{ and } 2.$$

In these ten experiments the average winner's score is

$$(7) \qquad \frac{2 + 5 + 3 + 2 + 3 + 6 + 2 + 7 + 3 + 2}{10},$$

which reduces to $\frac{35}{10}$, or simply 3.5. The reader's result need not, of course, be the same as mine.

Now we will figure out what the average winning score will be if more and more games are played. Collecting repetitions in the numerator of (7), we can rewrite (7) as

$$(8) \qquad \frac{4 \times 2 + 3 \times 3 + 0 \times 4 + 0 \times 5 + 1 \times 6 + 1 \times 7}{10}.$$

The numerator of (8) records that the winning score 2 occurred four times; the score 3, three times; the score 4, not at all; the score 5, not at all; the score 6, once; and the score 7, once.

Next we rewrite (8) as

$$(9) \qquad \tfrac{4}{10} \times 2 + \tfrac{3}{10} \times 3 + \tfrac{0}{10} \times 4 + \tfrac{0}{10} \times 5 + \tfrac{1}{10} \times 6 + \tfrac{1}{10} \times 7.$$

In (9), $\tfrac{4}{10}$ is the fraction of the ten games for which the winner's score is 2; $\tfrac{3}{10}$ is the fraction of the games for which the winner's score is 3, and so on.

The expression (9) suggests that we estimate what fraction of the games will have a winning score of 2 (or 3, or 4, $\cdots$) if millions of games are played. What number would replace the fraction $\tfrac{4}{10}$, obtained in our experiment?

Let us work out what fraction of the games would, over the long run, have a winning score of 2. In the first two throws of the penny we have four possible outcomes:

(10) $H\,H$ $H\,T$ $T\,T$ $T\,H.$

The first and third of these four cases produce the winning score of 2. Since the penny is supposed to be unbiased we would expect each of the four cases in (10) to occur equally often if many experiments are performed. Therefore we would expect the winner's score to be 2 in two-fourths of the games. For the long-run estimate we would have $\frac{1}{2}$ instead of the experimental result $\frac{4}{10}$. This is no contradiction; the ten-game experiment serves only as a guide to our thinking, not as a prediction of what would happen over millions of experiments.

Next, what fraction of the games will, in the long run, have a winning score of 3? (In our experiment the winning score of 3 occurred in three-tenths of the games.) To have a winning score of 3, the two teams have to be tied at the end of the first two points, and then one team has to score two points in a row. Inspection of (10) shows that the two teams are tied at the end of the first two points in two-fourths of the games. Thus in one-half of the games the winner's score will be more than 2. What fraction of these games that have a winning score of 3 or more will have a winning score of 3? The half for which the third and fourth points are either $H\,H$ or $T\,T$. Since $\frac{1}{2} \times \frac{1}{2} = \frac{1}{4}$ we see that in one-fourth of all the games, the winning score will, in the long run, be 3. (It is interesting to compare this $\frac{1}{4}$ to $\frac{3}{10}$ of our experiment.)

The reader may show that the winning score of 4 will tend to occur in one-eighth of all the games. Similarly, the winning score will be 5 in one-sixteenth of the games, and so on.

Taking our cue from (9), we suspect that the average winning score will tend to be

(11) $\frac{1}{2} \times 2 + \frac{1}{4} \times 3 + \frac{1}{8} \times 4 + \frac{1}{16} \times 5 + \cdots .$

We are faced with the problem of summing an endless series that resembles a geometric progression but which, unfortunately, is not one. We expect the sum of the first N terms of (11) to get closer and closer to the average winning score; and we expect that score to be about 3.5. Pausing for a moment to get a feel for the problem, let us at least sum the first four terms. To three decimals we have

$$\frac{1}{2} \times 2 + \frac{1}{4} \times 3 + \frac{1}{8} \times 4 + \frac{1}{16} \times 5 = 1 + \frac{3}{4} + \frac{4}{8} + \frac{5}{16} = 2.562.$$

The reader may compute the sum of the first twelve terms and make a guess as to the value of (11).

We will assume that the series (11) has a sum (that is, that it does not mis-behave like the harmonic series). This assumption can be justified, but doing so would require too long a detour. Let us call the sum of *(11)* W. We will now find W by exploiting the similarity of *(11)* to a geometric series.

We have

(12) $$W = 2 \times \tfrac{1}{2} + 3 \times \tfrac{1}{4} + 4 \times \tfrac{1}{8} + 5 \times \tfrac{1}{16} + \cdots.$$

Though *(12)* is not a geometric series, let us try the technique we used to find the sum of the geometric series *(3)*. We now multiply *(12)* by $\tfrac{1}{2}$. This gives

(13) $$\tfrac{1}{2}W = 2 \times \tfrac{1}{4} + 3 \times \tfrac{1}{8} + 4 \times \tfrac{1}{16} + 5 \times \tfrac{1}{32} + \cdots.$$

Just as we subtracted *(4)* from *(3)*, we will subtract from

(14) $$W = 2 \times \tfrac{1}{2} + 3 \times \tfrac{1}{4} + 4 \times \tfrac{1}{8} + 5 \times \tfrac{1}{16} + \cdots$$

the relation

(15) $$\tfrac{1}{2}W = 2 \times \tfrac{1}{4} + 3 \times \tfrac{1}{8} + 4 \times \tfrac{1}{16} + \cdots.$$

Instead of cancellations, this time we obtain

(16) $$W - \tfrac{1}{2}W = 2 \times \tfrac{1}{2} + \tfrac{1}{4} + \tfrac{1}{8} + \tfrac{1}{16} + \cdots.$$

Since $\tfrac{1}{4} + \tfrac{1}{8} + \tfrac{1}{16} + \cdots$ is a geometric progression with $a = \tfrac{1}{4}$ and $r = \tfrac{1}{2}$ we see that *(16)* simplifies to

(17) $$W - \tfrac{1}{2}W = 2 \times \tfrac{1}{2} + \tfrac{1}{2}.$$

Simplifying both sides of *(17)* we obtain

$$\tfrac{1}{2}W = \tfrac{3}{2},$$

and so W is 3. The problem is solved.

Exercises

1. Find the sum of these endless geometric series.
   (a) $\tfrac{1}{4} + (\tfrac{1}{4})^2 + (\tfrac{1}{4})^3 + \cdots$ (Answer: $\tfrac{1}{3}$)
   (b) $1 + \tfrac{2}{3} + (\tfrac{2}{3})^2 + \cdots$ (Answer: 3)
   (c) $1 - \tfrac{1}{2} + \tfrac{1}{4} - \tfrac{1}{8} + \cdots$ (Answer: $\tfrac{2}{3}$)

2. Let $S_N = \dfrac{1}{1 \times 2} + \dfrac{1}{2 \times 3} + \dfrac{1}{3 \times 4} + \cdots + \dfrac{1}{N \times (N+1)}.$

   For example,

   $$S_3 = \frac{1}{1 \times 2} + \frac{1}{2 \times 3} + \frac{1}{3 \times 4}$$

   which, decimally, is 0.750. Compute to three decimals (a) S_1, (b) S_2, (c) S_3, (d) S_4, (e) S_5, and (f) S_6.

3. See E 2. Prove that $S_N = 1 - (1/(N+1))$. (*Hint:* Note that $1/(1 \times 2) = (1/1) - (1/2), 1/(2 \times 3) = (1/2) - (1/3), 1/(3 \times 4) = (1/3) - (1/4)$, and so on.)

4. See E 3. Prove that S_N of E 2 approaches 1.

5. Let S_N equal $1/(1)^2 + 1/(2)^2 + 1/(3)^2 + \cdots + 1/(N)^2$. For example, $S_4 = \frac{1}{1} + \frac{1}{4} + \frac{1}{9} + \frac{1}{16}$, which, to three decimals, is 1.423. Compute to three decimals (a) S_5, (b) S_6, and (c) S_7.

6. See E 5. Using the facts that $1/(2)^2$ is less than $1/(1 \times 2)$, $1/(3)^2$ is less than $1/(2 \times 3)$, $1/(4)^2$ is less than $1/(3 \times 4)$, and so on, prove that each S_N of E 5 is less than 2. (*Hint:* Use E 2, E 3, E 4.) It can be proved that $1/(1)^2 + 1/(2)^2 + 1/(3)^2 + \cdots = \pi^2/6$.

7. Using E 6 prove that if $S_N = 1/1^3 + 1/2^3 + 1/3^3 + \cdots + 1/N^3$, then S_N is always less than 2. It is not known whether

$$1/1^3 + 1/2^3 + 1/3^3 + \cdots = C$$

is related to π^3 as intimately as $1/1^2 + 1/2^2 + 1/3^2 + \cdots$ is to π^2. It is not even known whether C/π^3 is rational.

8. We proved that s_N for the harmonic series gets arbitrarily large as N increases. Show that s_N grows "slowly." Specifically, prove that
   (a) s_4 is less than $1 + (\frac{1}{2}) + (\frac{1}{2}) + (\frac{1}{2}) = \frac{5}{2}$;
   (b) s_8 is less than $s_4 + (\frac{1}{4}) + (\frac{1}{4}) + (\frac{1}{4}) + (\frac{1}{4})$, hence less than $\frac{7}{2}$,
   (c) s_{16} is less than $\frac{9}{2}$,
   (d) s_{32} is less than $\frac{11}{2}$.

9. In this appendix we have considered sums of numbers. In Chapter 3 (E 30, E 31, E 32, E 33, E 34) similar questions were considered for products of numbers. Show that in those five exercises the two forces operating are:
   (1) one force influencing the product A_N (or B_N) not to approach 0 (the terms are close to 1);
   (2) one force influencing the product A_N (or B_N) to approach 0 (the terms are less than 1).
   Note how they balance.

10. Compute the average winning score in 20 experimental games, and compare it with the theoretical result, 3.

11. Compute to three decimals the sum of the first 15 terms of (*11*).

12. Show why the winning score of 4 will tend to occur in one-eighth of the games. (*Easy way:* The two teams share the first two points, share the second two points, and one team gets both of the third pair of points.)

13. See E 12. Show why the winning score of 5 will tend to occur in one-sixteenth of the games.

14. What is the average number of points scored in the volleyball games between Hawaii and Texas? (*Hint:* Why is the average loser's score 1?)

15. A bug is taking a walk on the real line. He starts at 0, and at each step goes either 1 to the right or 1 to the left. Thus, after one step he is either at 1 or -1. At 2 and at -2 there are bug traps. If many bugs take such promenades, what is the average number of steps they take before they fall into a bug trap? (*Hint:* Show that this is E 14 in disguise.)

The problem of the two teams, the problem of the balanced penny, and the problem of the wandering bugs illustrate the part of probability devoted to *the random walk*. Mathematics of the random walk is applied, for example, to the percolation of a fluid through some object, the spread of smoke through air, or the motion of colliding and rebounding neutrons before capture by the lead casing of a nuclear reactor.

Reference

1. *W. Feller, *An Introduction to Probability Theory and its Applications*, vol. 1, 2nd ed., 1957, Wiley, New York. (If a team is to win by k points, then the average winning score is $k(k + 1)/2$; this is implicit in a more general result proved on pp. 317–318. See pp. 311–318 (and the index) for more information concerning the random walk.)

SPACE OF ANY
DIMENSION

In Chapter 15 we referred to the impossibility of building algebras on spaces of dimension other than 1, 2, or 4. This appendix tells what is meant by space of any dimension: 1, 2, 3 or more.

We can describe every point on a straight line by using one real number, telling how far that point is from the point that we choose to label 0, and whether it is left or right of 0. This places on the line a scale such as this,

(1)

$$\cdots \quad \underset{\substack{-4 \;\; -3 \;\; -2 \;\; -1 \quad 0 \quad 1 \quad 2 \quad 3 \quad 4}}{\rule{6cm}{0.4pt}} \quad \cdots$$

which tags every point with a real number. In *(1)* we have dotted heavily the points whose tags are integers. Note that the line is *one*-dimensional and that each point is described by using only *one* real number.

When we go to dimension two—the plane—it is the custom to tell where a point is by first selecting two perpendicular lines,

and then describing any point in the plane by its relation to these two lines.

To do this, place on each of the two lines a number scale. Then any point *P* in the plane is described by the two numbers given by the rectangle drawn in this manner:

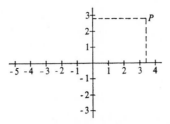

The particular point we chose is described by 3.4 and 2.8. We could call *P* "the point (3.4, 2.8)," keeping in mind that 3.4 refers to the horizontal line and 2.8 to the vertical. [The point (2.8, 3.4) is different from the point (3.4, 2.8).] Note that the plane is *two*-dimensional and that *two* real numbers are required to locate a point.

Now let us go to dimension three, ordinary space. To pinpoint a location in space we can proceed in this manner: We select a plane in space and a line perpendicular to that plane.

(2)

In the plane, we select two perpendicular lines meeting the line *L* in (2). Then we place on each of the three lines the real number scale. Drawing these lines in perspective, we now have

Any point *P* in space is described by the point *P**, which is directly below (or above) *P*, combined with a number on *L*, which tells how high (or low) *P* is.

For example, consider this *P*;

with P^* the point $(5, -4)$ and with height 7. The point P is located by the *three numbers* $(5, -4, 7)$. The order in which the three numbers is written is as important as the order in which we write names: given name, middle name, family name. (John Charles Thomas is a different person from Thomas John Charles or Charles John Thomas.) Thus the X and Y of the plane are written first, in their usual order; the third, or right-hand number, describes the height of the point. Note that space is *three*-dimensional and that *three* real numbers are required to locate a point.

Summarizing, we see that a line corresponds to the set of reals, the plane to the set of pairs of reals, and space to the set of triplets of reals.

It is very easy to conceive of the set of quadruplets of real numbers; for example, $(-7, 6, 0, \sqrt{2})$ is a quadruplet, and so is $(2, \pi, -107, 19)$. The reader is urged to devise a few quadruplets himself. He will find it no harder to write a few quintuplets of real numbers, such as $(10, 15, -\pi, -\sqrt{2}, \frac{1}{2})$, and even toss in a sextuplet, such as $(-1, 2, -\frac{1}{2}, \frac{2}{3}, \frac{3}{4}, 0)$.

It is no harder to think of the set of all quadruplets of real numbers than it is to think of the set of all triplets of real numbers. The set of triplets of real numbers has a convenient geometric model—space. We can "see" the set of reals as the line; the set of couplets of reals as the plane, and the set of triplets of reals as space. But no one, no matter how hard he squints, will "see" the set of quadruplets as some sort of geometric object.

However, if the reader wants to think of four-dimensional space geometrically, visually, here is one way. Consider the set of all arrows that can be drawn in the plane. The feather is described by two real numbers and the point by two real numbers. Thus the set of quadruplets of real numbers can be thought of as representing the set of all arrows in the plane.

It is the custom to call the set of quadruplets of real numbers "Four-dimensional space" or "Four-space," the set of quintuplets "Five-dimensional space" or "Five-space," and so on. With equal ease, we may speak of "Twenty-space"; that is, the set of all 20-tuplets of real numbers.

Any set S in one-to-one correspondence with the set of k-tuplets (such that two elements close together in S correspond to k-tuplets which are close together, and two k-tuplets close together correspond to two elements close together) is also called a k-dimensional space. For $k = 1$, 2, or 3 we have as examples of such sets, the line, the plane, and the space in which all material things are found.

Even though S can be conumerous with spaces of different dimensions (see E 27 of Chapter 16) it can be proved, with the aid of Sperner's lemma, that S cannot be simultaneously of two different dimensions. The rather technical proof for this fact is to be found in R 1 of Chapter 2.

It is very easy to define an addition, $\oplus$, on k-space. For example, with $k = 4$, we can define the "sum" of two 4-tuplets $(a, b, c, d) \oplus (A, B, C, D)$ as $(a + A, b + B, c + C, d + D)$. The reader may check that $\oplus$ is commutative and associative. The same method defines, for $k = 2$, the $\oplus$ that we obtained geometrically in Chapter 15 with the aid of parallelograms. As mentioned in Chapter 15, it is impossible to define a multiplication, $\otimes$, in four-dimensional space such that $\oplus$ and $\otimes$ together satisfy all the rules of algebra.

Exercises

1. Show that the set of circles in the plane is part of a 3-space. (*Hint:* A circle is described by its center and its radius.)

2. Show that the set of rectangles in the plane whose sides are horizontal and vertical is part of a 4-space by showing that such a rectangle can be described by
   (a) its length, width, and center;
   (b) its lower left corner and its upper right corner; or
   (c) its area, its upper left corner, and the length of its diagonal.
   (Topology guarantees that methods (a), (b), and (c) will all yield the same dimension.)

3. A baseball pitcher determines the speed of the ball, the rate of its spin, the axis of spin, the direction in which the ball is thrown, and the time at which it is thrown. Show that the batter requires seven numbers to describe the pitch.

Reference

1. D. Hilbert and S. Cohn-Vossen, *Geometry and the Imagination*, Chelsea, New York, 1952. (Further examples of spaces are to be found in pp. 157–164.)

INDEX